*Practice of
Wildlife Conservation*

The mountains of Alaska and northwestern Canada owe much of their charm and picturesque quality to their wildlife. (Dall mountain sheep photographed by Dr. Adolph Murie.)

Practice of Wildlife Conservation

LEONARD W. WING, Ph.D.
Agricultural and Mechanical College of Texas

JOHN WILEY & SONS, INC., NEW YORK
CHAPMAN & HALL, LTD., LONDON

Copyright, 1951
BY
JOHN WILEY & SONS, INC.

All Rights Reserved

This book or any part thereof must not be reproduced in any form without the written permission of the publisher.

PRINTED IN THE UNITED STATES OF AMERICA

To
WILLIAM GILBERT FARGO
and
ALDO LEOPOLD

Preface

My experience in teaching the subject at the college level and in working with various conservation departments and their personnel has indicated the need of a general textbook covering the broad field of wildlife conservation and management. The book tries to blend the theoretical and scientific aspects with actual field practice along lines that experience has shown to be desirable and workable. In so doing, the book considers the land picture existing today, after man has interjected himself into it.

The personnel that will staff our public agencies, private organizations, and institutions in the future are in our classrooms today. I have long included the study of the organizational and administrative phases of conservation in my classes. This comes at the end of the courses, just as the general material in these areas comes at the end of the book, after the student has been grounded in the fundamentals of management.

I have assembled the material in a form that seems to me workable on the basis of our present stage of development. I have found it essential to good instruction that the biology of wildlife be integrated with management practice in preparing a student for future work, even though the student has had earlier courses in vertebrate biology. This makes the offerings usable also by students not having so complete a background in natural history, such as students of forestry, range management, or agriculture, as well as for students who enroll because of their outdoor interests. It should also make the book useful to others than students. Because some confusion exists about the legal aspects of wildlife conservation, as well as hunting controls, Chapters 11 and 12 treat the subject with more detail than would otherwise be advisable in a general textbook.

The book has been written with extra regard to readability, for I know that many of its readers will not be versed in or care to read ecological, biological, or management jargon. No one who studied long with the late great Professor Aldo Leopold could conscientiously do otherwise than use the simple English language wherever possible.

I find that the average student does not have the time to hunt widely in the voluminous literature (the fund of wildlife literature runs into thousands of papers) for reading material. On the basis of my experience, instead of extensive documentation and citation in the text, I have tried to suggest some comprehensive works, mostly those readily accessible, and to hold the number down. Students who wish to go further—and I hope that there will be many—will find references in many of the suggested readings. In addition they should consult the journals, where important papers currently appear. The *Journal of Wildlife Management* is an indispensable source of current and detailed studies too numerous to mention. Other important information appears in *The Auk, Wilson Bulletin, Condor, Journal of Mammalogy, Copeia, Bird Banding, Journal of Forestry,* and *Audubon Magazine.* Among collected papers the *Transactions of the American Wildlife Conferences* and *Transactions of the American Fisheries Society* are gold mines of information. Most states put out reports and even periodicals (such as the excellent *California Fish and Game*). Eventually, I hope, each state will have a field manual for its own particular area and conditions. Processed and mimeographed material containing important current reports are the *Wildlife Review, Progressive Fish-Culturist, Pittman-Robertson Quarterly,* and various wildlife leaflets and reports.

LEONARD W. WING

College Station, Texas
April, 1951

Acknowledgments

It would be difficult indeed to really acknowledge all who have contributed something to this book. In fact, I doubt whether I can remember all the people from whom I have received ideas, suggestions, or information in one form or another. Often the good idea clings in the mind long after the memory of its reception has faded. If anyone recognizes his own ideas or suggestions, I am both pleased and grateful.

I wish particularly to note the help of several people. Aldo Leopold, Ralph C. Hawley, Frederick M. Hamerstrom, Jr., William B. Davis, Douglas E. Wade, George Petrides, and Charles F. Yocom read early drafts and offered many pertinent suggestions herein incorporated. R. William Eschmeyer, Clarence Tarzwell, Clarence Pautzke, and Frank Knapp checked the material in Chapters 17 and 18. Vernon A. Young made many important contributions to Chapters 4, 8, 10, 11, and 12. Ernest Swift, A. H. Smith, and T. D. Little read Chapters 21 and 22 and suggested many clarifications. Ernest Swift and Harold Loughary read parts of the manuscript now portions of Chapter 24. Harrison F. Lewis's reading of Chapters 21, 22, 23, and 24 resulted in several important changes. John T. Emlen examined the material on the bobwhite and valley quails. Richard H. Pough reviewed the sections on rare, threatened, and persecuted species.

Burton Lauckhart, Clarence Tarzwell, Robert L. Webster, the Great Northern Railway, and the Montana Game and Fish Department contributed several photographs, as indicated in the appropriate legends. Other photographs are my own.

The several drawings used in the text are the work of Anne Hinshaw Wing.

Contents

CHAPTER		
1	Conservation and Management	1
2	The Biological Base of Management	19
3	The Biological Base of Management (Continued)	37
4	Techniques of Field Investigations and Practices	54
5	Techniques of Field Investigations and Practices (Continued)	71
6	Farm Game and Its Management	91
7	Farm Game Birds and Mammals	107
8	Forests and Forest Wildlife Management	124
9	Game Birds of the Forest	140
10	Forest Game Mammal Management	160
11	Forest Game Mammal Management (Continued)	173
12	Game Management in the Open Range	194
13	Southern Wildlife Species	207
14	Northland Wildlife	218
15	Fur-Bearer Management	234
16	Wildfowl Management	249
17	Lake Fish Management and Improvement	270
18	Stream Improvement and Management	285
19	Songbird and Non-Game Conservation and Management	297
20	Treatment of Rare, Threatened, and Persecuted Species	311
21	State Powers and Controls	318
22	Federal Wildlife Controls in the United States	333
23	Provincial and Federal Wildlife Spheres in Canada	346
24	Administration and Regulation	351
	Index	365

Conservation and Management

Definition. Wildlife management is the branch of conservation that handles wildlife as an attribute of the land. Although it is concerned primarily with production, it may at times be called upon to undertake control measures that will preserve a species or hold its population in bounds. Such control measures, however, are secondary to production. A comparison with forestry has considerable merit. Forestry is the branch of conservation that handles forests for the purpose of producing a crop of forest products. These may be tangible, like lumber, or intangible, like recreation. Yet foresters direct forest-fire activities, which are protection rather than production.

Game farms and fish hatcheries usually are not part of wildlife management programs; in fact, game farms and fish hatcheries, like fur farms, take on aspects more of animal husbandry than of conservation. Often, however, game or fish managers must deal with artificial stocking, particularly in some states.

The exact kinds of wildlife included under wildlife management will differ with different people. But the principal divisions are often listed as follows (even though one or two may not be included in this book):

Shell-fish management
—Fish management
—Game management
—Fur-bearer management
Non-game animal management
Wild plant management

Mention must be made also of still another conservation category, one that exists only by reason of human esthetic enjoyment. Realization in recent years that pristine areas are passing has brought forth a concept of *wilderness*—of wilderness which perhaps is designated best as the "essence of climax ecology." Wildlife managers are called upon for work and advice in connection with wilderness areas and wilderness wildlife, and so with some reason wilderness management may be considered at least an ally if not a part of wildlife management.

Wildlife Management and Allied Fields. Though the field of wildlife management is young, it is by no means an example of spontaneous generation. If that were so, wildlife management would be an orphan among science, art, and industry. Just as no modern organism is without ancestors or relatives, so no modern field of knowledge is without allies and antecedents.

Wildlife becomes an integral part of the *land* when we use the term in its broadest sense, even though wildlife is a mobile and fluctuating part of that land. *Land use* tries to determine the various forms of use, especially the highest, and also to formulate programs to bring about that use. Hunting, fishing, trapping, and the like are forms of natural-resources utilization and for that reason, at least, contribute to "land utilization."

Animal wildlife depends upon plant life for food and protection either directly or indirectly. Indirect dependence is a second-hand dependence, as when the wolf eats the deer that feed upon browse. A study of the dependence of animals upon plant life involves *botany;* even more it involves *ecology*, of which one branch, *wildlife ecology*, is the foundation of management operations. Wildlife ecology, to use an analogy, bears the same relations to wildlife management that *silvics* bears to *silviculture*. Wildlife ecology has been called "fericology," but that term has not been adopted.

The dynamic phase of wildlife management, which we call environmental manipulation, deals with improvement of the environment; it is based upon biological principles, which in turn are founded upon adequate knowledge resulting from sound research. Environmental manipulation is of recent origin and is predicated upon the belief that favorable conditions for wildlife can be brought about by dynamic operations. Because it has a position analogous to that of improvement work in forestry, environmental manipulation was once given the name *fericulture,* which denotes its correspondence to silviculture.

As an animal science wildlife management impinges in part upon *zoology;* yet because it is "practical" it is far from being a branch of "classical" zoology. A basic knowledge of the principles of zoology is requisite and a knowledge of the habits of animals indispensable for anyone working in the field of wildlife management. The relationship that wildlife management bears to zoology is similar to that which forestry bears to botany.

Wildlife management must consider laws, regulations, and their enforcement, and in so doing it touches upon *public administration*.

The organization of conservation departments is a matter of concern to both public administration and wildlife management, as is also the collection and expenditure of public funds, whether appropriated funds or money collected by licenses and fees.

Society has given approval of the use of some wildlife resources for recreation, and somewhat different from problems of administration are a number of social and economic problems in the relation of hunters, fishermen, and trappers to landowners and to the general public. The fact that wildlife supports a multimillion-dollar industry need not concern us at the moment; the knowledge that such an industry exists will be sufficient.

Problems of the Wildlife Manager. We have seen by the preceding brief discussion that wildlife management is a profession involving several fields of human activity; therefore, we do not need to proceed far to discover that a multiplicity of problems is brought down upon the wildlife manager. One of the first matters of conflict facing the wildlife manager in the field and the administrator in the office is the clash between wildlife use and human use of the land upon which the wildlife lives. It is obvious that such conflicts are bound to arise. They arise also on questions of preferences and tolerance. Thus the same animal may be "good" in one setting and "bad" in another, according to its life habits. A coyote is a valuable mousetrap on a cattle ranch, but it may be harmful on a sheep ranch.

In addition to being called upon to increase the wildlife population of an area, the manager may be expected to control or to reduce populations that have grown to exceed the permissible stand. This might be expressed in a different form by simply stating that part of the manager's job is to keep the wildlife population within the limits of human tolerance. It may be added, however, that such problems seldom arise.

Many land uses take precedence over wildlife management, and it must be recognized that wildlife, like any other natural resource, is subject to priorities in favor of more valuable and more important uses. Due attention to this may obviate many a conflict.

Increased pressure for more and cheaper hunting, fishing, and trapping is another source of difficulties. Anyone willing to pay a small fee in the form of a license may hunt, regardless of his capabilities or sportsmanship. The old custom of "free" hunting is giving way slowly to the pressure brought about by changes associated with occupation of the land. As yet few hunters are willing to recognize landowner rights, or to pay fees and charges for the use of the land upon which they hunt, fish, or trap; hence the wildlife manager is projected into the middle of the "trespass nuisance."

Limitations to Management. Just as we have problems facing wildlife management, so do we have limitations to its application. These limitations may be classified for convenience as *biological, economic, administrative, and public policy.*

Biological problems need not be discussed here as they will be covered in suitable places throughout the text.

One of the most important *economic* limitations is the cost of producing game, fish, and fur. (This might be stated pointedly, "How much can be produced on a one-dollar license?") *But it should be understood clearly by all that it is the wild-raised game and fish that provide the hunter and fisherman with his catch and that his license money contributes only slightly to producing what he hunts.* Not all license money can be put into production; administration, overhead, protection, and various other activities claim shares. Thus nicety of judgment is required in determining when contributions to the cost of producing are too great for the value of the product; the law of diminishing returns operates in the woods as well as in the factory. It is generally more economical to increase production by increasing the amount of habitable territory than it is to bring about greater density on existing territories. The possible unoccupied area, however, is eventually used up and further operations must be on existing range.[1] The possible range is definitely limited for fish by the amount of existing or impoundable water, but the limits of range for terrestrial game are less exact.

In view of the fact that land devoted wholly to wildlife purposes (either as refuges or as hunting grounds) requires capital outlay, wildlife work is generally restricted to cheap lands and multiple-purpose land. Though they require lower capital outlay, cheap lands usually need more developmental expenditures, which sometimes exceed the difference between the purchase price of good land and poor land.

To be mentioned but not discussed here are *administrative* and *public policy* limitations. Because a matter is desirable or feasible, it is not necessarily legal; conversely, undertakings that are legally possible are not necessarily feasible or desirable.

[1] Note that the term *range* may have two different meanings: (*a*) the geographic area inhabited by a species and (*b*) habitat occupied by individuals. The latter sense is used principally for big game, especially in the West. Thus we may speak of "summer range," "winter range," "deer range," or even "quail range."

Biological Aspects of Hunting and Fishing. One of the questions frequently asked by the layman and one that seems appropriate to discuss here is this: "Are hunting and fishing biologically justifiable?" or, phrased in another way, "Is the actual killing of fish and game biologically unsound?"

Nature always has potential provisions for more young than are actually required to replace the parents, for it is an inexorable law of nature that not all may reach adulthood. The potential surplus is always sufficient to maintain a capacity breeding stock of a vigorous species under normal natural conditions. Absence of such a potential surplus marks species that require special consideration.

Because winter is generally the "pinch period," it usually sets the carrying capacity of the range. No area can carry a greater population than the pinch period permits, wherefore the number of animals in excess of the carrying capacity form a "surplus." A *margin of safety* is needed to care for normal expected losses, however, and all animals in excess of the carrying capacity and the margin of safety constitute the *biological surplus*.

The biological surplus is doomed; the range cannot support it; it must disappear during the pinch period. Biologically speaking, man is but another decimating factor with which wildlife must cope. It is biologically sound for man to take the biological surplus, the loss of which will not affect the species because the capacity population and its margin of safety are not disturbed. There can be no biological objection to taking this surplus by whatever means are chosen—so long as the take is confined to the biological surplus. On the other hand, hunting, fishing, and trapping are biologically unsound when there is no biological surplus or when the take exceeds the biological surplus.

There are other considerations than biological, however, and we must not overlook them. It might also be biologically acceptable to kill a certain percentage of song birds for sport, food, or any other reason, just as is now done with mourning doves in the South, but it would hardly be sporting or esthetic or within the bounds of public policy to do so in our culture. Hence, the biological aspects are not all the story.

Before the subject is dropped, the student should be warned to distinguish clearly between evidence and appeals on biological grounds, and appeals on social, humanitarian, political, or emotional grounds. Few subjects, in fact, have had so little discussion on biological grounds and so much on emotional grounds as wildlife conservation. It is not intended to dismiss all non-biological aspects without consideration; these aspects are of great importance, and some will be taken up in later chapters.

It should be noted also that there is no synthetic production of wildlife. At best, management simply controls and regulates the positive needs and reduces the negative limitations. It is a rearrangement of nature's forces, not the substitution of something for them. Because we deal with biological rather than physical principles, there is no such thing as a single formula of universal application. Management must be fitted to local conditions.

TABLE 1.1

ANIMALS OF VARIOUS GROUPS IN THE UNITED STATES AND NUMBER REGARDED AS GAME, GAME OR COMMERCIAL, AND INJURIOUS

(After McAtee with adaptations)

	Approximate Number of Species	Game Species Number	Game Species Percentage	Game or Commercial Species Number	Game or Commercial Species Percentage	Reckoned by Some as Injurious Number	Reckoned by Some as Injurious Percentage	Non-Game or Non-Commercial, hence "Harmless" Number	Non-Game or Non-Commercial, hence "Harmless" Percentage
Freshwater fishes	600	88	14.67	132	22.00	378	63.00	90	15.00
Amphibians	138	0		3	2.17	3	2.17	132	95.65
Reptiles	149	0		24 *	16.11	60 *	40.26	70	46.98
Birds	811	69	8.51	69	8.51	142 †	17.51	600	73.98
Mammals	670	82	12.24	198 ‡	29.55	189 ‡	28.21	399	59.55
Total	2368	239	10.09	426	17.99	772	30.26	1291	54.52

* Five species (including crocodile, alligator, and snapping turtle) are the same in each group.

† Seventy-six of these species are protected by the Migratory Bird Treaty.

‡ One-hundred and sixteen species (fur bearers) are the same in each group; many of these are protected by state laws.

Status of Vertebrate Species. The status of each of the 2368 vertebrate species living within the borders of the United States shows that only 10.09 per cent can be classed as "game" species (Table 1.1).

Only 7.09 per cent have commercial use, and 30.26 per cent are classed as injurious—by some people at least. Of the whole 2368 vertebrates, only 1291 or 54.52 per cent are not classed as game, commercial, or harmless species—and therefore "harmless." It seems obvious to a biologist or conservationist that the American viewpoint is very badly distorted when nearly one-third of our higher animals are "injurious," so called, and when only about a half are "harmless," so called, or lacking in commercial or game "usefulness."

General Economic Values. With the exception of fur bearers and food fishes, wildlife is not generally the subject of commerce in the same sense that lumber, petroleum, or minerals are commercial articles, but wildlife does possess definite economic values, nevertheless, and it seems fitting to discuss a few of these briefly. Wildlife managers who depend solely upon economic values of wildlife to justify their work fail to appreciate wildlife economics; wildlife managers who ignore economic values likewise fail to grasp their import fully.

It is not possible to determine with any degree of accuracy the dollars-and-cents value of wildlife to the people of the United States, Canada, or any other country. Estimates, however, have been based upon crop saving, recreational uses, and other positive wildlife values, and a 1921 estimate gave the insect-suppression value of birds as more than $444 million dollars in the United States. The exact role of birds as checks upon insects has been so confused by exaggeration and emotional argument that it is difficult indeed to estimate the role and value of birds as crop protectors. Though any general estimate must necessarily be largely a matter of conjecture, it is probable, considering all possible sources of economic worth, that the value of wildlife to the people of the United States and Canada is in the neighborhood of 2 billion dollars a year.

Innumerable are the ways in which wildlife has direct economic value, and even values which would seem to be purely esthetic frequently give rise to demands that in themselves are economic. The amateur photographer, for example, who goes to the wild to take pictures creates additional demand for photographic supplies. Because he cannot be said to be hunting game for sustenance, even the hunter must be hunting for some kind of thrill, and this thrill is an emotional one. Among the purely economic values are not only furs and other valuable products but also animal work, like the impounding of water (by beavers), suppression of insects, and control of disease-carrying rodents. Wildlife values are so many and so varied that it seems best to tabulate the principal ones.

Classification of Economic Values of Wildlife

Positive values.
  Esthetic (nature study, presence).
  Recreation (hunting, fishing).
  Useful products derived from wildlife.
    Food.
    Wearing apparel (made from fur and hides, plumage).
    Manufactured articles (made from fur and hides, plumage, whale products, fish oils).
    Down, ivory, whalebone.
    Fertilizer.
  Useful activities of animals.
    In the wild state:
      Distributors of plants and animals.
      Scavenger service.
      Impoundment of water.
      Protection of human health (control of disease-carriers such as rats and mosquitoes, experimental animals).
      Sources of employment for human beings (protectors, biologists).
      Crop saving, insect suppression, control of harmful animal life.
    In captivity:
      Trained animals.
      Zoo specimens, circus exhibits.
      Animals used for scientific experiment.
Negative values.
  Destruction of property.
  Competition and predation.
  Disease reservoirs.
  Encouragement of undue trespass.

Direct Income. In the early history of man, the chief value of wildlife to human beings was for subsistence. Primitive man used the flesh of animals for food, the skins for wearing apparel, shelter, and boats, and the bones for implements. Before the arrival of the white man, Indians of this continent were almost wholly dependent upon animals for food and clothing, though some Indian tribes supplemented their food supply by rudimentary agriculture. Many primitive peoples of today still depend heavily upon wild animals, although the number of primitive people declines.

The number of people that can be supported by an area is greatly limited under a "wildlife economy." It seems probable that fewer than 750,000 Indians occupied the present United States and Canada in 1492. As the population of this area now totals more than two hundred times this figure, it would appear that the subsistence value of the land under a wildlife economy was less than $\frac{1}{200}$ of its value under our present economy.

Market hunting supplied a direct income to some people for a long period of time, but now market hunting has given way to "recreational" use, which indicates that recreation is the "higher form" of utilization. Market hunting continues today in the form of whaling, commercial fishing, and trapping because there is relatively little conflict between the recreational and market values of those forms that are still used commercially. The sale of *game fish,* however, has almost ceased, and for the most part the fishes that are considered as *food fish* are those usually found in large schools or at a distance from population centers, and those that have poor "sporting" value. Most fur bearers, having low value for recreational purposes, are still hunted and trapped for fur, but wherever a conflict has occurred between the use of a species for fur and its use for sport, the latter has won invariably. Like fur bearers, whales have never been particularly valuable for public recreation; yet it must not be assumed that they (or any other wild animal) or the mere knowledge of them may not give a deep thrill to many people. By that token, they have esthetic values that would be lost if they disappeared.

Indirect Income. The principal indirect income from wildlife is from recreational use, which may be considered under two classes: recreational income and recreational pleasure.

Indirect Income from Wildlife

Recreational income.
  Recreational services.
    Guiding, boat rental.
    Board and lodging.
    Repair of equipment.
    Summer camps.
    Rent or support of dogs and horses.
  Recreational goods.
    Guns, ammunition, tackle.
    Out-of-door clothing.
    Boats.
    Cameras, souvenirs.
  Transportation.
    Railroad, stage, boat, airplane.
    Automobile (garage, gasoline).
  Licenses, fees, royalties, taxes.
  Land rental.
Recreational pleasure.

The money spent for recreation is often great. As determined by field interviews in three Ohio areas, the expenditures and bag by squirrel hunters, counting all items, varied from nothing to $20 for a day of hunting. The average expenditure was $1.63 a hunter, and the cost of each squirrel bagged averaged $2.70 for all three areas. The averages for the individual areas were $0.90, $1.32, and $6.53, respectively; the last-named figure was highest owing to the distance traveled in reaching the areas. Similar expenditures have been reported in Texas. Such figures no doubt rise or fall with changes in economic conditions.

The time spent afield probably indicates the "recreational pleasure" obtained. The hunters, in the Ohio example cited, averaged 4.6 hours afield and walked 5.6 miles (perhaps somewhat overestimated); they required 3.4 hours to see and 6.2 hours to bag each squirrel.

The number of licenses issued by the states rose from a total of about 3 million in 1930 to 7 million in 1938 and 12 million in 1947. The density of hunters in some states runs to a score or so for each square mile; it averages about 4.

Land Rental. Hunting and fishing form the principal purposes for which wildlife lands are leased. Actual leasing of hunting and fishing grounds is not new, for it seems certain that lands were leased for hunting in England at a very early date. The leasing of lands on a large scale, however, is comparatively recent and constitutes a potentially important source of revenue for landowners, particularly for owners of range and forest land and land of marginal value.

In some parts of the country, it is possible for an owner to secure sufficient revenue to pay his taxes and more by leasing his holdings for hunting purposes. In a number of leases, the rental has been fixed as the amount of the taxes. Because this relieves timberland owners from periodical cash outlays for taxes, it enables them to carry cut-over land until a second crop of timber matures. When hunting carries the burden, many acres of timberland can be kept on the active tax roll, instead of becoming tax-delinquent, ownerless, public land. Farmers may lease duck and muskrat marshes and sometimes the hunting rights on their property. Leasing may involve trading, as the trading of hunting rights on farm land for grazing rights on club property.

Hunting and fishing clubs are cooperatives that secure hunting and fishing privileges for members. Clubs may rent hunting or fishing areas, own them outright, or own part and lease the rest.

The leasing of hunting lands for hunting purposes by clubs and individuals is common in the southern states where sportsmen from other sections of the country spend considerable sums of money in renting tracts of land for quail hunting. Local people are sometimes paid for caring for dogs and horses and for acting as guides.

In the South also there is a far deeper respect for property rights of others than there is in the North, East, and even the West. Hunters object far less to landowners' maintenance of rights or to their charging others to use them. Texas ranchers lead in charging for hunting privileges. Squirrel hunting rights in Texas have an average rental of 18.6 cents an acre; deer hunting brings more. The amount of money brought into a community is sometimes an important part of the local income, especially where the land is poor for agriculture and farm income is correspondingly low. As much as $6,000 has been obtained from hunting rents a season on an 11,000-acre Texas ranch.

Capital Land Values. Many parcels of land have greater value than they might otherwise have because some form of wildlife is present. Lands near lakes and rivers, for example, are often admirably suited for resorts or commercial hunting lodges. Sportsmen have purchased wild lands in order to have an area for hunting deer and other wildlife; occasionally several sportsmen band together to buy hunting lands. They may buy jointly or purchase adjacent parcels individually and erect a hunting camp for the combined use of all upon one of the parcels.

Sometimes such lands are of submarginal nature, even for forestry purposes. Money received by the owners in selling these lands to sportsmen is value created by game; for that reason the entire selling price must be credited to the wildlife side of the ledger.

Marshes not useful for ordinary farming purposes may be very valuable as areas for hunting waterfowl, or they may be of great economic worth for muskrat trapping. Many marshes now used exclusively for muskrat trapping yield more income from fur than they formerly yielded from marsh hay or pasturage.

Trout streams generally have the highest theoretical value of all comparable hunting or fishing areas. A Forest Service study found that, during 1936 and 1937, trout fishermen removed 1212 pounds of fish from Tonto and Horton Creeks in Arizona. The meat value, at then existing local prices ($0.60 a pound), amounted to $727.26. The streams have a combined water surface of 24.48 acres, and the yearly production averaged $29.71 an acre. Capitalized at 6 per cent, the value of the creeks was $495.17 a surface acre, based only upon the meat value of the trout.

The cost to the fisherman approximated $7.50 for every pound of trout obtained, which indicates a recreational value *twelve and one-half times the meat value.* Under these conditions, it is probable that the yearly recreation value assignable to the entire watershed of these streams is perhaps $10 an acre, while that of the streams is $750 a water acre. If we capitalize this at 6 per cent, we shall find the result amazing indeed.

Cooperatives and Land Pools. There are three main types of game pools, though the exact mechanism by which they operate varies from area to area or from state to state. These types are (*a*) commercial pools, (*b*) farmer pools, and (*c*) farmer-sportsmen cooperatives. The commercial pool or "club" is generally operated with one man as the central figure. He may be a game-farm operator who stocks the area immediately before the shooting season. The legal provisions in such cases are usually liberal enough to permit the taking of a major portion of the release (generally pheasants). Experience seems to indicate that the game-farm owner unintentionally stocks the surrounding countryside as well as the lands over which he holds leases. Some commercial ventures of this sort are only variations of tourist lodges and dude ranches.

The farmer pools (such as the famed Williamston plan) usually begin as organized efforts on the part of the landowners to combat the trespass nuisance. Though farmers may receive some income under these plans, from their viewpoint they generally receive enough protection against unworthy trespass to make the money received of minor importance.

Farmer-sportsmen cooperatives are usually small organizations composed of a few farmers and their sportsmen friends, usually residents of neighboring towns. The farmer-sportsmen cooperatives are generally the most successful of game pools, for all the participants are on a friendship basis. In practice the farmers supply the land and perform such routine tasks as may be necessary for the betterment of the game, and the sportsmen supply the necessary funds for the purchase of fence, eggs, stock, winter feed, and material. All members participate equally in the hunting.

Public Shooting Grounds. Several states, and more recently the federal government, have embarked on forms of "socialized hunting" under the name of "public shooting grounds." The arguments for such programs fall along several lines, principally that, because the public, by law, charges a license fee for the privilege of hunting, it morally obligates itself to provide the licensee with a place to hunt. Another argument strongly advanced is that landowners (whether farmers or hunting clubs) deny the private individual access to choice fishing and hunting grounds. It cannot be disputed that the private individual has been denied free access to hunting and fishing spots; it is a fundamental truism that growth of a nation means greater occupation of the land by private owners and therefore less land for others to use freely for their own private purposes. Still another line of reasoning is that unless he is wealthy the individual cannot afford to pay rental or club expenses for his hunting, an argument that in essence is really one for transferring some of the cost from the individual to the public.

Under "socialized hunting" as provided by public shooting grounds, the only net change is substitution of the state for the private landowner as the proprietor of lands over which the hunter travels. Socialized hunting has come to the fore chiefly in waterfowl areas along some of the coasts and in the Great Lakes region. It has also been suggested for upland game hunting. Public shooting grounds do not increase the supply of game for the hunter, but they do increase the kill by encouraging overshooting. Theoretically, they provide a place where the non-landowner may have hunting without paying for it himself or by paying but a nominal charge. Yet this idea is a fallacy, for the public must pay either through increased taxes to support public shooting grounds and their administration or through extra taxes to offset loss of the property to the tax rolls. In any event there is not enough available land to provide hunting for everyone in the amount that everyone may wish to hunt.

Public shooting grounds have been located near or adjacent to refuges, particularly those of the inviolate type. Sometimes parts of refuges have been opened under terms of law; unfortunately, choice parts of the refuge have been so opened. The net result of public shooting grounds so far seems only to add to the decline in many species of game with no great benefit to the public as a whole, even though a minority may have profited personally. Shooting grounds may be open to all who come regardless of numbers, or they may be restricted to lottery tickets or to a limited number of hunters on a first-come-first-served basis.

Wildlife as a Tourist Attraction. It is frequently stated that deer and other wildlife are of greater value to the inhabitants of a region as "tourist bait" than as objects of pursuit. Resort owners recognize this and universally advertise the fish and game to be found. In recent years roadside museums and roadside zoos have sprung up (often in connection with backwoods filling stations) for the purpose of luring tourists. States and provinces have found it necessary to regulate the roadside zoos because they too frequently tend to become inhumane or unfit quarters for wild animals.

Fishing and hunting derbies have been officially frowned upon also in several states and provinces on the ground that people should go fishing and hunting for recreation and sport, not for automobiles, boats, and other prizes.

Nature trails and trailside museums have been established near centers of population, in connection with parks, and in other areas frequented by tourists and nature hikers.

Great satisfaction is derived by tourists from the mere knowledge that wild conditions are present, even though they see no wildlife. This has been aptly stated by Adolph Murie who wrote:

> I believe that many of us are benefited by the mere knowledge that wilderness exists. We would suffer a definite loss if suddenly we should learn that the jungles of South America had disappeared.

It is this satisfaction that has brought about the establishment of national, state, and provincial parks and of wilderness areas wherein primitive conditions are maintained in an undisturbed state. Much discussion has been aroused by the need for additional wilderness areas and parks and for better protection of those already established. The genuine need for wilderness areas has been demonstrated adequately, although conservationists are not in general agreement regarding standards for such areas.

Royalties and Taxes. Wildlife is a resource belonging to the public as a whole, and use of this public resource for private purposes is governed by such conditions as the state (the agent of the public) may impose. It is reasonable for a state to ask some cash return for the privilege of converting public property to private use. Revenue from this source takes various forms, such as licenses, permits, royalties, severance taxes, privilege taxes, ammunition taxes, sporting-goods taxes, tags, seals, and stamps. Licenses and permits have two chief functions, to regulate and control and to yield revenue, but one or the other of these functions is often lost to sight.

Miscellaneous Products. Numerous products from wildlife were at one time important items of commerce, but for the most part the general use of wildlife for economic products has ceased. A few examples, however, will be given.

State Birds, Trees, and Flowers

Commercial eiderdown comes from the plumage of eider ducks and forms an important source of revenue in Iceland, some Scandinavian countries, and parts of Labrador. The people zealously protect the eider ducks, in some places not even allowing extraneous noises for fear that the birds may be frightened. The eiderdown is gathered from the nests and cleaned before being baled and exported. Plumage from other species was formerly an important item of commerce and trade to the millinery industry.

The great slaughter of bison left quantities of bones on the plains or under cliffs. For a number of years settlers were able to gather these bones in sufficient quantity to ship by the carload for use in making fertilizer; in a few places, bison bones are still gathered for shipment. Another use of wildlife for fertilizer is the guano industry, confined mostly to rocky islands off the coast of Peru. Guano, the dried excreta of cormorants (guanay) and bats, accumulates on arid islands where the birds nest in huge rookeries. It may also accumulate in caves used by bats. When the bird islands of Peru were discovered, the guano lay many feet deep; later dozens of boats engaged in the trade. The guano industry is now carefully regulated by the Peruvian Guano Commission, which has undertaken a scientific study of the trade and the birds in order to increase the industry through management measures. In actual practice the guanay birds are returning to the land some of the fertility that has been washed seaward.

Among other products obtained from wildlife might be mentioned buttons, pearls, and ivory, the last from elephants (particularly the African elephant) as well as from the walrus of the Arctic region. Of considerable interest is "fossil ivory," derived from extinct relatives of the elephant in the Northlands.

State Birds, Trees, and Flowers. The designation of a state bird, flower, or tree, officially through legislative act or by common consent, recognizes the attraction value of nature, including wildlife. We may with justification indicate this action as a cultural one. The tabulation lists the state birds, trees, and flowers that the various states and provinces have adopted.

	Bird	*Tree*	*Flower*
Alabama	Yellow-shafted flicker	......	Goldenrod
Alaska	......	......	Forget-me-not
Arizona	Cactus wren	......	Saguaro
Arkansas	Mockingbird	Pine	Apple blossom
British Columbia	Thunderbird (*legendary*)	......	......
California	Valley quail	Redwood	California poppy
Colorado	Lark bunting	Blue spruce	Colorado columbine

	Bird	Tree	Flower
Connecticut	Rose-breasted grosbeak	......	Mountain laurel
Delaware	Cardinal	Holly	Peach blossom
District of Columbia	Wood thrush	......	American Beauty rose
Florida	Mockingbird	Cabbage palmetto	Orange blossom
Georgia	Brown thrasher	Live oak	Cherokee rose
Hawaii	......	Coconut	Hibiscus
Idaho	Mountain bluebird	......	Lewis Mock orange
Illinois	Cardinal	Oak	Violet
Indiana	Cardinal	Tulip tree	Zinnia
Iowa	Goldfinch	......	Wild rose
Kansas	Western meadowlark	Cottonwood	Sunflower
Kentucky	Cardinal	Tulip tree	Goldenrod
Louisiana	Brown pelican	Magnolia	Magnolia
Maine	Black-capped chickadee	Pine	Pine cone and tassel
Maryland	Baltimore oriole	......	Black-eyed Susan
Massachusetts	Veery	......	Trailing arbutus
Michigan	Robin	......	Apple blossom
Minnesota	Goldfinch	......	Moccasin flower
Mississippi	Mockingbird	Magnolia	Magnolia
Missouri	Eastern bluebird	......	Hawthorn
Montana	Western meadowlark	......	Bitterroot
Nebraska	Western meadowlark	......	Goldenrod
Nevada	Mountain bluebird	......	Sagebrush
New Hampshire	Purple finch	......	Purple lilac
New Jersey	Goldfinch	......	Violet
New Mexico	Road runner	......	Yucca
New York	Eastern bluebird	......	Rose
North Carolina	Carolina chickadee	......	Dogwood
North Dakota	Western meadowlark	Green ash	Prairie rose
Ohio	House wren	Buckeye	Scarlet carnation
Oklahoma	Bobwhite quail	Redbud	Mistletoe
Oregon	Western meadowlark	Douglas fir	Oregon grape
Pennsylvania	Ruffed grouse	Hemlock	Mountain laurel
Rhode Island	Bobwhite	Maple	Violet
Saskatchewan	Sharp-tailed grouse	......	......
South Carolina	Carolina wren	Cabbage palmetto	Jessamine
South Dakota	Western meadowlark	Cottonwood	Pasque flower
Tennessee	Mockingbird	......	Iris
Texas	Mockingbird	Pecan	Bluebonnet
Utah	Gull	Blue spruce	Sego lily
Vermont	Hermit thrush	Sugar maple	Red clover
Virginia	Robin	Flowering dogwood	Flowering dogwood
Washington	Goldfinch	......	Coast rhododendron
West Virginia	Cardinal	Sugar maple	Rosebay rhododendron
Wisconsin	Robin	......	Violet
Wyoming	Western meadowlark	......	Painted cup

Suggested Reading

Designations of Wildlife Areas. Areas devoted wholly or partly to wildlife purposes may vary in ownership, organization, and purpose. Whether in public or private ownership, they vary in name and allowable uses. Logical designations and the functions which fall to each can be listed as follows:

Classification of Areas Used for Wildlife Purposes

Name	Purpose	Other Allowable Uses
Sanctuary.	Absolute protection.	None.
Reserve.	Scientific study.	None.
Refuge.	Protection of certain species (or all species during a part of the year).	Any use not in conflict with refuge purpose.
Preserve.*	Wildlife management on a harvest basis.	Preserve uses may be secondary to other uses, in which case any use is allowable. If preserve idea is primary, other uses not in conflict are allowable.

* Other names often used are game area, game management area, game cooperative, game pool, and shooting preserve.

SUGGESTED READING

Bennett, Hugh Hammond, 1939, *Soil Conservation,* McGraw-Hill Book Co., New York.

Gabrielson, Ira N., 1941, *Wildlife Conservation,* The Macmillan Co., New York.

Gordon, Seth, Jr., 1941, "A Sampling Technique for the Determination of Hunter's Activities and the Economics Thereof," Jour. *Wildlife Management,* 5:260–278.

Graham, Edward H., 1944, *Natural Principles of Land Use,* Oxford University Press, New York.

Graham, Edward H., 1947, *The Land and Wildlife,* Oxford University Press, New York.

Grange, Wallace B., 1949, *The Way to Game Abundance with an Explanation of Game Cycles,* Charles Scribner's Sons, New York.

Havemeyer, Loomis (Editor), 1935, *Conservation of Our Natural Resources,* The Macmillan Co., New York.

Henderson, Junius, 1927, *The Practical Value of Birds,* The Macmillan Co., New York.

Henderson, Junius, and Elberta Craig, 1932, *Economic Mammalogy,* Charles C Thomas, Springfield, Ill.

Hillcourt, William, 1950, *Fieldbook of Nature Activities,* G. P. Putnam's Sons, New York.

King, Ralph T., 1938, "What Constitutes Training in Wildlife Management?" *Trans. Third N. A. Wildlife Conf.:* 548–557.

Leopold, Aldo, 1933, *Game Management,* Charles Scribner's Sons, New York.

Palmer, E. Laurence, 1949, *Fieldbook of Natural History,* Whittlesey House, McGraw-Hill Book Co., New York.

Stevens, Ross O., 1944, *Talk about Wildlife for Hunters, Fishermen, and Nature Lovers,* Bynum Printing Co., Raleigh, N. C.

Stoddart, Laurence A., and Arthur D. Smith, 1943, *Range Management,* McGraw-Hill Book Co., New York.

Van Dersal, William R., 1937, "The Dependence of Soils on Animal Life," *Trans. Second N. A. Wildlife Conf.:* 458–467.

2

The Biological Base of Management

Wildlife management is premised upon the fact that there are inherent biological characteristics of a species that favor or hamper management efforts. Thus if a character favors management efforts, we are working with natural biological principles; if it hampers us, we are working against them. These characteristics are treated here as the *biological base of management,* but elsewhere administrative, political, economic, agricultural, and other phases of management practice are considered. Inasmuch as all attributes operate simultaneously, wildlife management must take all into account, and the respective emphasis upon any or all is fundamentally a problem of decision, whose excellence will be governed by the judgment, knowledge, and experience of the man making the decision.

Food and Shelter. The fundamental needs of everyday animal life are food and shelter, to which all others are subordinate. Quantitative lack of food means starvation, emigration, or wandering; qualitative lack means physical weakness, loss of vigor, low reproduction, slow decline, and perhaps slow death. Lack of shelter in quality or quantity means low population success.

By "shelter" we mean locations where an animal may carry on its living activities in safety, where it may feed in safety, and where it may breed in safety. Shelter must protect from the elements as well as from "enemies." But of as great importance as protection from *real elements* and *real enemies* is satisfaction of the *instinctive needs of the species.* The instinctive behavior pattern is relatively fixed and operates upon the animal continually, though stress of exigencies (such as starvation or parental fear) may dull it. A bobwhite, for example, instinctively shuns poor cover, as though it fears that something will happen to it if it ventures into insecure areas.

Shelter must satisfy the animal pattern and the threshold of instinctive security. The mockingbird requires trees and open grassy areas, which is one reason why it is as abundant in southern home grounds as the robin in northern gardens. But if the lawn grows to tall grass, weeds, or brush, the mockingbird departs, to return again only when the grass forms a greensward again. Some birds, for example, may need perches higher than the surface of the forest canopy, and so the cutting of giant "wolf trees" may evict them just as a growth of brush may evict the mockingbird.

Pocket gophers become pests sometimes in irrigated alfalfa fields, but accurate leveling of the surface reduces the suitability to pocket gophers and therefore cuts down infestations. This simple act of perfection actually becomes a *management practice* based upon the animal preference for rough surfaces, which is a form of shelter suitability.

Food Chains. In all animal environments exists a series of energy transfers, beginning with the plants that derive their energy from the sun and, by photosynthesis, combine it with carbon dioxide, water, and minerals. Transfer of energy from the sun to the plants initiates the system. The plant-eater then gets its energy from the plant and passes it on to a meat-eater; henceforward transfer of energy is from one meat-eater to another, always from a smaller and more numerous prey to a larger (or fiercer) and less numerous predator. This series of energy transfers has been called *food chains* because of the linkage of each step to the others (Fig. 2.1). Food chains rarely exceed four or five links, by which time the end is reached—a predator with no apparent enemies. The top link of the food chain is generally controlled by territorial demands, which are strongest in predators. The many food chains of an animal community together form a *food web*.

Predation. Fundamentally predation is nothing more or less than a step in the energy cycle that we call food chains. At any stage in this energy cycle, organisms may cease to exist and the energy contained in their bodies may be converted by decomposition back into constituent compounds, then reincorporated into the habitats and made available for use again. But the transfer of energy may not cease so abruptly; it may be carried on up the food chain from animal to animal. Beyond the herbivores, we call this energy transfer *predation*.

If there were no hindrances to expansion, the biological pressure of any organism would soon expand it so greatly as to leave no room for

Predation

other life. That an organism does not crowd out all others is clear evidence that most biological pressure is doomed to dissipation against environmental resistance. This means simply that most reproduction must fail. It is obvious that every animal has some great advantage or it would not exist. On the other hand, every animal has some great weakness; otherwise no other animal could survive.

Nature has many ways of cutting down the biological pressure, and predation is one of them. Others are weather hazards, starvation, disease, accidents, and non-breeding. Predation, as should be ex-

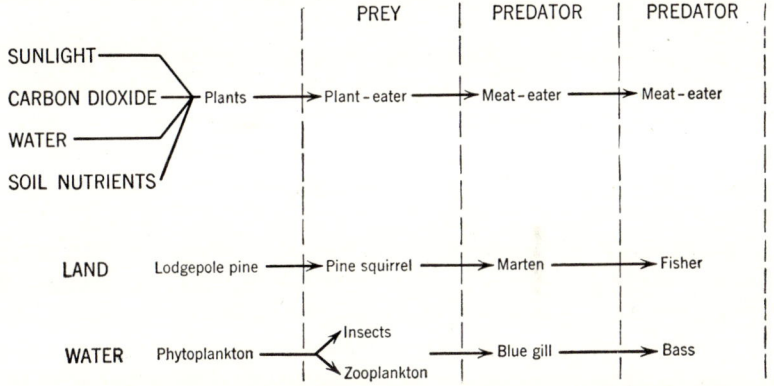

FIG. 2.1. Food chains such as these on land and in water transfer energy from plants to plant-eaters, which in turn pass it on to meat-eaters.

pected, varies with the number of animals in excess of the capacity of the environment to support them. It thus varies with the changes between biological pressure and environmental resistance. When environmental resistance builds up, the predation losses mount. As it declines, the losses decline. The same process occurs also if changes take place in the biological pressure.

Predation losses fall most heavily upon the less vigorous classes— the immature and the past-mature. Animals in their prime years are quite capable of caring for themselves unless weakened by disease, starvation, or other factors. Predation on the less vigorous animals indicates normal conditions. Predation upon prime animals usually indicates a weakness or breakdown in the environment.

Size of Food. The ability of an animal to conquer largely determines the *upper limit* to the size of animal food that an animal may eat. But fierceness and banding together may make up for lack of size, as shown by the weasel that preys upon much larger rabbits, or the wolf packs that preyed upon the bison of the prairies (the bison in turn banding together for greater defense). Among invertebrates and some vertebrates poisons serve to make up for lack of size or fierceness.

Structural limitations occur also, as the merganser shows when it tries to swallow a fish too large and has it lodged in the throat, but many birds and mammals bite off pieces or break up fruits that they cannot swallow whole. Thus insectivorous birds take bites out of a caterpillar, and wolves tear their prey. Usually the bill or jaw is powered especially for this.

The *lower limit* is governed by the size below which the animal is not compensated for its time. An eagle would not find it profitable to search the stubble fields for grasshoppers, but a kestrel does; the wolf would starve if it searched for mice as the fox does. But during times of abundance, as during a high of the lemming cycle, even the wolf may find it profitable to undertake mouse-feeding because of the unusual abundance of small units.

The food habits of herbivores, such as the grazing of bison or the browsing of deer, do not usually follow the rule of lower limits because plants stand still and allow "mass production." Seed-eaters may be limited, however, just as may meat-eaters. The sharp-tailed grouse, for example, can hardly afford to pick composite seeds one at a time like a goldfinch, and so the grouse usually feeds upon composites only when it can pick off whole heads in a mass-production act.

The number of food items in the stomach gives some idea of the food habits of animals towards their lower limit of food size. More than 10,000 seeds have been found in the stomach of a mallard, but these were obtained by eating flower-heads. The remains of some 5000 ants, which must have been picked up almost singly, appeared in the stomach of a yellow-shafted flicker. (The sticky tongue of the flicker, however, makes it possible to eat several at a time, though the ants must walk in almost singly.)

Food Quantity. In the course of evolution, the quantity of food eaten has become adjusted to the size of the animal, its activity, and its metabolic make-up in relation to the calories provided by the food. Herbivorous foods have fewer calories than animal foods, and a rather larger digestive system is needed to extract energy from them. The digestive system of a bovine is large and bulky in comparison to that of a carnivore. The intestine is especially long, and the stomach large and paunch-like. Animals feed upon more concentrated or more natural foods in cold weather than they do in warm weather. Blue grouse in pens, for example, fed upon grains freely until a cold snap hit, whereupon they deserted the grains for Douglas fir needles characteristically eaten by the species in winter. Sharp-tailed grouse have been found likewise to desert grains in feeding stations for the usual winter food of buds during cold spells. Hot-weather foods, on the other hand, may often be largely moisture-producing.

We have few figures on the number of calories in foods eaten in the wild or on the caloric demands of wild animals. Fats contain about 275 calories an ounce, proteins 120, and carbohydrates 120, though the calories actually released in the body seem to be several per cent less. The number of calories required varies, though not proportionately, with the animal bulk. Young animals require more than adults for each pound of body weight, and active animals require more than sluggish ones. Small animals require more per unit of body weight than large ones, especially in cold regions. The larger size of northern representatives of a species and the smaller size of southern ones reflects heat conservation and radiation needs. This tendency toward increase of size in cold climates and decrease in warm ones is known as the *Bergmann principle*. Man requires from 15 to 20 calories a day for each pound of body weight, but the caloric requirements of birds and mammals in the wild may be several times this number.

The caloric contents of common foods, according to nutritionists, are as tabulated. The values may provide some basis for evaluating wild foods.

Food	Calories per Pound	Food	Calories per Pound
Lean beef	800	Asparagus	80
Tenderloin beef	1600	Cabbage	65
Chicken	960	Carrots	100
Turkey	1200	Spinach	75
Eggs	1600	Mushrooms	200
Fish	550	Lettuce	65

One fair-sized ground squirrel should supply enough calories to last a coyote for a day or so (even if the squirrel is not particularly fat, as ground squirrels usually are), and one ptarmigan might sustain an arctic fox for several days. But it would take many pounds of the average forage to carry a deer for 24 hours.

As already indicated, the amount of food required to produce or sustain a pound of a wild organism is usually greater when spread over young than over adults or over small units, like small birds, than over larger ones. The amount of food required daily for newly hatched young may be as much as 50 per cent or more of the body weight. Some small insectivores are reported to consume more than their weight in animal food daily. It takes several times the body weight to produce a grown animal, and twelve times the body weight may be a conservative figure for a carnivore and perhaps thirty times for a herbivore. A pound of bass will need from 4 to 8 pounds of blue gills.

Food Quality. The basic food needs of an organism are *fats, proteins, carbohydrates, vitamins, minerals,* and *water* in varying proportions for energy and body repair. Sometimes food must also be eaten for *storage* in the form of body fats, as shown by the laying on, under the influence of endocrine glands, of fat by birds in preparation for migration or by mammals in preparation for hibernation. The digestive ability of an organism and its instinctive selection pattern, as has been previously mentioned, are adjusted to the food requirements of the body. Although it is a safe rule that natural foods suffice and usually are best for an organism, study of nutritional needs seems likely to indicate possibility of improvement.

Animals are able to recognize differences in foods, and some of these differences are clearly apparent to us. A fertilizer experiment on tree seedlings produced greater sucrose concentration in the leaves of maples after nitrogen fertilizing; deer fed upon the fertilized plots more than others. Deer eating laurel leaves in the Appalachian Mountains seemingly have greater immunity from toxic effects than have cattle, not because deer have a greater immunity but because they restrain their consumption of laurels. Animals are not always similarly affected by foods, however, even though the animals may be closely related, and so we may not judge deer foods, for example, by what a cow eats.

Water. Water requirements vary with the food, the weather, and the animal's ability to conserve water. All animals produce metabolic water, but only desert animals as a group have developed *water conservation* to the stage where they can exist indefinitely on metabolic water. Water conservation is attained by *habits*, such as nocturnal or burrowing habits that allow escape from diurnal heat and low humidity; by *structure*, such as possession of scales or protective skin; or by *physiological habits*, such as the excretion of dry feces that waste little water.

Physiological Needs. It is obvious that a number of factors enter into the eating habits of animals. Perhaps the most important internal ones and the hardest to measure are the physiological needs of the organism. Possibly abundance and habit, as much as physiological requirements, determine many of the foods eaten, as indicated, for example, by the shifting in *key species* from area to area in the elk and deer range. Many animals feed largely in proportion to the abundance of the various foods in the habitat. The body needs of the animal no doubt do influence habits, but measuring these needs is difficult. We recognize "meat hunger" (probably protein lack) in our own bodies, and no doubt animals have similar cravings. The water craving certainly is definite. The abandoning of grains in favor of needles and buds by the blue grouse and sharp-tailed grouse, as previously mentioned, may reflect a body need, although independent response to instinct cannot be overlooked. (The blue grouse mentioned were young during their first winter and their first experience with snow and cold, which rules out habit.) Nestling birds are fed a diet high in moisture and protein, which is an instinctive adjustment of the parents to their growth requirements. Even fruit- and seed-eating birds feed the young a diet largely of insects. A high protein diet is essential for growth and body repair, and an adequate protein intake assures a stable mitotic rhythm. (The mitotic rhythm goes on continually, though more or less inversely to body activity; it reaches its highest point just before dawn, during sleep.)

Taste no doubt enters into the eating habits of animals, particularly of mammals, and to a lesser degree into the habits of birds. The *low palatability* of foods in fall and the ready eating of them in late winter may reflect differences not necessarily associated with body needs. We know surprisingly little of the relationship of palatability and body requirements.

Starvation and Survival. Most of our interest in starvation concerns survival in cold weather. The body temperature control normally maintains a balance between the production, or intake, and the outgo of heat. An excess of production or intake, or a lowering of outgo, means a rise in body temperature, which if prolonged above normal means death. A gain of outgo over production means a drop of body temperature and ensuing lethargy, which may not be particularly serious. But if the downward trend continues, freezing to death results.

The production of heat is normally adequate to care for outgo when food is sufficient. A well-fed bird or mammal is not likely to freeze to death within its normal range. Only under extreme circumstances, such as wind exposure, ice encrustment on the body, wet plumage, or wet pelage, may heat loss be great enough to cause freezing to death in a well-fed bird or mammal in its own habitat. Because fish are poikilothermous and live in a liquid medium, they need fear freezing only in areas where the water freezes to the bottom. Solid freezing may occur in mountain lakes but seldom elsewhere.

The bird or mammal in its native range has time enough during the short hours of the winter day to obtain sufficient food to carry through the long night, but whether or not it can find the food is another story. Animals seek shelter during the night or during severe weather, and this habit probably maintains the balance between heat production and loss. In mountain and hilly country animals may shift their day and night positions to take advantage of warm currents or strata of air. No doubt an animal in the wild feels cold just as we do, and the discomfort of cold releases instinctive reactions. These may take the form of fluffing the plumage, seeking shelter, or turning to the wind, as well as production of more heat by increased oxidation in the cells. Shivering with cold is a muscular activity for heat generation. If oxidation uses up available heat resources, the animal freezes to death.

Migratory birds seem to be unadjusted to the winter day-night ratio in their breeding range and are therefore unable to carry through long nights at low temperature. In the higher latitudes the alien house sparrows roosting in rafters and silos have been known to freeze to death during extremely cold nights, while sparrows burrowed into straw stacks and hay mows survived. Native birds have survived in the woods at the same time. Some similar relationships of game birds and mammals, particularly exotic species, to weather have been noted. But the bird or mammal that is evicted from or unable to reach suitable shelter in inclement weather may die of cold even in its home range.

Body Size and Weight. Although body weight and weight changes are good indexes of human health, they are definitely limited in indicating the health of a wild animal. Generally speaking, only in cases of starvation or prolonged unfavorable conditions will body weight readily indicate serious range trouble, but range indicators themselves will already have shown the same thing in a more practical way. Areas of poor soil or forage perhaps may consistently produce below-average animals; body weights can indicate this, and the preparation of habitat standards of growth and body weights might be a useful undertaking for the wildlife biologist.

Among fish, body size and weight are especially important characters because fish have *indeterminate growth;* the age of fish can be determined from scales. The growth and size of fish are clearer indicators of the conditions in the habitat than the same traits are for land animals.

Body tissue, stored fats, water content, and food in the digestive tract all combine to form body weight. Body weight varies daily, weekly, and seasonally. Since increased fat deposition as a prelude to migration increases the body weight of migratory birds, their weight at the migration seasons is significant.

Mass increases as to the *cube,* and surface with the *square,* so that increased size benefits animals in cold regions by giving less surface per unit of mass. The same mass in more units is an advantage in warm regions where radiation of heat has greater importance than its conservation. As already mentioned, representatives of a homoiothermous species tend to be larger in cooler regions and smaller in warm regions in accordance with the *Bergmann principle.* It is thus normal for the bobwhite to weigh 130 grams in Texas and 190 grams in Wisconsin; a 75-pound Florida deer is as normal as a 200-pound Ontario one.

Animals of the cold climates tend to reduce projections and extremities (*Allen rule*) as a protection against heat loss. The ears of the Arctic hare, for example, are much smaller than those of rabbits inhabiting mild climates. Long-tailed mammals rarely reach areas of intense cold; thus only short-tailed cats (*Lynx*) reach the Arctic, as compared to the long-tailed ones (*Felis*) farther south.

Psychological Needs of Animals. The psychological responses of animals include the satisfaction of instinctive requirements, following of innate and conditioned patterns, reactions to stimuli, and reactions to the disturbances attendant upon the "sense of well being." Feeding upon meat by a carnivore is basically a response to the meat-eating instinct. Meat is good for carnivores because they have evolved a digestive system for its use and an instinct for choosing it. The odor of meat releases the feeding reaction, though it may be dulled if the animal has eaten its fill. Only foods within the instinct pattern release the feeding reaction. A rabbit responds to clover but not to a mouse, just as the fox recognizes the mouse but not the clover as food. The feeding reaction of the phoebe is released by a flying insect but not by a crawling ant. A passing minnow or flashing bait will release the preying instinct of a bass, though it will not interest a clam on the bottom. The adjustment of reactions and releases is thus a basic instinct pattern for each species.

The need for shelter has already been discussed, though that need is also basically a matter of instinctive requirements and their satisfaction. The instinct pattern of the prairie chicken causes it to seek the open, but that of the ruffed grouse sends it into the forest. Conditions that satisfy one repel the other. Within the major habitat choice are different instinct patterns; the sage grouse seeks the open, but invariably only sagebrush (*Artemisia*) provides the chief component of its instinct pattern.

Habit and *tradition* no doubt play an important part in the operation of the instinct pattern, but sometimes it is hard to separate instinct from habit or tradition. Habit may be considered as repeated acquired acts of an individual, whereas tradition is combined of the collective acts handed down by association from generation to generation. The wintering and breeding of many populations in restricted areas generation after generation can be explained by tradition. In the same way, many big game animals of the West regularly cross certain passes or routes year after year by tradition. Similarly, prairie chickens have returned for many years to the same booming grounds, even though none today could possibly have boomed there a score or even several score years ago. Many of these booming grounds are situated on little rises of ground, but many others, it must be added, appear to differ not at all from the acres of surrounding prairie.

Territory. The role of territory is indeed a critical one, worthy of a whole chapter or even a book, and the student should certainly go deeper into it by further reading. Although some animals appear to have no discernible territorial demands, most of the species with which the field biologist or wildlife manager will work are territory-conscious.

The most significant territory is breeding territory, as shown by so many common birds and mammals, particularly predatory ones, in which territorial aspirations are especially pronounced. Each animal takes up an area from which it (usually only the male) excludes others of its kind. Territory has a number of biological functions, but its most important action from the management standpoint is the limitation of numbers. A marsh may have quantities of food for canvasback or mottled ducks, but still the number of breeding pairs may be only six if there is territory enough for only six, for the concept of territory includes both space and habitat needs. Territory may become so small as to include only the nest proper among colonial birds, yet so large as to embrace square miles among the predators.

Biologists recognize *winter territory, flock territory, roosting territory,* and sometimes additional or specialized types in addition to *breeding territory.*

Territorial animals assert their ownership in many ways, such as by singing or driving out intruders. Territorial animals ordinarily do not interfere with other species except where shortage of essential needs brings on interspecies strife, as among hole-nesting birds. The biologist can determine territory in the field, especially among birds, by watching for conflicts, the sign of territorial consciousness. Marked animals make it especially helpful in working out territorial relations, but marking, banding, or trapping is not always essential. One who has watched mottled ducks on the Gulf Coast marshes need only watch the males drive out intruders to identify territorial holdings. Even though the male mottled duck drives out intruding males and even pairs, he ignores tree ducks in the same rice fields.

Home range, as the name implies, is the area over which an animal wanders without excluding others. Most rodents have home ranges, often but a hundred yards across, over which they travel freely, each individual with his own separate range overlapping those of others. Individual territory in the sense of exclusive occupation is absent; deer, rabbits, and others exhibit this same home-range tendency.

Sex Ratios. Ordinarily we think of only two types of mating habits, monogamy and polygamy, with sex ratios accordingly adjusted. In the state of monogamy two individuals, male and female, pair together for breeding. The pairing may be of varying duration; it may be for copulation only, for production of one nest or litter of young, for an entire season, or for life. The last occurs usually in predatory birds and mammals. Obviously monogamy, except when it is temporary, demands a one-to-one sex ratio.

Polygamy among animals in our region involves a single male mated to several females rather than the converse type of polygamy where several males are attached to a single female (which has been reported elsewhere). Successful polygamy requires an uneven sex ratio—that is, more females than males. Otherwise the conflicts of males seeking mates or territory for breeding would result in a lower breeding efficiency. There seem to be three principal means for achieving in nature the uneven sex ratios necessary for polygamy: deferred maturity, differential sex mortality, and communal courtship.

The sex chromosomes are produced equally at maturation, and differential sex mortality occurs after that. Deferred maturity may be morphological or physiological, as it is in young males that reach full maturity a season or more later than the young females. But deferred maturity seems most likely to reflect a low sex-hormone level of the young male. Thus young gobblers produce viable sperm at one year of age but do not mate with females in the wild, apparently because of competition from adult males. Young females, however, reproduce at the age of one year. By the second year, the gobbler is able to compete with older gobblers. In the same way, young buck deer are unable to serve females because of competition from old bucks. Only when old bucks engage in conflict and leave the does unattended can young bucks succeed in serving the does. First-year male blue grouse can successfully fertilize the eggs of captive females, but they do not do so in the wild. These first-year males do not develop the secondary sexual characters of the older males, nor do they engage in the elaborate courtship performance of the mature male. In fact, they probably perform none of the characteristic courtship acts in the first year.

Promiscuity has been reported in some species, particularly among the prairie grouse (prairie chicken, sharp-tailed grouse, and sage grouse). It may occur also among some rodents and perhaps among some of the larger herbivores, such as the bison and caribou. The males of the prairie grouse group carry on a communal courtship in which the males congregate at dancing or booming grounds, where they remain during the breeding season. Each male has his own little stand, usually a short path, where he performs throughout the season. The females come to the courtship grounds for copulation. The males stay within the limits of their respective stands, which assures undisturbed mating between females and chosen males irrespective of the sex ratio. Dominant males, however, may do most of the breeding, and young or less dominant ones may do none. Communal courtship thus may be but a manifestation of promiscuity.

Mobility. Mobility is a measure of the wandering habits of animals, and it probably measures a combination of instinctive nervous tendencies and physical ability. The bobwhite, for example, is an animal of low mobility, as evidenced by its spending days or weeks in a circumscribed area. Rarely does the average bobwhite die a distance as great as a mile from its hatching place. The mourning dove, on the other hand, is rather more mobile, and occasionally very much so. In the dry regions, for example, it may fly many miles daily for food or water. The average white-tailed deer moves little during the day or season as compared to the elk or mule deer, which are more mobile. Carnivorous birds and mammals have a mobility greater than that of their prey.

Breeding Potential and Productivity. Every animal has a capacity to breed that is far greater than the actual number of offspring that reach maturity. The average mature bobwhite female lays 14 eggs and lives perhaps through two laying seasons. Thus the original pair would have increased to 16 the first year and 128 the second if all eggs hatched, all young matured, and all young in turn were successful in reproducing. This theoretical breeding rate under ideal conditions is the *breeding potential,* low in large animals but high in many fishes and insects. The breeding potential measures the reproductive capacity of the species.

Within the environment exist untold factors that resist the expansion of a species—unfavorable weather, enemies, mistakes, starvation, and many others. Collectively, we term these *environmental resistance.* The operations of environmental resistance upon the breeding potential reduces the number of young reaching maturity and gives *productivity,* the actual reproduction attained. Together with the surviving individuals, it gives the *population,* and so population may be expressed as the difference between the breeding potential and environmental resistance. Mathematically it may be expressed as: $P = BP - ER$. We shall see in the analysis of population biology that a further refinement of our working concept of this formula becomes necessary.

Density and Saturation Point. The number of animals relative to space gives the *density,* often measured in terms of units per 100 acres, though many westerners and northerners use the section (640 acres). Thus a high density of deer might be 4 per 100 acres, or about 25 to the section. This can also be expressed as about 25 acres per deer.

It has been noticed that, throughout the range of a species, the maximum density reached in the choicest of environments remains about the same. This maximum appears to be a measure of the spatial needs of the individual, rather than the amount of food and cover available, and seems to be independent of the environment. It has been designated as the *saturation point,* and for practical purposes it represents the lower limit to which the species will permit itself to be squeezed. The saturation point of bobwhites appears to be about one to two acres, of the mockingbird one to a half-acre. *The saturation point is a function of the animal psychological pattern, rather than of the land.* Obviously it limits the number of breeding individuals possible in an area, just as the space needs of laying hens limit the number that can be housed in a chicken coop and still give maximum egg production. But here the parallel ends, and a good rule to follow has been stated as "all bets off in the slums of domestication or confinement."

Carrying Capacity. Land has attraction or lack of attraction to a species according to how well it supplies the life essentials. As has been said before, these essentials are food, cover, and such other requirements as the species may have. Obviously the critical time of the year will be most important, and in our regions the pinch period usually is winter, although it is summer in the dry lands. The number for which an area can provide essentials and thus carry through the pinch period is designated as the *carrying capacity*. It stands to reason that, regardless of the essentials available, an area can never carry more than the *saturation point*. It stands to reason also that an area will not be able to sustain more than its carrying capacity in safety and that all above this capacity are subject to loss, just as all water in excess of 4 quarts is subject to loss if it is poured into a gallon jug or if the container shrinks to a gallon.

Ecological Factors. Many factors affect animal life, and it would require volumes to discuss all of them. Perhaps the most fundamental of the ecological factors is *climate*. The influence of climate and weather exceeds that of all others in the long run, and often in the day-to-day life of the animal also. The chief elements are *temperature, humidity, precipitation,* and *wind*. There exist many lesser ones, such as *cloudiness* and the progressive changes that have gone on for ages. But there are seasonal variations, however, that are of transcendent importance, such as drought, severe winters, and cold springs.

Birds and mammals have developed temperature control and are called *homoiothermous,* meaning a temperature constant regardless of the surrounding medium. Others are called *poikilothermous* because their temperature rises and falls with the surrounding medium. In common language we call them warm-blooded and cold-blooded. Without temperature control, land animals of cold or cool regions would become inactive in winter and often at night. Their penetration into cold and cool regions would be restricted or impossible but for their warm-bloodedness.

For the most part, animals are unable to withstand prolonged temperature much above blood heat, but 122° F seems to be the top limit for plants. Coagulation of body proteins appears to be the initial effect of high temperature in tissue, just as formation of ice crystals in the cells is the first destructive effect of freezing. Yet no atmospheric temperature is too low for plant and animal life as such, and life exists in all land and water areas of the globe.

Ecological Factors

The ecological effect of the light is rather marked, particularly upon marine organisms. It plays an important role in the success of many plants, as we may readily see in shade-tolerant forest trees. It also influences bird migration and perhaps hibernation of mammals. Animals that are active in the daylight are designated as *diurnal;* those active at night, *nocturnal.* Animals of the twilight are said to be *crepuscular.*

The *oxygen* content of the atmosphere is roughly 21 per cent, and that of water may reach 10 per cent at freezing temperature. (It is zero at boiling.) Some fish, like the trout, have become adapted to a high oxygen content; others, like the catfish, can live in waters low in oxygen. Pollution and stagnation reduce the oxygen content of water.

Water varies also in its mineral and organic content; water at the head of some mountain streams is practically distilled water. Sea water, too, varies in fertility as well as salinity; fertility reaches its richest point in the high latitudes and its poorest in low ones. Water in the air (humidity) affects evaporation from the body of animals, but only animals especially adapted to dry air are able to survive in the desert. Animal and plant life both become richer with an increase of humid conditions.

The *soil* plays an important role in determining the plant life upon which animals depend. It is truly said that only rich soils support a rich fauna. Plants grow faster, produce more, and are more luxuriant in rich soils. Soil studies show that soils may be low in potash or phosphates as well as trace elements, and animals living upon the forage of these soils may show nutritional deficiencies. In *experimental aquariums* fish have demonstrated greater differences in growth in water *conditioned* through use by others of their kind than in unconditioned water. This has not been shown for animals in the wild but each stage of plant succession seems to condition the site for the following one. Artificial maintaining of ecological unbalance may disturb the microflora and microfauna of the soil and give "soil sickness."

Topographical influences are most apparent in mountain lands, especially near the dry margin. North-facing slopes are wettest, south-facing ones driest. West-facing slopes are usually drier than east-facing ones because the sun pours in during the afternoon when the air temperature is high.

A rise in altitude means cooler conditions, for temperature declines at about 3.5° F for each 1000 feet of altitude. Although in a general way this has an effect similar to that of a poleward movement, it is not directly so because the day length remains the same. Organisms at high altitudes receive far more insolation, particularly in the short end of the spectrum, than polar ones. Nevertheless, Arctic conditions and Arctic species extend southward on mountain tops and higher altitudes, just as southern species spread northward in the valleys and lowlands. (Although the area above timberline is often called *tundra*, it should properly be called *mountain tundra*.)

Environment. The mixing of plant species, one of the most important of ecological factors, has been designated as *interspersion*. An even-aged or single-tree forest has far fewer animals within its borders than an all-age or mixed forest. Most animals need several different vegetation types, perhaps three or four, although a few, like the bison of the grasslands, seem able to live on one. Maximum populations require adequate vegetation types within the mobility limits of the species. The *edge effect* is but an expression of interspersion at the junction (*ecotone*) of two or more vegetation types.

Environmental factors are sometimes listed as *welfare factors* (food, water, shelter, etc.) that benefit the species, and *decimating factors* that act upon the individual (accidents, starvation, enemies, etc.); both are related, and the absence of a welfare factor may mean the presence of a decimating factor, as when lack of food means death by starvation.

Ecological Succession. In a given area certain groups of plants tend to grow and certain groups of animals to live. Climate determines those that shall occupy an area, though soil and other factors play a subordinate role. The sequence of change from bare ground to the plants and animals characteristic of an area follows definite steps which are called *stages*. The entire process is called *ecological succession* (plant succession and animal succession). Each stage follows in definite order the preceding stage and will in turn be succeeded by the proper stage until the end or *climax* is reached. The climax is the permanent stage that maintains itself under the given climatic conditions.

Ecological succession is a one-way street, irreversible in nature. As land managers, we can throw the succession back to a lower stage (though we may not hit the one we aim for) by plowing, burning, and other operations. We can speed it up by planting and like helps to nature, though just how successfully we can bypass a stage is open to question.

The succession stages on land (*xerosere*) beyond the bare ground or bare rock stage may be listed as:

Forest Region	Grass Region
Crustose lichens	Crustose lichens
Foliose lichens	Foliose lichens
Moss	Moss
Annuals	Annuals
Perennials	Perennials
Shrubs	Climax grass
Climax forest	

The succession stages in water (*hydrosere*) are:

Submerged
Floating
Reed-swamp
Sedge-meadow
Shrubs (if a forest region)
Climax (forest or grass depending upon region)

Examples of plant succession are:

	Years
Pacific Northwest	
Bare ground	
Lichens and mosses	1–2
Annuals	1–3
Forbs	2–5
Shrubs	5–20
Douglas fir	20–300
Hemlock	Permanent
Tennessee Highlands	
Bare ground	
Annuals	1–3
Forbs	2–5
Grass	4–6
Shrubs	5–15
Forest	Permanent

Ecologists use the term *climax* to denote a vegetation stage adjusted to the climate so that it is permanent. A subclimax is one persisting for long periods as if it were a climax, often as the result of fire or soil (*edaphic*) conditions.

Ecological Divisions. Several major ecological regions have been set up for convenience in biological studies, and concepts of *life zones*, *biomes*, and *biotic provinces* have resulted. All have great merit, although none fits all needs, and much can be said for each one. The biologist on the ground, however, will find it easier to use *vegetation zones,* such as post oak, oak-hickory, and spruce-fir. An example of altitudinal vegetation zones in the northern intermountain region is:

Sedge-grass	Ponderosa pine
Spruce-fir	Fescue-wheat grass
Arborvitae-hemlock	Wheat grass-blue grass
Douglas fir	Sagebrush-grass

SUGGESTED READING

Allee, W. C., Alfred E. Emerson, Orlando Park, Thomas Park, and Karl P. Schmidt, 1949, *Principles of Animal Ecology,* W. E. Saunders Co., Philadelphia.

Allen, Glover M., 1925, *Birds and Their Attributes,* Marshall Jones Co., Boston.

Chase, Warren W., and Elizabeth B. Beard, 1947, *Teaching Aids in Wildlife Management; Outline of the Principles of Wildlife Management,* Edwards Bros., Ann Arbor, Mich.

Clements, Frederic E., and Victor E. Shelford, 1939, *Bio-ecology,* John Wiley & Sons, New York.

Daubenmire, R. F., 1947, *Plants and Environment; a Textbook of Autecology,* John Wiley & Sons, New York.

Elton, Charles, 1936, *Animal Ecology,* The Macmillan Co., New York.

Errington, Paul L., 1942, "On the Analysis of Productivity in Populations of Higher Vertebrates," *Jour. Wildlife Management,* 6:165–181.

Errington, Paul L., 1946, "Predation and Vertebrate Populations," *Quart. Rev. Biol.,* 21:144–177, 221–245.

Grange, Wallace B., 1949, *The Way to Game Abundance with an Explanation of Game Cycles,* Charles Scribner's Sons, New York.

Hamilton, W. J., Jr., 1939, *American Mammals; Their Lives, Habits, and Economic Relations,* McGraw-Hill Book Co., New York.

Hesse, Richard, W. C. Allee, and Karl Schmidt, 1937, *Ecological Animal Geography,* John Wiley & Sons, New York.

Kyle, H. M., 1926, *The Biology of Fishes,* Sedgwick and Jackson, Ltd., London.

Leopold, Aldo, 1933, *Game Management,* Charles Scribner's Sons, New York.

Mayr, Ernst, 1939, "The Sex Ratio of Wild Birds," *Am. Naturalist,* 73:156–179.

McAtee, W. L., 1947, "The Distribution of Seeds by Birds," *Am. Midland Naturalist,* 38:214–223.

Nice, Margaret Morse, 1941, "The Role of Territory in Bird Life," *Am. Midland Naturalist,* 26:441–487.

Oosting, Henry J., 1948, *The Study of Plant Communities; an Introduction to Plant Ecology,* W. H. Freeman Co., San Francisco.

Pearse, A. S., 1939, *Animal Ecology,* McGraw-Hill Book Co., New York.

Pitelka, Frank A., 1941, "Distribution of Birds in Relation to Major Biotic Communities," *Am. Midland Naturalist,* 25:113–137.

Weaver, J. E., and F. E. Clements, 1938, *Plant Ecology,* McGraw-Hill Book Co., New York.

Welch, Paul S., 1935, *Limnology,* McGraw-Hill Book Co., New York.

3

The Biological Base of Management (Continued)

The forester talks about timber stands and concerns himself primarily with the management of timber stands. The wildlife biologist deals with *animal populations,* which are in a sense analogous to timber stands. (Game managers sometime use the term *game stand.*) An understanding of animal population biology is fundamental to management practice.

Internal Adjustment Factors. As we saw previously, population results from the action of two forces: breeding potential and environmental resistance. The breeding potential is relatively fixed for a species, but it may vary a little in different parts of the range. Those species living in the warmer parts of the range may have more broods or litters a year than those of the high latitudes, where the short season usually permits birds to nest but once and mammals to have few litters. The number of bird eggs varies also, tending to be larger in the cooler regions. Probably these geographical variations are genetic variations of populations, just as geographical variations of genetic origin occur in color, size, and song. These variations are important population adjustments to climate. Cold-blooded vertebrates behave similarly to warm-blooded ones in many of their adjustments.

Changes occur in the reproductive rates of animals as their numbers increase, and reproduction tends to drop when numbers increase to a maximum. These phase changes or alternations, which will be discussed shortly, represent internal adjustment factors of the organism. The population formula should take account of these internal adjustment factors (IAF) and be represented as

$$P = \frac{BP}{IAF} - ER$$

The Population Curve. Years ago investigators noted the tendency of populations to rise rather rapidly in their initial stages, then rise more slowly, and finally to reach a stable level. This tendency has been designated as the S or *sigmoid curve* of population. Although this curve has been demonstrated very clearly in laboratory experiments and human census figures, its demonstration as a principle in the wild is not so clear. Several cases of exotic animals in new environments show that the sigmoid curve of population does operate in unconfined (not necessarily native) populations. Thus the exotic rabbits released in Australia built up a total that faithfully followed the population curve. The English sparrow, so far as available evidence shows, did the same thing, and the starling and pheasant currently demonstrate this principle. Fish also show it in newly built ponds or ponds that have been restocked after fish have been removed.

Evidence appears to indicate that some populations may actually rise above the leveling-off stage and then drop down before becoming stabilized, a factor that may be involved in some of the reported declines of pheasants and Hungarian partridges after an apparent high degree of successful establishment. The leveling process involves many factors of environmental resistance, among them competition for space. Space, we must not forget, is as limited and space requirements are as fixed for animals in the wild as for orchard trees or field crops.

Minimum Numbers. Several species and races of birds, mammals, and fishes have become extinct in North America, along with additional ones elsewhere in the world. Somewhere along the downward path the population numbers are believed to have become too few for rebuilding of the species, and extinction was the result. About 200 birds seemed the fateful low for the heath hen. This minimum number for recovery has been termed the *extinction threshold*. A vigorous species in optimum or equivalent range may conceivably not have a low density limit; one gravid doe rabbit might be sufficient to populate an indefinite area, which was almost an actual occurrence in Australia. The same may be true for the starling and similar vigorous species, but the large number of failures in importing exotics indicates that the ability to establish a population is possessed by few organisms. Experiences with Hungarian partridges indicate a few successes with large plantings where small ones failed; the matter of minimum numbers seems to have marked the difference.

The size of an isolated remnant that can survive also measures the effect of minimum densities. Forty acres is assumed to be the minimum isolated woodlot that will hold ruffed grouse. About ten antelope appear to be the minimum herd that can survive independently, and approximately eight bobwhites the minimum number that can survive as an independent covey. Groups below the minimum number must merge with others or disappear.

No doubt small areas fail to satisfy the life requirements of a species, even though the acreage may be greater than the average territory of a pair. Psychological requirements probably enter into the minimum, for coveys and herds instinctively watch for unfavorable approaches of enemies and other animals. Small group size upsets the instinctive balance, but how far reaching it may be we cannot say. During the winter, small flocks of gregarious birds display significantly greater nervousness than the main body of the flock. The firmer sense of security in the normal flock probably assures more living success.

Estrus cycles are known for mammals, but similar occurrences in birds have not been established. There exists, nevertheless, a sequence of physiological and psychological developments associated with the approach of breeding seasons, and mating success requires a minimum number for pairing of individuals in the same stage of development.

In a thinly distributed population there is less chance for members of the two sexes to contact each other than in a population of normal density. Thus if only one pair of deer lives in Texas, they might roam for a lifetime without getting out of the state and never find each other; the only pair of sturgeon in Lake Michigan might swim for a century and never meet. These examples are extreme, but they illustrate the fact that too thinly spread populations mean no survival.

Phase Alternations. Chance relationship between random phenomena is 50:50, but when we deal with a run of three, the chance relationship becomes 2:1. Thus the chance of any year being wet or dry is 50:50, but, if the second year is wetter than the first year, the chances of the third year being drier than the second is 2:1 because we are considering a run of three. The same 50:50 ratio for a run of two, and 2:1 ratio for a run of three, holds for any other random data. This includes animal populations. If the relationships are not 50:50 or 2:1 for the respective runs, definite causes other than chance are indicated.

The breeding potential systematically presses upward against environmental resistance, and any downward or leveling-off tendencies, temporary or permanent, usually are significant. A sustained small variation from random builds up in time. Increases in population are normal directional expressions of reproduction; declines are more complex.

In a state of nature the *biological balance* represents the evolutionary adjustment between breeding pressure and environmental resistance. In a general way, as had been said elsewhere, the number of eggs laid or young born during the breeding period reflects the *life hazards* of the species. Thus the salmon that lays thousands of eggs has a much greater life hazard than the bear that gives birth to a single cub in alternate years. But the pressure for increase exists in both cases and is upward; hence, any trends other than upward are variations from the *animal normal*.

Alternations occur in nature, some readily explainable but others not. A breeding population tends to decrease its productivity with *increase* of abundance and to increase it with a *decline* in numbers. This alternation is an inverse relationship of abundance and reproduction. Flight years of northern birds, particularly grosbeaks, tend to alternate so that grosbeaks are usually absent the year after a flight but return the second or *alternate* year. Red-breasted nuthatches come in large numbers in about two out of three years, which is reminiscent of random numbers in runs of three. We do not know why these birds show alternating phases rather than the regular yearly visits that are normal for migratory birds.

Growth Rates. Animal growth follows a general pattern of rapid increase during the days immediately after birth or hatching, followed by a tapering off and final cessation as maturity approaches. Fish, some invertebrate animals, and possibly other animals show a tendency for slower growth when population pressures are high.

Small animals mature faster than large ones, just as bushes grow more rapidly than trees. Mice, for example, may reach maturity in less than a month; goldfinches leave the nest when about ten days old. But grouse and larger animals take all summer or even several years to reach maturity.

Animals characteristically have determinant growth, a type in which the animal early reaches a definite size and then stops growing. But fish have *indeterminant* growth and continue to grow throughout life, like a tree. In fish, growth has a seasonal tendency associated with nutrition, greater in warm weather than cold, which accounts for *annuli* in scales, usable for age determination. Indeterminant growth does not commonly occur in birds and mammals, except in such instances as the horns of bighorn sheep (which, like fish, have seasonal growth marks that make age determination possible) and the hair and beard in man.

Sexual maturity may be delayed for some time after *physical maturity* is reached. Among birds, for example, the bald eagle reaches full size in the first summer of life, but it does not breed until it is three or four years old, when sexual maturity presumably is reached. The attainment of sexual maturity before physical maturity does not usually occur in vertebrates, though it may occur among large and slow-growing animals. Human females may breed at twelve or thirteen and continue to grow for several years thereafter, just as a heifer may breed during its second year and grow larger for another couple of years. Similar irregularities have been reported among big game, but they are not usual. Among invertebrates regular breeding may occur in the larval state, which is called *paedogenesis*. The breeding of young animals, like subadult bald eagles, is sometimes called paedogenesis also.

Gregariousness and Flocking Habits. Animals of the open habitats tend to be more gregarious than those of other habitats. Burrowing rodents, like prairie dogs and ground squirrels, provide an example of such gregarious behavior. The great herds of bison and caribou also exemplify the gregariousness of open-country animals. The big-game herds of Africa live in the savanna, the tropical grassland. Predators of the open country also tend to become gregarious as a complementary adjustment to prey gregariousness.

Forest birds and mammals show far more solitary habits than those of the open or brush; those of the brush have intermediate habits, just as brush is intermediate between open vegetation and the forest canopy. The forest hinders vision as well as physical passage, and forest animals come to rely heavily on a keen sense of smell rather than vision and speed. Fleetfootedness, fast flight, and keen eyesight characterize animals of the open. Deer, though evolutionarily a recent invader of the forest, already show this difference; the mule deer is faster of foot and keener of sight than the whitetail, but the whitetail has the keener sense of smell.

Flocking habits reflect gregariousness, which reaches its peak in winter or sometimes in the migration seasons. The decline of gregariousness with the coming of the breeding season in most birds, for example, presumably reflects the increase of antagonism associated with sex hormone elaboration. The shift from gregariousness during most of the year to solitariness in the short breeding season needs considerable study. Colonial birds show gregarious tendencies throughout the breeding season, but even colonial birds show solitary traits in the breeding season, as though they nest together but live alone.

The largest flocks (which probably indicates high gregariousness) occur among migratory birds and the smallest among sedentary ones. Pileated woodpeckers, for example, rarely band together in numbers greater than a pair. Migrating hawks usually migrate in singles or small groups; the Swainson and broad-winged hawks, however, often migrate in large flocks. It seems likely that the concentration of migrating predatory birds in flocks gives less opportunity for hunting successfully than the same number scattered and migrating individually. The Swainson hawk and especially the broad-winged hawk have solved this dilemma by migrating almost straight through to winter or summer quarters.

The inception of flocking in birds begins in midsummer, sometimes among males before nesting is over. The initial grouping seems to be by family groups and aggregations thrown together by habitat distribution. Flocking begins earlier in high latitudes, sometimes many weeks before that in low latitudes; likewise flock break-up occurs later, and the solitary period is consequently shorter in high latitudes.

Some psychological control that is not understood regulates the size of the flock. Some species gather into huge flocks, whereas others rarely form flocks larger than a few individuals. The passenger pigeon flocked in numbers running into millions, but the mourning dove seldom forms flocks larger than a few dozen. The white-necked raven flocks may number several hundred, but the American raven flock infrequently reaches even a dozen. Rafts of scaup ducks may total 10,000, but mergansers usually flock in units of fewer than a score. Whole families may show the same trend. The cats and wrens seldom group together, for example, but the bovines and icterids almost always go in flocks.

Sex and Age Flocks. Some differences occur in flocking habits of the two sexes and of the old and young. Males of many waterfowl band together during the latter part of the breeding season, and this tendency for *packs* to be made up mostly of males may continue into winter. Where this occurs, the young usually remain with the females; even in fall and winter the males found in flocks that are largely female are usually birds-of-the-year. Young mammals likewise often run with the females, while the old males group together after the breeding season. Young of an earlier litter among a few carnivores may remain with the mother and her succeeding litter. This is true of young females more than it is of young males.

Wintering bird populations show a tendency for the males to winter farther north and the females farther south. Geographical disproportions in sex ratios indicate this tendency. Similarly male birds move northward earlier in the spring than females do, as though males had greater resistance to cold, storm, and severe weather. Actually, however, their earlier migration is due to the fact that the breeding cycle starts a bit earlier in the male.

Species Associations. Different species in nature usually remain independent of each other, although some may be associated together, particularly in winter. Waterfowl are rather tolerant of each other and on occasion form interspecies flocks in migration and on winter grounds, but the usual mixture is a scattering of one species in a flock of others. The blue and snow goose associate together more freely than other geese, which probably reflects their close relationship, if not their unity of species. The prairie chicken and the sharp-tailed grouse associate together more than other gallinaceous birds, even to courtship display near each other. Mixing of broods may occur among them too. It may also occur between blue and ruffed grouse.

Among many of the smaller birds are several groups that associate together regularly in winter flocks. The chickadees, downy woodpecker, nuthatches, and brown creeper flock rather freely together, as do several of the Icteridae, Fringillidae, and Parulidae. Observable preferences occur between associating species, like the several chickadee species that associate with each other more than with other species, and with nuthatches more than with creepers. Within the groups occur also interspecies dominance tendencies that reflect this association, as when a species drives off one species more than another.

Mixed Stands. The earlier discussion of density did not mention mixed densities. The environment has facilities for only a fixed number of animals having the same or similar requirements, and the more closely allied these requirements, the greater the interspecies competition. We find little overlapping of requirements between caribou and passerine birds on the tundra, and the population of each is independent of the other. But elk and mule deer on many of the interior ranges have considerable overlapping of habitat requirements, especially food, and the combined density of the two (on a mass basis) remains substantially the same as either density singly. In the same way, pheasants and quail have overlapping requirements, and the total for the mixed populations is not the sum of the separate densities but substantially the same as the density of one singly. Adjustment of mixed density is proportionate to the overlapping of requirements in space, food, or cover. This has its parallel in horticulture, where an orchard may produce an additional crop of alfalfa between the peach trees but not of other fruits.

Social Hierarchy. A flock of animals proves to have a complex social structure, particularly in confinement. The position of an animal in the social hierarchy depends upon *dominance* of others, usually by greater physical ability. The wolf that leads the pack probably does so because it stands at the top of the *peck order,* not because others recognize its sagacity.

The peck order may be a *straight line,* in which case each animal dominates the ones lower in rank but defers to those having *peck rights. Triangular* or circular peck orders also occur: animal A, for example, dominates B, which dominates C, which in turn dominates A. Instead of peck rights, *peck dominance* may occur, in which case the dominant individuals do so only in a majority of their contacts with others.

Species Groups. Within animal species appear population groupings. It is known, for example, that in crosses between races of deer mice (*Peromyscus*) some of the interracial crosses are more fertile than others. Some may be practically sterile, just as for interspecies crosses. Among deer mice occur also "ecological races," which are taxonomically the same species and live in the same area but occupy different ecological habitats. Physiological variations of population groups seem to exist also. The greater ability of southern bobwhites to withstand prolonged relatively higher temperatures than northern quail is due in part to their smaller bulk and proportionately greater surfaces and in part to their lighter feathering. These bobwhite are taxonomically the same species, and sometimes even the same subspecies.

Grouse of the genus *Dendragapus* show another type of species grouping rather clearly. All belong to a single species *Dendragapus obscurus* (blue grouse), but within the species are two well-marked groups: the coastal sooty blue grouse group and the dusky blue grouse group of the interior. The sooty blue grouse is darker; the dusky blue grouse is grayer. Even well-marked vocal differences occur. These distinctions clearly are of evolutionary origin and denote closeness of relationship within the respective groups.

It should seem clear to the biologist that any transplanting or raising of animals for release must consider the problem of species groups and the possible effects, usually unfavorable, of introducing different genetic compositions into an existing population. This may be particularly applicable to fish transfers. The problem of species groups is added to other biological considerations, such as possible climatic maladjustments, which can be indicated in part by *climographs*.

Migration. Annual migration occurs among birds and mammals as well as among amphibians, reptiles, fishes, and some invertebrates. The spectacular north-and-south movement of birds demonstrates one of the great workings of natural rhythms. The northward movement in spring seems to be associated with the lengthening or total amount of daylight and consequent changes in the elaborations of hormones by the gonads, but some birds move northward from south of the equator, where daylight is declining during the northern spring. The southward migration seems more complex and less easily explained than the northward one; elaborations of gonadal hormones may not be involved so intimately.

Migrating birds follow a sequence of movement, some moving early, some late, and others in between. Early migrants consistently migrate early, just as late ones migrate late, year after year. These are fixed species habits. Species do not migrate early in the season one year and late the next, even though stragglers may vary from the main movement, or the main movement may vary within a few days year to year. Thus the blue-winged teal is an early fall migrant each year. The Canada goose moves northward with the advance of open water, but stragglers may still be moving in May. The black-polled warbler is regularly the last of the warblers to migrate in the East, long after others have gone by, just as the myrtle warbler is an early migrant. A five-year average of bird migration in one locality will still fit the migration sequence years later.

The general pathway of migrating birds is substantially the same year after year. Migrants that pass up and down the Atlantic Coast, for example, are not likely to move any distance away from it, in a body, during succeeding migrations. This fixity of habit has given rise to the postulation of "flyways." Individual birds, however, cannot be counted on to follow any expected migration route.

A few species of restricted range migrate almost as a population, but most move north and south over a "broad front," usually in flocks. Small birds are mostly *nocturnal* migrants, and others may be *diurnal*. Most waterfowl migrate by day, though nocturnal migration is also fairly common among them. The sudden appearance of birds in the spring often testifies to the arrival of nocturnal migrants. Even nocturnal migrants will continue to pass through while feeding in the daytime.

Wind and air movements play an important part in determining the pathway of migration within the limits set by the migration route. Thus the golden plovers that migrate across the western Atlantic from eastern Canada to South America drift westward under the influence of wind and earth deflection (Corioli's force) so that they automatically hit South America rather than passing into the South Atlantic. Their northward migration route, which brings them up the interior, is similarly influenced by world and continental wind systems and earth deflection.

But the actual guides that animals use in migrating are not clearly understood. Fish may be able to detect changes in currents or chemistry of the water, such as its salinity. Probably the bird finds its way over land largely by sight, for major landscape features appear even on moonless nights, though fog may obscure them. Northward and southward movement as such is probably considered best as a *tropism* response, with the actual accomplishment of it subject to considerable individual latitude. No doubt explanations of migration fall within the scope of physics and chemistry, and time will give us answers to most, if not all, of the unknown facts. There is no known special migration sense and no known way for migrating animals to sense faint earth impulses.

Birds migrate at *low altitudes,* mostly under 1000 feet, even over water. There are authentic reports of birds at altitudes above 3000 feet, but most of these reports are from mountainous areas so that the actual flight height is still low. Geese migrating from the interior across the Cascades have been observed clearing a 7800-foot ridge by several hundred feet. Thus they flew at an actual altitude of more than 8000 feet, yet they flew low as measured by ridge tops and high as measured by the valley floor of 1200 feet.

Banding records indicate that a wintering bird tends to return to the same winter ground in succeeding years, just as the bird tends to return to the same breeding area year after year. Big game withdraws to the same swamp and winter range year after year. Some populations breed and winter in restricted areas although others may be less fixed in their habits. The various races of geese show a fixity of winter and breeding ground. The fact that they mate for several seasons and that pairing takes place in migration and on the breeding grounds prevents much geographic mixing, which accounts for the large number of subspecies. Among birds that pair on the winter grounds, pairs may be formed of birds hatched miles apart, a fact that militates against building up of population groups among birds like the mallard duck.

Migration is well known among salmon and other fish, but it may differ from bird migration by involving a return to breeding grounds after the passage of years and then for only one breeding effort, rather than annual migration back and forth. Salmon migration is from fresh water, the young going to salt water for development and back to fresh water for breeding (*anadromous migration*). Eels reverse this and migrate to salt water for breeding and back to fresh water for maturing (*catadromous migration*). How these fish find their way is unknown, though within the respective media the explanations probably differ little from those for birds. Like fish, migrating seals and penguins seem to face the same problems in finding their way.

Altitudinal migration occurs in the mountain country, usually downward to adjacent lower country in fall. Mule deer and elk may migrate as much as 50 miles or so, but some mountain birds may move far out on the plains.

Concentration Areas. Wintering grounds of big game are well-known concentration areas of limited scope; winter concentration areas of waterfowl likewise are well known and limited. But many birds have concentration areas of very large size. The tree sparrows, for example, winter from southern Canada to the Gulf States, but their main winter concentration lies in a band across the midsouth, as do the winter grounds of the slate-colored junco and scores of other birds. Concentrations extend farther north along the Pacific Coast than along the Atlantic in response to the northward thrust of marine climate. Among some species, moving to winter quarters is actually a withdrawal to the more southerly parts of the range.

In closely related species that geographically replace each other (*allopatric species*), one usually declines in abundance as the other increases. Mallard and black ducks illustrate this complementary effect and so do the western and eastern meadowlarks. But closely related species of similar distribution (*sympatric species*) usually have similar concentration patterns, though the larger species generally has the more northerly distribution, as shown in the wintering habits of the Cooper and sharp-shinned hawks.

Hibernation and Aestivation. Mammals and other animals of lower mobility than birds cannot migrate, other than locally, to winter quarters. Many are unable to make even local movements to escape the dryness of summer. Aestivation and hibernation have been evolved as an answer to the problem; they differ only in time and ecological cause. *Aestivation* is a sleeplike condition of suspended activity for passing the dry periods; *hibernation* is the same type of suspended activity for passing the cold periods. Many ground squirrels, for example, go into *aestivation* in midsummer, which passes into the *hibernation* of winter without a break. The ground squirrel, *Citellus richardsoni,* may spend up to nine months in hibernation and aestivation.

Just as in bird migration, a great increase of fat deposition under the influence of endocrines marks the approach of hibernation and aestivation. This stored fat supplies the energy to keep the body alive. The animal seeks or prepares a sheltered place for its sleep; the ground squirrel, for example, builds a well-insulated nest of dry grasses in its soundly engineered burrow, and it may even plug the entrance tunnel. Bears seek caves, rock outcrops, hollow logs, and sometimes blowdowns and thickets in the forest.

The body temperature of a hibernating animal like the squirrel drops and approaches freezing temperature, so that the animal actually becomes torpid. The heart beats but a few times a minute, at most, and breathing is in proportion. All in all, life almost calls "time out" in these hibernating animals. The body temperature of bears, on the other hand, does not seem to drop so much, and no doubt the degree of life suspension varies from nearly complete in the ground squirrel to very little in black bears, fox squirrels, and others. Probably a complete series of gradations between ordinary physiological activity and hibernation occurs. Even the body temperature of the sleeping or resting animal normally drops below that during activity periods.

Population Reservoirs. Despite sex ratio balance or unbalance, a reservoir of unmated individuals, especially among birds, exists in the wild. The substitution of another mate, either male or female, for a lost one attests to the existence of the reserve supply. Experimental removal of members of a pair has demonstrated the immediate replacement, often in a few hours. This replacement has even taken place several times in the same nest, so that the final guardians were several foster-parents away from the young.

The state of abundance of this reservoir in nature is not clear, but unmated adults sometimes attach themselves to mated pairs. Early in the breeding cycle this may prove a handicap, but later, when the young need so much care, it probably represents a definite gain. Adults that form this reservoir may largely represent males not yet successful in establishing territories and females not successful in pairing. It would be natural for these to be mostly young animals. (It must be remembered that among territorial animals only males in possession of territories succeed in attracting females and that it is the *female that seeks the male* already established on a territory.) Some mammals attached to mated pairs are clearly young, but some past their prime have likewise become so attached.

Spread into New or Unoccupied Range. It is clear that considerable advance and retreat takes place at the periphery of animal ranges, especially on the poleward edges and dry margins. The northward advance guard of the bobwhite in the lake states may be cut back practically 100 miles during a particularly unfavorable winter. The dickcissel of the southwestern plains country regularly spreads and shrinks its range, as do several other dry-land forms. In the 1870's the dickcissel even spread into New England, where it became as common as the house sparrow, if we may judge by reports. It has not crossed eastward over the Appalachians since. In general, marked advance and retreat occurs among animals living in relatively inhospitable environments.

Some of the expansion in the past can be explained by animal movement into new habitat created by settlement, and some of it to northward march of climate that has been going on since Pleistocene times and that currently may reach about 75 miles a century. But southward, westward, and eastward moves cannot be so readily explained. Neither can spread of greater magnitude than climatic shift. Parallel changes in Scandinavia and other parts of the world rule out changes in the wake of settlement as a complete answer.

Spread of animals into vacant range is not well recorded. Even the spread of the English sparrow in America was incompletely recorded, but it seems to have been at the rate of perhaps 65 to 70 miles a year. The spread of the starling seems to have been rather less, perhaps only 50 miles a year. Apparently the spread was more rapid after the first years, just as population curves build up more rapidly after the initial period.

The spread of the rabbit across Australia was very rapid. The Hungarian partridge is reported to have spread at the rate of 5 miles a year from Ohio into Michigan (though slower later), 2 miles a year in Wisconsin, and 28 in Manitoba. The black rat spread across Ascension Island, a distance of 4 miles, within a few months of coming ashore from a shipwreck. As a result of several releases, the opossum has moved in California from 3 to 10 miles a year.

Data are now being accumulated on the spread of the nutria, a large South American rodent of inferior fur, released within the past few years in the Louisiana muskrat marshes, Puget Sound, and perhaps elsewhere. Between 1939 and 1947 the nutria averaged about 20 miles a year in spreading across the Louisiana marshes, but between 1935 and 1947 it progressed yearly only a quarter of that distance along the rivers in the Puget Sound region.

Nesting Colonies. Because marine and water birds must return to land for nesting, nesting grounds are in demand, and marine birds especially tend to be colonial nesters. A colonial nesting area, usually much restricted, is generally a rocky island, headland, or cliff, which may acquire the designation of "bird rock." To be suitable for many sea birds to launch into the air, a rock needs a precipitous slope to the windward. At the same time it must be isolated from foot enemies; hence, bird rocks are usually islands, or bluffs and cliffs of islands. Such rocks must also be located near rich sources of marine food that are adequate for the large population and its nestlings. These combinations make the bird islands highly valuable, all out of proportion to their size, and justify the great effort made to reserve or protect them for the birds or, as sometimes happens, for sea lions and other marine mammals.

Among the best known of the bird islands are those of the guano birds of Peru. Along the Atlantic Coast of the United States and Canada are found such noted bird islands as the Dry Tortugas, Green Island, Grand Manan, and Cape Hatteras. No less are those of the Pacific Coast, even though they are less highly publicized—Bird Rock, Three Arch Rocks, Farallons, and Bering Islands. Some bird islands, as well as nesting cliffs, occur in large rivers and lakes, such as the Columbia and St. Lawrence rivers, Great Salt Lake, and the Great Lakes.

Population Cycles. The rise and fall of population has long been known, even though the rhythmic character and implications have only recently been recognized. No satisfactory universal explanation has appeared, which reflects both our lack of knowledge and the probably separate causes of many pulsations. Shifts of range, such as of the dickcissel, may reflect population increase and consequent pressure inducing range advance, to shrink again with decline in population.

But many cycles are clearly increases and decreases of population levels with no change in range. The ruffed grouse and snowshoe rabbit, for example, periodically rise and fall in abundance within their ranges; no emigrations of these species are known, though some local movement may occur. Population rises of several northern birds, such as the snowy owl and northern shrike, are associated with southward flights, presumably because the stimulation to population increase strengthens latent migration tendencies.

The populations and flights of the snowy owl and northern shrike fluctuate around a mean of some four years, though not necessarily together. Four years is about the average for lemming rises and falls in the North, with which the snowy owl and several fur-bearer pulsations are associated. Rodents and rabbits of the North serve as the basic forage food for a chain of meat-eaters, and a decline in the food supply results in a complementary decline in the meat-eaters.

The magnitude of the population cycles is so great among some species as to seem incredible to an observer who has had no field experience with them. The snowshoe rabbit populations may reach more than 1000 to the square mile, at the high, and dwindle to but one or two at the ensuing low. Those of the ruffed grouse may fluctuate between 500 to the square mile, at the high, to one or two at the low. Some cycles, however, vary between such low limits as to be demonstrable only by statistical methods.

The more violent pulsations, or *macrocycles,* occur among northern animals that feed upon fresh vegetation, such as bark and buds (rather than seeds or whole plants) or the meat-eaters that feed upon these herbivorous animals. The less violent cycles, or *microcycles,* occur among animals that feed upon seeds, whole plants, and insects, and among most meat-eaters.

Macrocycles are also exhibited in animals dependent upon habitat relations that are easily upset by weather or drought cycles. Those animals of more stable or less narrowly restricted habitats usually exhibit microcycles, if any.

Causes of Cycles. The causes and workings of cycles are not clear. Some can be associated with climatic changes, as shown by the rise and decline of beaver abundance with long-time rainfall cycles. The influence of weather changes and associated occurrences seems paramount in many pulsations and related phenomena. Most prominent are the cycles in the Northland, where environmental strain on animal physiology is highest, but they may also occur in the tropics and in the seas. A 7-year cycle has been reported for guano birds of Peru and a 9-year one for Atlantic salmon.

Although cycles may occur singly, a species usually shows the influence of several related cycles at the same time. Thus some animals show 4-year, 5½-year, 9-year, 11-year, 22-year, 34-year, or longer cycles in combinations of two or more.

The over-all determinant or control of cycles seems to lie in the disturbance of the physiological adjustment of animals to their environments. The common element of disturbance is weather and climate. Solar radiation may have direct bearing through ultra-violet changes, but more important are the indirect influences through weather changes.

Some local or individual cycle changes can be explained on local or individual grounds. Thus the 34-year shift of the ocean current known as *El Nino* brings on a 34-year shift in a whole series of phenomena along the northwest coast of South America. The intricate relations of predator and prey can conceivably set up a pulsation likely to continue, but such has not been demonstrated in the wild. Irruptions of disease may on occasion result in local declines, but disease has not been shown for great areas except correlative to existing physiological disturbance.

Prolonged Physiological Stress. The whole matter of the relationship of environment to the animal involves animal physiological balance in a most intricate manner. The physiological structure of the body ordinarily is sufficiently resilient to rebound from lesser, short-time stresses. But prolonged ones bear heavily at times upon bodily functions and may produce reverberations that are more influential than short-lived but greater strains.

In general, on the basis of our present knowledge, most prolonged strains in the wild are likely to result from weather conditions; this is particularly true in the life of the individual. A drought, for example, may result in marked animal distress from lack of fluids for normal bodily functioning. The drain from desiccation and heat must be counterbalanced by intake of water, but drying of vegetation lessens the available moisture. Insects that might otherwise be available usually retreat to protected spots with increase of dryness and thereby become less available to wildlife. High air temperature, which may occur during heat spells in summer, can raise the body temperature above normal and cause distress. The actual operation of high body temperature is not well known for birds and only fairly well known for some mammals. The first symptoms of distress in the bird are shown by opening of the wings and rapid breathing through the mouth; the latter action loses considerable moisture from the lungs.

Although it is difficult to observe directly in the field the workings of physiological strains environmentally induced, it should be obvious, nevertheless, that they are present in varying degrees. They are important to the conscientious biologist and wildlife manager, and it is unfortunate that we lack means for measuring them in usable terms. Awareness of them and search for workable methods for their determination are the best approaches that can be suggested at present. The observation and other field techniques in the two chapters that follow offer some help to the resourceful field man.

SUGGESTED READING

Allee, W. C., 1938, *The Social Life of Animals*, W. W. Norton and Co., New York.
Allee, W. C., Alfred E. Emerson, Orlando Park, Thomas Park, and Karl P. Schmidt, 1949, *Principles of Animal Ecology*, W. E. Saunders Co., Philadelphia.
Chapman, Royal N., 1931, *Animal Ecology with Especial Reference to Insects*, McGraw-Hill Book Co., New York.
Deevey, Edward S., Jr., 1947, "Life Tables for Natural Populations of Animals," *Quart. Rev. Biol.*, 22:283–314.
Dewey, Edward R., and Edwin F. Dakin, 1947, *Cycles; the Science of Prediction*, Henry Holt and Co., New York.
Dice, Lee R., 1945, "Measures of the Amount of Ecologic Association between Species," *Ecology*, 26:297–302.
Dymond, J. R., 1947, "Fluctuations in Animal Populations with Special Reference to Those of Canada," *Trans. Royal Soc. Canada*, 41:1–34.
Elton, Charles, 1942, *Voles, Mice, and Lemmings*, Oxford University Press, Oxford.
Errington, Paul L., 1933, "The Nesting and Life Equation of the Wisconsin Bobwhite," *Wilson Bull.*, 45:122–132.
Errington, Paul L., 1945, "Some Contributions of a Fifteen-Year Local Study of the Northern Bobwhite to a Knowledge of Population Phenomena," *Ecol. Monographs*, 15:1–34.
Grange, Wallace B., 1949, *The Way to Game Abundance with an Explanation of Game Cycles*, Charles Scribner's Sons, New York.
Leopold, Aldo, 1933, *Game Management*, Charles Scribner's Sons, New York.
Lotka, A. J., 1925, *Elements of Physical Biology*, Williams and Wilkins Co., Baltimore.
MacLulich, D. A., 1937, *Fluctuations in the Numbers of the Varying Hare (Lepus americanus)*, Univ. Toronto Studies, Biol. Ser. 43.
Mohr, Carl O., 1947, "Table of Equivalent Populations of North American Small Mammals," *Am. Midland Naturalist*, 37:223–249.
Pearse, A. S., 1939, *Animal Ecology*, McGraw-Hill Book Co., New York.
Shelford, Victor E., 1929, *Laboratory and Field Ecology*, Williams and Wilkins Co., Baltimore.
Wetmore, Alexander, 1926, *The Migrations of Birds*, Harvard University Press, Cambridge.

4

Techniques of Field Investigations and Practices

Since a manual in itself would be needed to list all the field techniques available, only the more general ones will be covered here. Some specific methods will be discussed in the sections covering the species to which they apply; although this may involve a slight duplication, it seems best from the standpoint of organization. Actual management practice for various species will be given chiefly in other chapters.

The Game Survey. The extensive type of wildlife inventory is the *game survey,* which, as the name implies, is a general survey of existing species, their past history, present and past conditions, and the factors of environment that influence them. The survey covers only the major points and does not concern itself with details or manifestations of populations; instead it places emphasis upon the general aspects of wildlife and the environment.

Of necessity the game survey must utilize many data that are rough, but the major factors sought are so broad that it is not necessary to use only refined data to discover them. The size of the survey is unlimited; it may be a survey of a small property or a region; conceivably, it could encompass all the earth's land surface and the surrounding waters.

The first major game survey in this country was made by Professor Leopold and may well serve as the model for others, as it marked the beginning of the game survey as a tool of conservation. It represents a landmark in the technique of survey-making and merits careful study. But Professor Leopold's sage warning is still worth repeating, "When people run out of ideas, they start counting in hopes that somehow it will give them some."

The Sample Area in Determining Abundance

Relative and Absolute Abundance. Abundance of animals is designated in two ways: *absolute* and *relative* abundance. Absolute abundance is the exact population present and is determined by numerical counts upon definite areas. Relative abundance, as the term indicates, gives abundance in terms of related elements.

Relative abundance is reported in a variety of ways, such as individual animals per trap-night, hour, or mile, and by adjectives like common, rare, and very common. The relative abundance indicated by different observers may vary because of differences in observation experience and ability. The term *common*, for example, means different degrees of abundance to different people. Relative abundance thus based upon impression (adjective terms) is not so usable and reliable as that based upon a fixed unit. In a fixed-unit count, for example, one individual of a species observed once in 10 hours of observation would give a rating of 0.10 an hour; if once in 10 miles, a rating of 0.10 a mile. Should one individual have been observed in 10 days, the species would be given a *frequency of occurrence* of 0.10 and a *relative abundance* of 0.10. On the other hand, if 100 were seen on one of the ten days, the frequency of occurrence would remain 0.10, but the relative abundance would become 10.00. Frequency of occurrence is a form of relative abundance that is useful in indicating how widely a species is distributed; relative abundance is helpful in indicating proportionate populations; together they indicate the relative grouping of individuals as well.

Absolute abundance is reported as "so-many-on-an-area." We might speak of 50 grouse and 20 squirrels on the same area, or 1000 deer in a winter yard. We would not report absolute abundance as "so-many-to-the-unit," which is relative abundance, but as so many on a specified area.

The Sample Area in Determining Abundance. Usually it is physically impossible for an observer to count directly the population on a large area. The observer must turn to some method that will indicate the population on a whole area with reasonable accuracy and that will be within the physical possibilities of the observer. The *sample area* is the best method for this purpose (see also the section on censuses and censusing).

Proper selection of the sample or census plot is most important, and the observer must exercise care to select a sample plot that actually gives a sample. For best results the area selected should include all the habitats in representative quantities within the region; when that is not possible, separate samples are advisable for each separate habitat. Random selection of small plots may be done by throwing an iron ring of the plot size or by tossing a weight at random and using its resting point as the plot marker.

The commonest sample plot is the *quadrat,* the size and shape of which depend upon the population and area to be sampled. Quadrats for determining the amount of ragweed seed present might be only a foot square, whereas quadrats for sampling ruffed grouse populations would be 4 square miles. Instead of an equal-side quadrat, one can use an *extended quadrat.* Thus a quadrat for counting rodent burrows in the plains country might be 5 feet wide and several miles long. The extended quadrat has the advantage of being a continuous area that touches many different cover types and aspects.

Another sampling device is the *transect,* which is merely a line generally run with a compass in such a manner as to include representative territory. In actual practice the transect is an extended quadrat in which the width has been reduced to a line. The transect is convenient for quick sampling because it eliminates the necessity of laying out an area before starting. It does not need to follow exactly the same course upon subsequent operations if a fine degree of accuracy is not required. One might repeatedly compass due north through the forest from a given point for a definite distance and get comparable results each trip, even though he did not follow exactly the same course each time. This method has its chief value in large areas, remote regions, and rough country.

Exclosures and Inclosures. Control over the use of an area by various animals may be desirable in field studies. This control can be gained by fencing a sample plot with an animal-proof fence (Fig. 4.1). Such a fence for cattle is easily put up, but one for deer is more difficult, and one to exclude rabbits and rodents is still more so.

In the humid and low regions, which are generally forested, running the proper fence around the sample plot creates an exclosure with little disturbance of the plant life within, other than for the immediate boundary. But in dry regions, mountains, and other places where the rainfall or snowfall is critical, unless the exclosure is large, even a single strand of fence wire may materially change the conditions within, especially by influencing the dropping of snow and moisture and the drying effect of wind. Exclosures of wooden poles, such as corral-like ones, may not give a true comparison between conditions within and without unless they are larger than the usual exclosure.

A fine-mesh poultry netting set in a trench will generally turn rodents, although a band of sheet iron may also be needed. Turning the fence bottom outward in a trench generally eliminates all digging underneath. No suitable exclosures for birds and tree squirrels can be constructed except by cutting treeless belts around the boundary to prevent squirrel movement over the fence or by covering the plot with a netting. Netting will work satisfactorily also for some types of bird investigations, such as the study of alleged crop damage in grains and fruits.

Fig. 4.1. Rabbit- and stock-proof exclosure. Edwards Plateau, Texas. (Photograph by Omer E. Sperry.)

Inclosures for special purposes might consist of netting over a tree or over a single flower, but small inclosures are uncommon in actual management practice. Islands in lakes sometimes serve the purpose of inclosures. The inclosure may be fenced to exclude animals (Fig. 4.1).

Censuses and Censusing Methods. Without censuses it is not possible to know with any degree of certainty the status of the population on an area. A census may be a sample, though it is often more, and it may cover the species for which management or research has been or will be devised, as well as related species which may affect the principal species. In addition it is desirable and sometimes necessary to include ecological factors.

A census is a definite *enumeration,* and censusing is the process of enumerating; censuses are always reported in numerical terms. Estimates, on the other hand, may be reported in round figures or, as is common, in comparative terms.

The use to which the data will be put largely governs the time of the census, although there are three main census periods in game-management practice: breeding season, fall, and winter.

The fall census is generally a *pre-hunting* census followed by the post-hunting or *early winter* census. The pre-hunting census indicates the population present; the post-hunting or early winter census reveals the population that has survived the hunting season, the population the area holds as it goes into the winter. The post-hunting census compared with the pre-hunting census indicates the kill during the hunting season. It is a useful check upon inspection reports of hunters and hunter bags. The *late winter* census shows the population that has survived the winter and is present as the breeding season begins. The late winter census compared with the post-hunting census helps to determine the effect of winter upon the population.

Breeding season censuses usually consist of nest counts, den counts, and brood counts.

A *nesting census* indicates the number of birds breeding. A *brood* census indicates the number of young and furnishes data regarding the early success of the breeding period; carried through the season, it indicates the success of the breeding season.

Wildlife biologists employ various census methods, most of which depend upon observation. Perhaps the simplest census type, though not necessarily the easiest, is that made by a single observer (or by several observers) censusing waterfowl or other birds. For this census, few techniques are employed other than straight observation. The number of ducks is recorded for known areas, or a relative abundance figure is obtained during a unit of time or travel distance. The number of birds in a raft of ducks can be approximated by estimating the size of the raft and allowing one square yard of surface a bird. Rafts or flying flocks of ducks (and other birds) are estimated also by counting the number in a segment and applying this factor to the whole area covered by the aggregation. A good technique for counting a flock is to count a segment of 10, then mentally double this over the flock for 20, then redouble it for 40, and so on to the last segment, which can be apportioned if it is less than a whole segment. Enlargements of photographs help also. If two people work together, one observing and the other recording, flocks can be counted in groups of five and ten, or even sex counts can be made if a dimorphic species.

Thus the observer can call off "three males, two females, etc.," at any speed and the recorder can record in prepared columns or lines.

The "Lincoln index" arrives at an estimate of the total population by applying the ratio between the number of animals marked and marked animals reported killed, to the total killed by hunters. Thus if 10 per cent of the marked animals were killed, the total population should be approximately 10 times the total number of animals killed by all hunters. This is subject to many possibilities of error, one of which is the mixing or distributing of the banded birds in a thorough manner. It probably could be applied on other species than waterfowl, and perhaps by observation of marked animals. An equation for the Lincoln index would be:

$$\frac{\text{Killed marked animals}}{\text{Total marked animals}} = \frac{\text{Total kill}}{\text{Total population}}$$

The number of dens of coyotes, foxes, and other animals gives a rough population index if a pair of adults is allowed for each den. But the field man must bear in mind that animals other than owners may visit such dens. Except when young are small, dens of such animals as woodchucks would need an allowance of one animal for each burrow.

The *King method* of censusing ruffed grouse uses a 4-square-mile grid system laid out as definite cross lines through the woods, usually at 80-rod intervals. The census-taker walks the grid lines, so that he travels 32 miles for 4 square miles (Fig. 4.2). He counts the grouse that flush and determines the *flushing distance* for each grouse by pacing (or estimating) the distance between the point where the observer stood and the point at which the bird flushed. The average flushing distance of all the grouse is then computed and, together with the length of line covered, used to determine the population by the formula:

$$P = \frac{AG}{LF}$$

where P = population,
A = area of census plot in square yards,
G = number of grouse flushed,
L = length of census lines in yards,
F = twice the average flushing distance in yards.

It often happens that the flushing distance is not determined for all birds seen. The average is then computed for only the grouse for which flushing distances were obtained, but the total number of grouse (G of the formula) is used in computing the population. Ten grouse on 32 miles of line seems the probable minimum number for which the system is reliable. Although the average flushing distance is customarily used, some other figure, such as harmonic mean, might be used for some studies.

A modified form of the King method determines the grouse population for each separate ecological type crossed by the census lines and then combines the totals for the final figure.

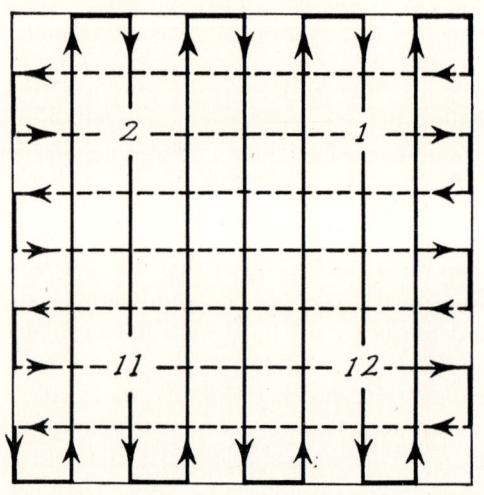

Fig. 4.2. Gridiron pattern of a census plot for the King census method. The grid lines are laid out along 40 lines, or their equivalent, on a 4-square-mile area. The direction of walking is indicated by the arrows, which in the illustration preferably would be for starting in the upper right or lower left corners.

Although this method has been developed for ruffed grouse, it has possibilities for adaptation to other species by proper modification. It is a *detection-distance* technique applicable to many readily visible species, like birds. A *visual distance,* determined as the distance a man's body from his hips down is visible, has been used with success in the Edwards Plateau brush country for white-tailed deer. The visual distance can be marked on the maps of the census lines for convenience; its width measures the strip covered. Counting is done along prepared lines at sunset.

A system of obtaining relative figures on pheasants by driving along country roads and counting the pheasants seen from the automobile has been devised in Ohio and used also in other states, including Iowa.

Censuses and Censusing Methods

Apparently this system works with some success in areas where the land is flat and conditions are uniform. The method is used in the fall between six and eight in the morning of clear days. The automobile travels 20 miles an hour while the pheasants are counted. The ratio between birds seen and population present is given as follows:

Birds to the Mile	*Indicated Population* (acres to the pheasant)
1	18
2	7–9
8–10	4–5

The drive is one of the most commonly used methods of censusing. Men are lined up along one edge of the area at definite intervals, and at a given signal all proceed across the census area, maintaining the original spacing during the drive. Counters are usually stationed along the sides of the area to record animals that pass out. Each driver counts "cutbacks" (animals that plunge through the line of drive) to his right, except the man on the left end, who counts cutbacks on both his left and right unless he follows on the outer boundary. In drive-censusing birds such as pheasants, as well as some mammals, counters sometimes may be stationed on high points to count all cutbacks within their designated areas, as well as birds that fly out of the census area. In this way the drivers, who may be untrained men, are relieved of the duty of recording animals flushed. The driven area, though usually rectangular, can be of any shape; the triangle has the advantage of enabling the drivers to converge from three sides.

Counts of some species are best made by coursing back and forth across an area, a procedure that flushes most of the individuals that are present. Often it is advantageous to use a trained dog because a good dog gives assurance that fewer game birds, particularly, will be missed. Airplane counts are made of elk, mule deer, antelope, and waterfowl (Fig. 4.3). The airplane enables the observer to cover a large territory, to see most of the animals present, and to mark their location on a map. A skilled pilot can often "jump" most of the big game within an area by circling at a low altitude (from 300 to 800 feet) and returning if necessary. The plane should fly back and forth across the census area rather than at random. Plane flights are of value in censusing waterfowl in areas of concentration and in regions of difficult access. Usually the plane is flown at an altitude of 75 to 200 feet while the pilot and observer check birds on each side of the flight course. In the breeding season waterfowl can be counted for about 40 rods on each side of the flight transect, which gives a quarter-mile strip for both sides. Fall and winter concentration-area counts generally cover all water areas rather than transects. Some waterfowl, especially teal, may jump up into the plane's path, but most of them can be avoided by a skilled flyer. Ground crews making sample

FIG. 4.3. Herd of elk on the Sun River Range. This aerial photograph shows a portion of the herd. (Photograph from Montana Game Department.)

counts in the area give correction factors when their figures are compared with the air count of the same sample areas. These correction factors are applied to the totals from the air counts for a final total.

Airplanes have also been used to follow migrating or homing birds. Most birds ignore a plane circling them at 200 to 400 yards, but in following geese a distance of about 1000 yards must be kept by the plane.

It is possible to obtain a rough idea of the abundance of deer and other species by track counts along fire lanes, in mud and snow. Tracks in snow have been used with some success in the western mountains to check deer migrating to the lowlands. The number of *beds,* especially in snow, can be used in estimating the population present; in a similar manner rabbit *forms* may give some indication of rabbit abundance. Perhaps one of the most novel censusing methods has been employed by foresters in India for censusing tigers, which come to water holes nightly. The location of these watering places being known, it is a simple task to determine the number of tigers that have come to them on any particular night. Untrained natives who are employed in this work smooth the soil around the water holes the night before so that any visiting tigers will leave tracks. The next day the natives carefully mark the size of tracks on a stick, which they take to the forester, who determines the size of the tracks by measuring the marks on the sticks. By this means not only the number of tigers is revealed but also the general age and sex classes are determined.

Nesting counts are made by drives or by a patient search for nests. A weighted rope or fish net dragged between two observers often flushes incubating birds in open fields; a third person, walking between the other two, watches for flushing birds. Nests are also counted in hay fields after the hay has been cut. Large areas can be covered when the ropes or nets are tied between cars or horses.

Data on number of pheasants can be obtained from the number of crowing grounds; likewise the number of sharp-tailed grouse or prairie chickens resorting to dancing and booming grounds will give some indication of population.

Trapping is usually resorted to for censusing small mammals, and seining for censusing fish. Each trap exposed overnight is rated as one *trap-night* so that 100 traps on one night and 10 traps on 10 nights would give 100 trap-nights. Some use has been made of fish poisons to get counts in small ponds.

Creel censuses and bag reports have come into favor as methods for obtaining a record of the take. Creel report blanks are filled in by the fisherman or investigator.

A method of limited use in counting breeding birds is the *singing male* census formerly used by the Biological Survey. Because birds tend to be territorial and relatively fixed in the breeding seasons, regular observation of territory gives a highly reliable count. This is the basis of all *breeding-bird censuses.* Counts of colonial nesters can be made easily on the nesting grounds; cooperative help may be needed for hole-nesters, such as martins, and chimney swifts.

Checking stations for obtaining information on the kill are generally placed on roads leading to game areas, at fishing docks, and at places of concentration along streams. In addition to the fish or game taken, the creel census and bag reports usually include other pertinent information such as the size of the items taken, locality where taken, and information about the fisherman or hunter. Sometimes sample fish scales are kept for age and growth-rate determination. Material for study of food habits, growth, body measurements, parasites, and the like may also be gathered at checking stations.

Measuring the Cover. There are various standard measurements of cover, yet each area presents its own individual cover problems. Cover measurements fall into five principal categories: *composition, density, quantity, quality,* and *availability.*

Composition is simply the percentage of plants of each species present. Density is the number of plants or stems to the unit area (the acre is usually the most convenient unit although hectares can be used). Quantity is the amount of cover (in part a combination of composition and density). The quality of the cover, and to some extent other measurements, varies with the wildlife species the observer has in mind—good mouse cover might be poor moose cover. Availability is determined by progress of the season and to some extent by accessibility.

Various other possible measurements are aspect, visibility, light penetration, temperature, wind protection, and predator protection.

Cover for cottontails has been rated by a grading system that will be found of value under many conditions. This system uses the following characteristics: height, density, durability, canopy, debris, and shade.

Forage and Range Capacity Determination. Though information is available regarding the needs of livestock, so little is known about the forage requirements of herbivorous big game on diversified range that the methods used for livestock range determination are the best as yet available for big-game range work. The requirements of big game are not necessarily the same as those of livestock; indeed, the requirements of big game itself vary not only between species but also between seasons in the same species. The carrying capacity of the range for big game and livestock is governed by several factors, chiefly the size of the area, palatability of species, density of the vegetation, and forage-acre requirement of the animals.

Determination of Proper-Use Factor. Palatability has been used in two distinct senses: (*a*) the relish or avidity with which animals take plants, and (*b*) the average percentage of the available growth of a plant species that is removed by the grazing of the animals on a properly utilized range. The second sense (*b*) has been called "proper-use factor," which will be used here, and palatability will be restricted to the first sense (*a*).

The methods used to determine the proper-use factor vary with the vegetation, the locality, and the season. The first requirement in proper-use factor studies is the determination of the chief forage species used by big game in an area to be surveyed during a given season. Such determination is obtained by the following methods:

(*a*) Observe the feeding animals during definite periods throughout the season by the use of binoculars (at least 8×). Spotting scopes and especially the 24× binoculars are valuable for antelope when used from a point of vantage. Determine the plant species and plant parts eaten immediately after the animals move on. To be of value this method requires care but, when skillfully applied, gives palatability and forage species data.

(*b*) Establish check plots of a definite size in all major ecological types where game feeds, and examine the plots at intervals for feeding data. These check plots are excellent for use on winter range.

(*c*) Snow trailing in winter (with or without binoculars) frequently gives good results for browse determination, but not for grasses because the appearance of the latter does not reveal when they were taken or by what animal.

(*d*) Stomach analysis of a representative number of animals is quite accurate for both woody and herbaceous material and is especially desirable for identification of herbaceous material in winter.

Any two of the methods listed, if employed correctly, should reveal not only the *key species* but also the minor species of plants that make up the dietary of big-game animals. Experience has showed, however, that game animals do not take key species equally on large ranges and that minor species of one locality may become key species, or almost key species, in another locality.

Proper-use factor tables obtained by these methods must be considered reliable only for the region where they are obtained.

Determination of Plant Density. The plant density from the standpoint of big-game animals may be defined as *the percentage of ground surface which, when viewed from above, appears to be completely covered by foliage within easy reach of the animals.* The methods used for livestock-range determination are the best available for game-range determination, but it must be remembered that irregularities may occur in using them for game work. Experiments with game animals in large inclosures comparable to livestock range experiments are needed in order to make comparisons with field observations.

Of the following four methods, the first two are the most common:

(a) The *reconnaissance method* is widely used. The examiner passes through vegetation types and makes a mental "moving average" of density and composition of grasses, herbs, and woody browse species. The three field adaptions of this method in general use are the *gridiron, transverse sketching,* and *triangulation* methods.

(b) *Square foot density,* or *point observation method,* samples the vegetation by randomized and replicated plots which obtain more quantitative data than the reconnaissance method. Many 100-square-foot quadrats (radius of 5 feet 7.8 inches) are located at random. The density is determined by a square-foot wire frame for each species covering 0.5 square foot (0.5 per cent density) or more; one square foot of vegetation is thus equivalent to a density of 1 per cent.

(c) The *weight estimate method* is based upon actual weights in grams for each species at a given time in definite quadrats that are patternized (gridiron) or randomized. The experienced field man can estimate forage weights with considerable accuracy and thus speed up range determination.

(d) The *volume palatability method* uses the volume of forage produced; thus it uses height, a datum omitted by most other methods. The volume rating is combined with the palatability to give the "volume palatability" rating of each species.

Carrying Capacity in Forage Acres. The *forage-acre* factor (Y) is obtained by multiplying the proper-use factor (P), which is a percentage, by the density (D): $Y = PD$.

The *forage acre* (F) is defined as an acre covered with vegetation (100 per cent or ten-tenths) which can be properly and fully utilized. In actual practice it is seldom that more than 80 per cent of the forage can be used and the plant cover survive. The forage-acre is obtained by multiplying the area (A) by the forage-acre factor: $F = AY$.

The *forage-acre requirement* (R) is the amount of forage (in forage acres) needed to sustain a mature animal without injury to the range. The forage-acre requirement of big-game species has not been worked out, but in range management the forage-acre requirement is determined by means of carefully conducted experiments on a representative range stocked to secure proper utilization during the given period. The forage-acre requirement for one head for one month is obtained by dividing the forage acres by the number of animal months (M_1) of utilization secured in the experiment:

$$R = \frac{F}{M_1}$$

Because the experiment gives only the forage-acre requirement for the season of the experiment, experiments carried through several seasons are needed to obtain the average grazing capacity of the range. The forage-acre requirement also must be determined separately for each type of range.

The carrying capacity of the whole range in animal months (M_2) is determined by the formula

$$M_2 = \frac{PDA}{R}$$

The number of animals (N) that the range can carry is obtained by dividing the number of animal months by the number of months (S) during which the animals use the range:

$$N = \frac{M_2}{S}$$

The determination of forage and range capacity for big game is not so easy as it may seem; in fact determination of density and composition of the vegetation is baffling at times. The square-foot method in winter elk surveys seems the best method devised to date. The browse may be clipped off to the browsing diameter for each species on the various sample plots and wet and dry weights taken. The carrying capacity can then be estimated on the basis of the weights in relation to the proper-use factor. It appears that the weight-estimate method is applicable also on summer range.

All range determinations require considerable additional investigation before they can be given full confidence. Censuses of the animals are also needed, as the forage density and poundage data lose significance in solving big-game survey problems unless animal-population determinations for correlation purposes can be made with a good degree of accuracy. The determination of carrying capacity on a range supporting both livestock and big game is complicated by the differences in forage requirements between the different classes of livestock and the species of game. Elk and moose use the upper story because they browse shrubs and trees that are higher than those within reach of deer or livestock.

Mapping. Maps are essential in the study of wildlife or in making and carrying out management plans. Maps are convenient forms upon

Field Investigations and Practices

which to record operations and changes, and the student should learn early to make and read maps.

Maps vary from simple outline maps to complex maps showing detailed conditions. The maps generally used in wildlife management can be listed as *base maps, cover maps,* and *contour maps.* In actual practice it is usually best to use combination maps, making sure that

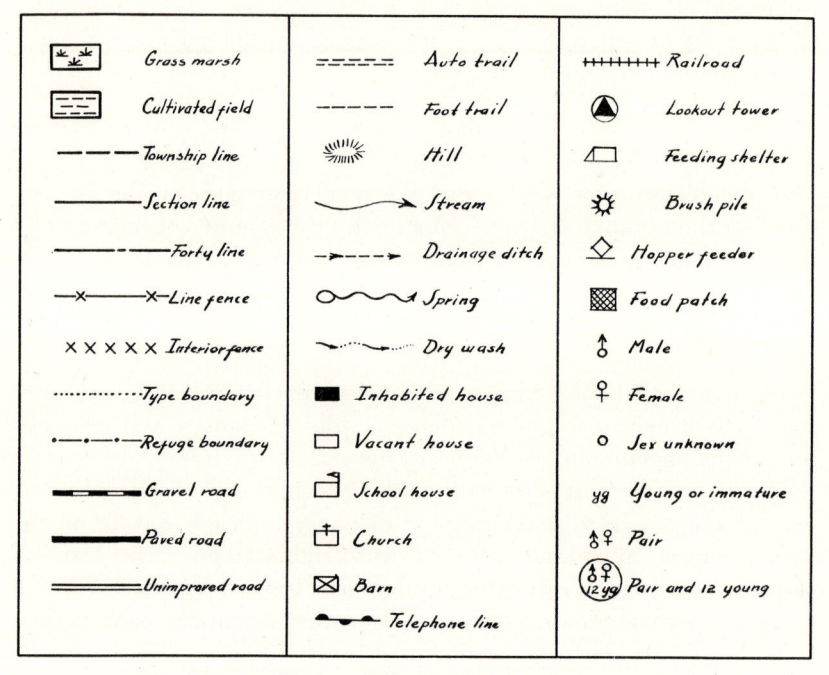

Symbol	Name	Symbol	Name	Symbol	Name
	Grass marsh	======	Auto trail	+++++++	Railroad
	Cultivated field	------	Foot trail	●	Lookout tower
------	Township line		Hill	⌂	Feeding shelter
———	Section line	~~→	Stream	✲	Brush pile
———-—	Forty line	-→---→	Drainage ditch	◇	Hopper feeder
—×———×—	Line fence	○~~→	Spring	▨	Food patch
× × × × ×	Interior fence	~...~	Dry wash	♂	Male
....	Type boundary	■	Inhabited house	♀	Female
—•—•—•—	Refuge boundary	□	Vacant house	○	Sex unknown
━━━	Gravel road	⌐	School house	yg	Young or immature
━━━	Paved road	✝	Church	♂♀	Pair
═══	Unimproved road	⊠	Barn	(♂♀ 12 yg)	Pair and 12 young
		~—•	Telephone line		

FIG. 4.4. Standard symbols for game management maps.

one does not overload them. With a base map at hand, a cover map can be constructed quickly by walking back and forth over the area and marking the cover on the base map. Cover can also be determined by ocular estimate from some high point of observation. Distances can be paced off, but measuring them is a better method. Without a usable base map the best plan is to make one with a plane table. A fairly good base from which to work is a map traced in such detail as needed from aerial photographs that may be examined in many county seats. A multiscope will materially aid in determining cover from aerial photographs. Maps are based also upon plat or property maps, which are generally less satisfactory, however, than aerial maps. Soil maps, topographic maps, and the like often are the easiest to obtain for bases.

The size of the cover map depends entirely upon the needs of the observer. Though a wall map may be of any size, for convenience it should not be greater than 4 or 5 feet in any one measurement. Field maps, on the other hand, must be of a size convenient to handle during the course of observations. Generally a sheet 8½ by 11 inches is as large as will be found convenient in the field, although larger maps, divided or folded, may be satisfactory. A map of 8½ by 11 inches, however, does not lend itself well to large areas; it is better to make a map in sections than to try to get too much information on one sheet. But the scale used is important. Standard symbols should be used for all mapping (Fig. 4.4).

SUGGESTED READING

Blair, W. Frank, 1941, "Techniques for Studying Mammal Populations," *Jour. Mammalogy*, 22:148–157.

Dalke, Paul D., 1937, "The Cover Map in Wildlife Management," *Jour. Wildlife Management*, 1:100–105.

Dice, Lee R., 1941, "Methods for Estimating Populations of Mammals," *Jour. Wildlife Management*, 5:398–407.

Gates, Frank C., 1949, *Field Manual of Plant Ecology*, McGraw-Hill Book Co., New York.

Gordon, Seth, Jr., 1941, "A Sampling Technique for the Determination of Hunters' Activities and the Economics Thereof," *Jour. Wildlife Management*, 5:260–278.

Hamerstrom, F. N., Jr., and James Blake, 1939, "A Fur Study Technique," *Jour. Wildlife Management*, 3:54–59.

Hillcourt, William, 1950, *Fieldbook of Nature Activities*, G. P. Putnam's Sons, New York.

Leopold, Aldo, 1931, *A Report of a Game Survey of the North Central States*, Sporting Arms and Ammunition Manufacturers Institute, Madison, Wis.

Leopold, Aldo, 1933, *Game Management*, Charles Scribner's Sons, New York.

Oosting, Henry J., 1948, *The Study of Plant Communities; an Introduction to Plant Ecology*, W. H. Freeman Co., New York.

Raisz, Erwin, 1948, *General Cartography*, McGraw-Hill Book Co., New York.

Ricker, William E., 1948, *Methods of Estimating Vital Statistics of Fish Populations*, Indiana Univ. Sci. Ser. 15.

Shelford, Victor E., 1929, *Laboratory and Field Ecology*, Williams and Wilkins Co., Baltimore.

Spurr, Stephen H., 1948, *Aerial Photographs in Forestry*, Ronald Press Co., New York.

Stoddart, Laurence A., and Arthur D. Smith, 1943, *Range Management*, McGraw-Hill Book Co., New York.

Taylor, Walter P., 1930, "Methods of Determining Rodent Pressure on the Range," *Ecology*, 11:523–542.

Webb, William L., 1942, "A Method for Wildlife Management Mapping in Forested Areas," *Jour. Wildlife Management*, 6:38–43.

Welch, Paul S., 1948, *Limnological Methods*, Blakiston Co., Philadelphia.

Wight, Howard M., 1939, *Field and Laboratory Technic in Wildlife Management*, Edwards Bros., Ann Arbor, Mich.

Young, Vernon A., and W. Leslie Robinette, 1939, "A Study of the Range Habits of Elk on the Selway Game Preserve," *Univ. Idaho Bull.*, Vol. 34, No. 16.

5

Techniques of Field Investigations and Practices (Continued)

Reading Sign. The ability to read sign is a valuable aid in the field, and no observer can ever become too proficient. Reading sign measures the ability of the observer to find evidence of animal activity in the field and to arrive at a reasonable understanding of the events that took place. Naturally, the sign may be of different degrees of clearness (Figs. 5.1 and 5.2), and the clearness will vary also with observers; that which is clear sign to the skilled observer may be poor sign to the novice. The actual seeing of sign in the field is not the whole of sign reading. Actually reading sign is almost entirely the problem of interpreting evidence. The student should begin with the most obvious sign and gradually work for an understanding of the abstruse.

Tracks and Trails. Good tracking snow is essentially the best medium in which to read much sign. The passage of animals and the various activities in which they have partaken leave impressions in soft snow (Fig. 5.3). The observer, however, may not always be so fortunate as to find snow at the time or in the places where evidence is wanted. Even so, it is rarely possible for an animal to pass for much distance without leaving some indications of its passage. Thus one can detect otter by slides along the streams that they inhabit and the male cougar by the deep scratches he makes in the earth or snow. Scats are expelled from time to time, and, if identifiable, they indicate the animal responsible for them. Similarly, indigestible parts of many foods are cast up in the form of pellets by many birds. When properly studied, these scats and pellets reveal important evidence of food habits. Runways are frequent, especially in grass and other heavy

72   Field Investigations and Practices

vegetation, and trails made by large animals are frequently cut deeply into the forest floor and desert soil.

Large animals leave trails that may be detected in vegetation by its crushed appearance. The length of time that has elapsed since the animals' passage can be judged to some extent by the amount of re-straightening of the vegetation. It must not be forgotten too that

Fig. 5.1. These shells evidence successful hatching by ruffed grouse because they have been opened at the large end by the escaping chick.

wounded animals may leave trails of blood, even if only a drop every hundred feet or more.

Often natural conditions are unsuited to the preservation of tracks, and then the observer can help himself by some simple operations. One of the simplest is to sift loose soil across a questionable spot so that any animal passing will be forced to leave tracks, or sand already in place can be smoothed and later visited from time to time to observe tracks. Mud found along streams and lake shores or around springs and water holes is excellent hunting ground for tracks, and, like sand, mud records new tracks if it is smoothed over to obliterate old ones. Bare spots in fields and woods are ideal for recording tracks, and special attention should be paid to the possibilities of ant hills and dust areas.

Tracks and Trails 73

FIG. 5.2. Deer sign on an aspen shoot rubbed by a buck removing velvet and polishing antlers.

FIG. 5.3. Raven sign in new-fallen snow.

Tracks are to be expected around used and unused dens, but the observer must again be cautioned that the animal making tracks around the mouth of a den is not necessarily the inhabitant, for animals often visit burrows that are not their dens.

Though it is usually impossible to note evidence of animal passage in the water, this is not always true. Fish create lines of roil along the bottom in shallow water, and land animals crossing streams or pools leave trails of muddy water, tracks in the bottom of the water, tracks on the bank, or bubbles under ice.

Kill Evidence. The finding of a dead animal presents an opportunity for testing an observer's skill and judgment in reading kill evidence. The first question to be settled is whether the animal died of natural causes or was killed. Animals in nature rarely die a natural death, although they may be on the road to a natural death when overtaken by disease or some predator. The method of killing may indicate the predator; the ground around the kill or marks on the body may also indicate the predator that is responsible or animals that have fed upon the remains.

Animals also visit carcasses of animals killed by others. A second animal innocent of the kill may possibly have been in the immediate vicinity at the time so that all the evidence points falsely to it as the killer. The condition of the carcass and the ground around it may indicate whether it has been lying there for some time, as well as whether the visitor came after death. Although the sequence of decomposition and visits of carrion insects are valuable indicators, our knowledge of these matters is scanty. At times the field man must draw upon a wide fund of information. For example, if an examination of feathers from birds found dead in winter reveals generalized molting, it indicates not predation but more likely a cripple from the fall hunting season, for molt takes place in fall rather than in winter. Lost feathers, however, are replaced in any season.

The condition of dead wild animals, when they are found, rarely lends itself to a post-mortem examination. A rapid examination of the body should be made for abnormalities. An internal examination of the principal organs, especially the lungs and liver, should be made when possible. Decomposition in the viscera usually precludes examination of any but freshly killed animals. Material for further study may be preserved in a 4 per cent formalin solution.

Evidence of Feeding. Animals betray their presence by methods of feeding; thus the badger and many others dig rodents, the bear tears logs or turns stones in search of insects, and rabbits, porcupines, and

Obtaining Evidence or Sign

mice chew the bark of trees. Obviously girdling done high in a tree would be the work of a porcupine because rabbits and mice do their girdling near the ground. Mouse-girdling can be distinguished from rabbit work by the neatness of eating as well as by the small tooth marks.

Both rabbits and deer clip stems, but the deer betrays its work by the crushed and ragged appearance of the stem, owing to the fact that the deer has no incisors in the upper jaw. Rabbits make a clean slanting cut. Red squirrels may clip the ends of pine branches, and sometimes it is a problem to tell whether the twigs were clipped by red squirrels or broken by ice. Perhaps the best known and most distinctive evidence of all animal feeding is the cutting of trees by beaver.

The place of deposition or eating of food which has been transported often indicates the animal itself. A knowledge of feeding habits and methods of caching is an invaluable aid. Wolves often cache food and use the nose in covering it over, but a cougar would scratch brush over it, and the bear would paw it over. Lesser animals have equally distinctive cache habits, as shown by the various squirrels, shrikes, and others.

Obtaining Evidence or Sign. Though direct observation and normal sign are usually relied upon for evidence of animal activity, the field man can materially forward his work by using methods that cause animals to reveal their presence or supply him with evidence. Perhaps the most widespread method is trapping and marking (which will be discussed later). Cameras set with pull strings and flashlights can require animals to take their own pictures, and some surprising results have been obtained by set cameras, even records of species previously undetected.

Birds that nest in holes often flush from the nests if a person scratches or raps smartly on the trunk of the tree.

Various elaborate mechanical devices have been used to record the visits of birds to the nest. Any person with a reasonable amount of ingenuity can construct a recording device. For most nesting birds and even for small mammals the simplest device is a marker that strikes a tape or drum when a bird makes a contact by stepping on a perch at the nest box, which in turn causes a magnet to pull the marker against the tape. Photo-electric cells may also be used.

Birds that use nest boxes are observed at their duties by means of a box with a glass side and a cover to place over the glass when the observer is away. It is advisable to have a blind or other device in which the observer sits unseen in darkness while he watches the bird through the glass, but recent advances in the manufacture of transparent mirrors offer many possibilities to the investigator, although the observer must be on the dark side of the mirror in order to use it like a window. Any mirror maker can make one by applying a thinner silver coat than usual and adding a cover glass.

Marking. Little need be said about the advantages derived from marking individual animals so that their movements can be traced. The practice is fundamental in many studies and applicable to many others.

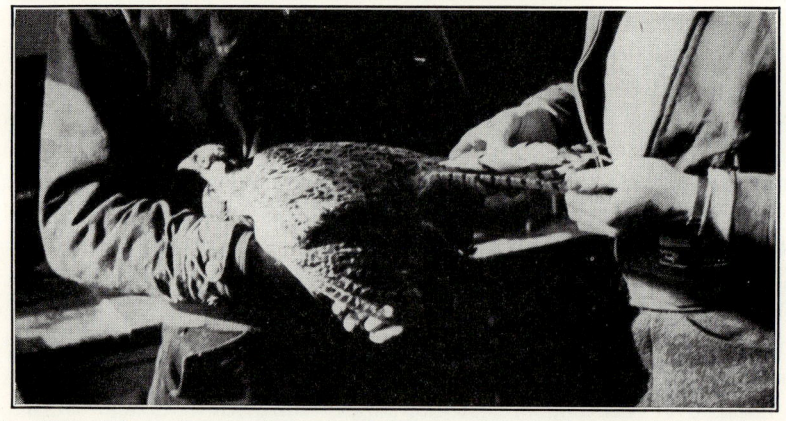

Fig. 5.4. A hen pheasant being marked by a white feather attached to the tail feathers.

A simple means of marking incubating birds is to smear colored paint around the edge of the nest so that the bird comes in contact with the paint, which thereupon makes a distinct mark on the plumage, but paint should be used with caution because it tends to mat feathers. Colored airplane dopes, like those used for model airplanes, are recognizable for a few weeks if applied directly to the feathers.

Feather marking offers many possibilities to the field man (Figs. 5.4 and 5.5). White feathers may be dyed various colors, though natural-colored feathers prove more satisfactory. Feathers to be dyed are boiled a few minutes in a strong vinegar solution before being placed in a strong solution of wool dye. Two basic dyes that have satisfactory affinities for feathers and hair are Malachite Green and Rhodamine B.

Colored feathers are attached to wing or tail by gluing the web of the colored feather to that of the natural feather with such a glue as

Marking

household cement; the shafts may be tied also and will even hold the feathers without cementing. The shaft of the colored feather may be cemented into the shaft of a natural one. In general colored feathers will last until the next molt. Colored markers of plastic or plastic fabric have been used with some success. They may be attached to the neck, wings, or back of birds and mammals with cement or metal clips. Plastic tags as well as metal ones are suitable for marking fish.

FIG. 5.5. A feather-marked and weighed sharp-tailed grouse ready for release. A rubber band holds the end of the tube closed until removed to allow escape of the bird.

Complete dyeing of the bird or mammal is useful for marking purposes. By attracting attention it is likely to increase the number of returns of banded birds as well as serving for visual reports. Combinations of colored patches formed during the dyeing process can be used. Pressure spray devices for marking animals also have merit.

Many animals are marked with serially numbered *bands* attached to the legs. Bird banding in Canada and the United States has been in progress for many years, and in the States bands are supplied by the Bureau of Biological Survey and its successor, the Fish and Wildlife Service. Use of any other bands should not be attempted. Numbered bands make it possible to identify birds upon recapture, but they help little in identifying individual birds in the field, though it is possible to band one series of birds on the left leg and another series on the right for place or sex identification. Colored plastic bands, either alone or in combination with the numbered band, are frequently added to identify individual birds (Fig. 5.6).

Sometimes one can clip certain tail or wing feathers in order to identify a few birds in the field, at least until the next molt. Clipping is advisable because pulled feathers are immediately replaced.

Mammals are marked (Fig. 5.6) by *tagging* (especially with ear tags), *toe clipping, tattooing, branding,* and *banding.*

Surgical clips of various sizes are obtainable at any medical supply house and, when numbered with a small die, are ready for fastening to the patagium (Fig. 5.6) of day-old chicks. When properly attached, the *wing clips* remain throughout life. Some fish tags will also work as wing clips. Great care must be exercised, however, lest the delicate wing bones be broken in attaching the clips. It is most practical to apply the clips immediately after hatching; otherwise, precocial chicks will be led from the vicinity of the nest by the parent bird. After hatching, precocial chicks can be kept at the nest by a low fence, but daily visits must be made by the observer because the parent may desert the young chicks if they are kept from following her. A hardware cloth or rag fence 5 inches high and 5 feet across is sufficient to hold the young and at the same time is easy to handle.

Big game can be traced and age of life recorded by means of bells like cowbells and sheepbells. Bells of one pitch can be used for bucks and another for does. If the observer has a good musical ear, bells of different pitch will identify individuals. Deer so marked sometimes learn to move with little sound from the bells.

Blinds. The blind, a structure built for the purpose of concealing the observer, is a necessary piece of equipment for close work where the observer wishes to watch animals without being visible to them. Animals under observation from a blind generally go about their activities in a normal and undisturbed manner. Perhaps the greatest value of the blind, other than for photography, is in the observation of nesting and feeding-station activities.

Blinds may be set upon the ground or set partially in an excavation, and they have sometimes been suspended in trees and over cliffs with ropes in the study of tree and cliff-nesting species, or placed upon platforms for study of marsh dwellers and nesting colonies. Floating and sunken oil-barrel blinds are very useful in watching waterfowl and other aquatic birds.

Blinds, which may be permanent, temporary, fixed, or portable, are constructed of roofing paper, burlap, brush, corn stalks, or any other available material (Fig. 5.7).

Marking 79

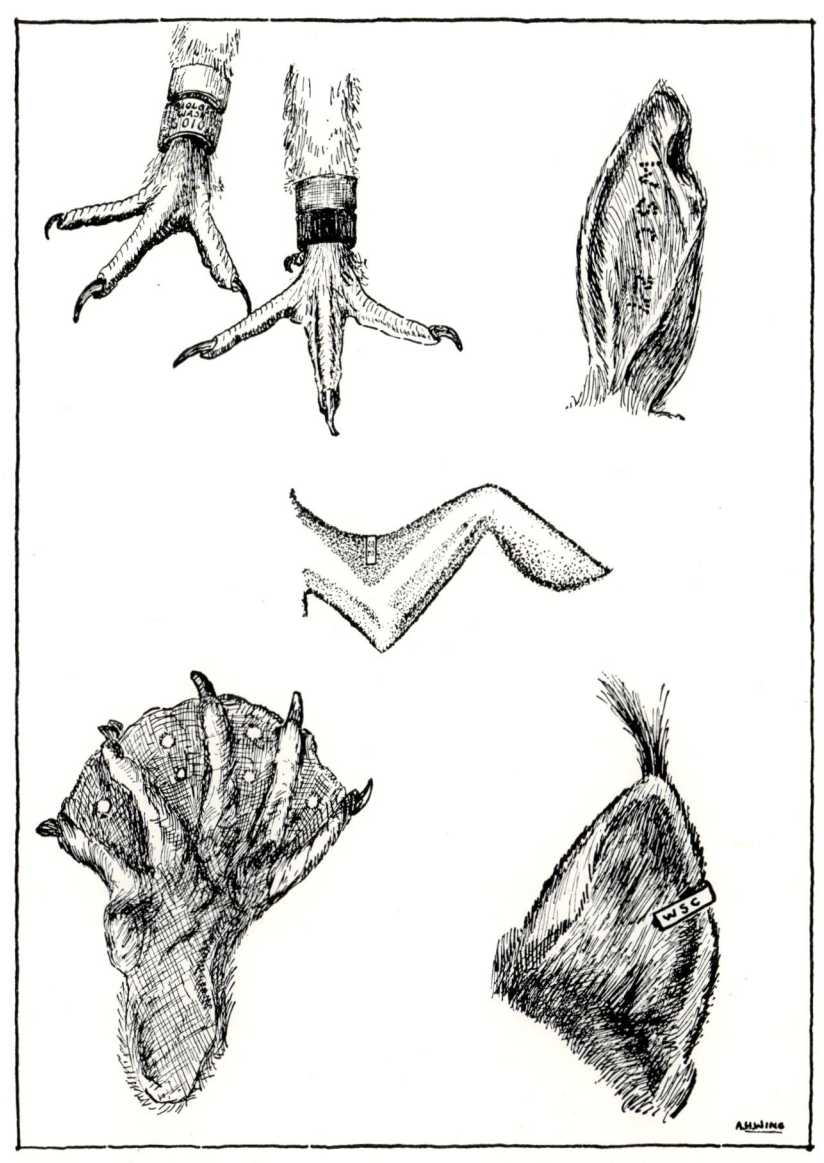

Fig. 5.6. Samples of marking techniques. Upper left, aluminum and colored plastic bands in combination. Upper right, tattooing in a rabbit's ear. Middle, numbered surgical clip attached to patagium of day-old chick. Lower left, marking beaver by punching holes in webbing of feet. Lower right, ear tags used for animals having large and tough ears.

The size of a blind depends upon the amount of its use and upon the number of people expected to use it, but in general it should be large because long hours spent in a small blind become exceedingly uncomfortable. Some species, however, become suspicious of large blinds. A good rule to follow is that blinds should not ordinarily be constructed shorter than the length needed for the observer to lie down. They can be made smaller if constructed over a pit. Observation holes in the side of the blind should be as small is is compatible with convenience. It is also advisable to provide a bench for cameras

Fig. 5.7. Constructing an observation blind of a frame covered by corn stalks.

and notebooks, as well as some kind of seat, for surely the comfort of the observer should not be overlooked.

Winter work in a blind usually entails discomforts, but the wise observer will foresee them as far as possible; especially will he dress warmly and pay particular attention to his footwear. Some degree of comfort is obtained by placing an oil lantern in an open and ventilated nail keg, sitting on the keg, and surrounding the body and keg with blankets. In very cold weather the observer can sit in a warm sleeping bag during the hours of observation. Needless to say, considerable comfort is obtained by installing a flooring of loose material.

Hair and Feather Identifications. Keys for hair and feather recognition are rather difficult to construct and use because of the complex nature of hair and feather identification. Hair and feathers can be identified to some extent by microscopic study and by comparison with known material, though familiarity is still the chief method of identification. Cross and longitudinal sections of hair are valuable for identificatation of both guard hair and fur hair. A simple method of sectioning hair is to imbed it in a Celluloid solution containing a small amount of dye. It is necessary to know the part of the hair from which the section came and to compare it with known sections from comparable parts of hair, as well as with hair from known parts of the animal body. The cross section of a hair varies with its position on the hair and the part of the body from which the hair comes.

Feathers found around nests or scattered in the woods are identified best by comparisons with bird skins. Elaborate keys have been developed for tracing feathers down to the family and order.

Food-Habits Research. Food-habits research is one of the important avenues of approach to the problems of life history. There are two methods of investigating the food habits of animals: field observation; and the examination of stomach contents, pellets, and feces. Sometimes one method must be applied and sometimes the other, yet in general a combination of the two is best because field observation furnishes a basis upon which to interpret data from stomach contents, pellets, or feces.

FIG. 5.8. Pellets of undigestible parts are telltale indications of food habits.

Reference material needed for stomach, pellet, and feces analysis is somewhat elaborate. A collection of all material that would be expected to occur in the samples should be at hand; this would be chiefly seed, skin, and skeleton collections. A collection of insects representative of local families, especially of Coleoptera, will be needed from time to time, and so will a collection of fish scales and local aquatic life. Because many finely comminuted plant parts can be identified only by their microscopic anatomy, reference slides of such material may be needed. Serological tests might also have to be made for identification of flesh, though such tests fail with cooked meat (as in identifying suspected venison in enforcement work).

The stomach contents, as well as pellets and feces, can be examined when wet or dried and studied later (Fig. 5.8) or preserved in a weak formalin solution for later examination. It is good practice to weigh the contents when fresh and after they become dry. Since there is no universal method of measuring the many items found in food samples, various investigators use different methods singly or in combination, depending upon the material and the purpose of the studies. Some prefer to report items by volume, some by weight, some by precentage of the total contents, and some by frequency of occurrence. Many investigators prefer volume and frequency.

Field Observation. The value of observation depends to a great extent upon the capacity of the observer to make observations and to preserve a judicial attitude in interpreting them. Time and place are important parts of observations; what may be an insignificant observation at one season or in one locality may be important elsewhere or at another time. Many are the factors that enter into the value and validity of field observation; yet it hardly seems necessary to discuss them here or to list the multitude of possible field observations.

The problem of "working up" field observations requires great concentration and careful discrimination, which is doubly true when observations have been made by others. Isolated observations unsupported by other observations should be handled with care as far as conclusions are concerned. It must be remembered, above all, that the value of conclusions varies with the amount and quality of data, and the amount of data in turn depends upon the number and accuracy of observations. The value varies likewise with the completeness of the analysis the investigator presents.

Though laboratory experimentation has supplanted observation in many fields to a great extent, the value of observation in wildlife studies is just as great as if not greater than ever before. *A connected series of carefully made field observations is quite as reliable as data from the most involved laboratory experiment.*

Field Experimentation. Field experimentation generally has been neglected as a tool of animal science; yet field experimentation is much more valuable than laboratory experimentation in studying wildlife problems. Conclusions reached from laboratory experiments are literally valid only for animals under those conditions; it is not legitimate to transfer bodily the results of laboratory studies to the wilds and there to apply them to wild populations. The essence of wildlife is *wildness,* and confinement destroys this important attribute. For this reason it is not possible to separate a wild animal from its environment and still have the same animal. A wild animal is an integral part of its environment and technically inseparable in wildlife research and management.

Field experimentation requires experimental areas for manipulations and control areas for checking (both areas must be alike and of the same character). Manipulations which are possible with field experimentation fall into three classes: additions, subtractions, and changes. During the process of making additive manipulations, something from the outside is added to the experimental area (such as shelter, food, or even other animals). On the other hand, subtractive manipulations remove something from the experimental area. Changes are manipulations which alter the experimental plot in some way but have neither added nor subtracted from the total of the plot. We could experiment with ruffed grouse drumming logs and their cover, for example, by removing some, by adding more, or by shifting the positions of the existing logs.

The size of the control and experimental areas depends entirely upon the subject of investigation; an experimental area for mice might be a few acres, whereas an experimental area for moose should encompass many square miles. The size depends upon the cruising radius, both daily and seasonal, of the experimental animals, and the physical action that the experimenter can accomplish with the means and time at his disposal. No set rule can be given for the size of the experimental and control areas.

Cooperation Studies. Sometimes considerable data, particularly of a mass type, can be obtained from hunters, farmers, and others by distributing creel cards, hunting forms, and questionnaires. On the whole, however, "mail-order" research is a poor substitute for a biologist afield. A score of interested hunters with a personal attitude towards the work of a biologist friend usually prove invaluable aids in gathering field data, and the biologist is fortunate who can command such interest.

Some investigations, particularly economic and administration studies, can be aided by the average hunter and fisherman. The sending in of body parts, such as scales, wings, tails, or feet, for sex ratio and age-class studies offers some chance for solicitation of help from the hunters and fishermen.

Wildlife Damage Investigations. One of the problems that will face a wildlife biologist sooner or later will be investigation of crop damage or other complaints. As a general rule, damage complaints tend to be grossly exaggerated and complainants unduly wrought up over their assumed loss. The mere fact that a wild animal passes through a field crop does not of itself indicate damage. In some areas farmers regularly let sheep go into bean fields to eat weeds, and many wild animals feed similarly upon plants other than crops.

A good pair of binoculars is essential in watching animals supposed to be destroying crops, for the observer can thereby locate the exact spot for close examination. This is especially true of bird invasions of grain fields. Doves, for example, do not scratch and can feed only upon waste or uncovered grains. Even sprouting grain in the crop may not indicate destruction; pulled grain would show a colorless section near the seed end where soil covered the stem, in contrast to the complete green of sprouting waste grain. A check of grain production can be made by placing netting over a plot and comparing it at harvest time with unprotected plots.

Study of damage to fruits is similar to that for field-crops; it involves combinations of observation, examination, and crop analysis. Farmers who plant unusual crops near concentration areas may well anticipate difficulties, and wildlife biologists can point out some of the difficulties in advance. For example, planting crops that are green all winter adjacent to coastal waterfowl concentration areas invites crop damage. Failure or inability to harvest a grain crop one year may bring on an influx of birds, and many can be expected to return the following season.

Binoculars and Other Optical Instruments. A good pair of binoculars is almost indispensable in carrying on field work. An $8\times$ binocular gives about all the magnification that can be held steady in the hand, especially when physical effort is great and nervous tension high. Objective lens smaller than 40 mm in an $8\times$ binocular should not be used. The recommended power and objectives are 6×30, 7×35, 8×40, 9×45, and 10×50. Some 6×42 and 7×50 glasses are exceptional instruments for field use, but cheap Japanese or other imitations of good makes are not worth purchasing. The weight of a 7×50 is usually great.

The light-gathering factor of a glass varies with the square of the objective lens divided by the power. Thus, a 6×30 binocular has a light-gathering ratio of 25, but the 8 × 30 has only about half as much. In bright sunlight, a low ratio works satisfactorily, but in cloudy weather, late afternoon, or in deep woods, the superior light-gathering of the large objective pays off.[1]

Spotting scopes and some telescopes are suitable for long-distance studies of antelope, waterfowl, and others. There are on the market some 24× binoculars that are extraordinary instruments for such work. They must be mounted on a tripod, but they can be used for many purposes in addition to distant observations. When mounted at a convenient site, they permit the observation of nesting and other activities without the need of a blind. A number of useful 16× navy telescopes have also appeared on the market.

Photography. Good pictures can help materially in carrying on field work, though the man who is even poorly skilled can make drawings or sketches of very great use, often more useful than photography. Pictures have a particular importance in illustrating material in reports of investigations, whether to be published or to be filed for future comparison. The service of photography in public relations, both still and motion pictures, black-and-white or color, can hardly be overestimated. Most administrative departments maintain a photographic file, and a comprehensive one, excellently indexed, is fundamental to public relations or education.

By means of *photographic stations,* usually identified by numbered stakes and even position marks for the camera, the biologist can make comparative records of seasonal or yearly changes comparable in coverage. It is sometimes possible also to demonstrate changes with time by photographing old sites as determined from earlier photographs. Ecological evidence can thus be acquired from pioneer-day photographs preserved in old family collections, early publications, libraries, and pioneer museums.

Choice of cameras, like the choice of binoculars or automobiles, is in part a personal matter. Cameras with extension bellows, ground-glass backs, and film-pack or roll-film adapters are the most versatile for black-and-white negatives. The best wildlife photographs are still being taken with the Graflex camera. The 35-mm miniature cameras are desirable for color pictures, and they are convenient for many black-and-white pictures also, though they do not take pictures of the quality of the larger cameras.

[1] The author personally prefers the 7 × 50.

Motion pictures are made on either 35-mm or 16-mm film, depending largely upon money available for film. The 8-mm size has nothing to recommend it for wildlife work. Thirty-five-millimeter film can be transposed to 16-mm size for loan films. Such films are usually made up with added sound track, but many people prefer to watch animals on the screen without the distraction of sound.

The type of motion-picture camera varies with individual tastes, though magazine cameras are often preferred. It is best to have a camera with a turret head and variable speeds, even single-frame control. Although telephoto lenses are essential, one that is larger than about $3\frac{1}{2}$ inches is seldom satisfactory. Larger ones are available, but the rigidity of the camera in the field is usually not great enough for such high power.

Field Collecting. Wildlife biologists universally are collectors of scientific specimens or items in the plant, animal, and mineral field. A small knapsack with vials and envelopes for seeds and small animals usually is part of a biologist's equipment. Small vials (2-dram, screw-top, druggists' vials are good) with a 70 per cent alcohol solution are convenient for small organisms. Seeds usually are placed in envelopes. A pair of forceps are useful; one may be carried safely in an old fountain pen, or with its points stuck into a cork.

Birds and mammals are preserved by removing the skin and stuffing it with cotton. An injection of zinc chloride in the belly and throat will retard decomposition in hot weather without hurting the skinning operations, though it may roughen the preparator's fingers. Fish, amphibians, and reptiles are usually preserved in 70 per cent alcohol or 4 per cent formalin. Often they are transferred to the alcohol after an initial period in the formalin.

Plants are collected whole when possible and carried in a metal container (vasculum) until they can be dried in a plant press. They are then mounted on sheets of good-quality cardboard.

Other field samples may be collected and preserved in appropriate ways, such as soil in sacks, water in vials, feathers in envelopes, or nests in boxes. Tree rings may be preserved in sections, for example, or as increment borings.

Field Notes. One of the most important duties of the wildlife man is taking notes or recording observations. Adequate and detailed written notes are essential in any serious field work, and the memory cannot be relied upon for recording data. Carefully recorded data can be worked over later, long after memory of them may have faded.

Field Notes

Field notes should contain more than symbols or other abbreviated notations whenever possible; they should be written completely, carefully, and with due consideration for clarity. The observer cannot foretell delays; he cannot know when it will become necessary or desirable for someone else to work over his notes. Often an observer transfers his operations to some other problem or territory before completing a project. He, as well as others, reaps some benefit from his labors when his notes are in such condition that another investigator may carry on.

Some observers prefer to use small notebooks in the field and later to rework the notes into a permanent form; others prefer to write the notes in permanent form at the moment of observation. Much can be said for either method, but the chances of error are reduced if permanent notes are made immediately. Some data can be recorded in tabular form, some by narration, and still others by carefully made measured drawings, sketches, and maps.

Prepared forms facilitate note-taking when many observations are expected to be of the same general type. They also have the advantage of uniformity, which the observer will appreciate when working up mass data later. Forms are necessary when many observers are recording notes on a central problem. Many of the multiple-copy commercial forms can be adapted to wildlife use, and they will speed up work. I.B.M. tabulating and sorting cards and Keysort sorting cards save much labor when organized for wildlife research.

Personal preference enters into the note-recording material, especially in the size of the notebook, which is not so important as commonly believed. A standard size, however, is best. The type of binder and color of paper is a matter of personal choice, except for the selection of a good rag paper. Notes can be written with carbon ink or a hard pencil; chemical inks tend to smear or run if the paper gets damp, and soft pencils will smudge. Dipping penciled pages in water reduces smudging. Beyond these few suggestions, the matter of notebooks is up to the observer.

Field notes, of either observation or experiment, must record the time, place, and conditions under which the notes were made. The weather, topography, cover, exposure, and related matters invariably enter the notebook; in fact all pertinent data should find its way there, and it is better to make the notes too voluminous than too sketchy. The amount of note-taking depends upon the individual and upon his observational skill. One field observer may spend all day in the woods and have nothing for his notebook, whereas another writes several pages after only an hour of observation.

A small note pad fastened to the steering wheel of a car or instrument panel is useful when traveling. A compass, altimeter, and watch may also be kept there. In making notations it is not necessary to separate numerals by commas; all numerals above 10 may be encircled to distinguish them from numbers below 10.

Reports. The field man will be required regularly to submit reports which, in general, fall into two classes: administrative and technical.

Administrative reports cover problems of administration and serve as material for *administrative decisions,* as well as to record conditions and recommend details. Reports of this type are usually the result of "trouble-shooting"—that is, the investigation of a complaint or a specific administrative problem. The administrative report presents clearly and briefly the findings of the investigator, together with recommendations for solution of the problem, and it may contain, therefore, the opinions of the investigator. In addition to serving as the basis for administrative decisions, administrative reports are filed for future reference because they indicate what happened, the conditions at the time, and what later was done or planned.

Technical reports cover general surveys or specific projects under investigation. The survey report may depend upon testimony of others, as well as the observations of the investigator; in fact it may contain almost any type of survey material. Reports on scientific projects cover intensive observations or experiments, and the observer presents his findings and his interpretation of them. This report does not present the opinions of the investigator except as they result from the particular investigation, whereupon they appear as part of the discussion.

In make-up the administrative report differs from the technical report chiefly in that it is more concise and that the beginning presents a brief summary and recommendation. The general outline of a report follows:

> Brief summary and recommendations (not more than one page in length; administrative reports only).
> Statement of problem, complaint, or objectives.
> The investigation.
> Data obtained.
> Discussion of the data.
> Conclusions and summary.

Technical reports for publication are "boiled down" considerably before being sent to press. Detailed observations are often not necessary or valuable enough for permanent record, but they should be tabulated or condensed so that the reader will not be lost in a maze of words.

In almost all government work, whether state or federal, report writing constitutes an important part of the duties of field men, although it sometimes seems to become the end rather than the means to an end. Small organizations may dispense largely with reports, as decisions are made not far from the point of observation, but it is not possible for administrators in large organizations to know all the technical details of their work, and they must depend upon reports of subordinates. The turnover of personnel in large organizations makes it necessary for reports to be filed in order to give continuity to the work. In smaller or less formal organizations the material that ordinarily goes into reports can be kept in notebooks and files until written up for publication or otherwise utilized.

Early in his training period the student should gain facility in writing reports because the ability to express oneself clearly is essential in transmitting and recording information.

SUGGESTED READING

Blair, W. Frank, 1941, "Techniques for Studying Mammal Populations," *Jour. Mammalogy,* 22:148–157.

Davison, Verne E., 1940, "A Field Method of Analyzing Game Bird Foods," *Jour. Wildlife Management,* 4:105–116.

Errington, Paul L., 1932, "Technique of Raptor Food Habits Study," *Condor,* 34:75–86.

Hamerstrom, F. N., Jr., and James Blake, "A Fur Study Technique," *Jour. Wildlife Management,* 3:54–59.

Hickey, Joseph J., 1943, *A Guide to Bird Watching,* Oxford University Press, New York.

Kalmbach, E. R., 1934, "Field Observation in Economic Ornithology," *Wilson Bull.,* 46:73–90.

Leopold, Aldo, 1933, *Game Management,* Charles Scribner's Sons, New York.

Lincoln, Frederick C., and S. Prentiss Baldwin, 1929, "Manual for Bird Banders," *U.S.D.A. Misc. Bull.* 58.

Mangels, Frederick P., 1938, "Colored Bands, Methods for Using Bands and Arranging Data," *Bird-Banding,* 9:94–97.

Mathiak, Harold A., 1938, "A Key to Hairs of the Mammals of Southern Michigan," *Jour. Wildlife Management,* 2:251–268.

Murie, Adolph, 1936, "Following Fox Trails," *Univ. Mich. Mus. Zool. Misc. Publ.* 32.

Pearse, John, 1947, "Identifying Injury by Wildlife to Trees and Shrubs in Northeastern Forests," *Fish and Wildlife Serv. Research Rept.* 13.

Seton, Ernest Thompson, 1925-1929, *Lives of Game Animals*, Doubleday-Doran and Co., Garden City, N. Y.

Shelford, Victor E., 1929, *Laboratory and Field Ecology*, Williams and Wilkins Co., Baltimore.

Spencer, Donald A., 1939, "Electrical Recording of the Activities of Small Mammals," *Jour. Mammalogy*, 20:479–485.

Stebler, A. M., 1939, "The Tracking Technique in the Study of the Larger Predatory Mammals," *Trans. Fourth N. A. Wildlife Conf.:* 203–208.

Wade, Douglas E., 1938, "Drought Intensity Measurements and the Effect of the 1936 Drought on Wildlife," *Trans. Third N. A. Wildlife Conf.:* 558–569.

Wadkins, L. A., 1948, "Dyeing Birds for Identification," *Jour. Wildlife Management*, 12:388–391.

Welch, Paul S., 1948, *Limnological Methods*, Blackiston Co., Philadelphia.

Wetmore, Alexander, 1927, "A Method for Keeping Notes and Files Dealing with Ornithology," *Condor*, 29:109–111.

Wight, Howard M., 1939, *A Field and Laboratory Technic in Wildlife Management*, Edwards Bros., Ann Arbor, Mich.

Young, Vernon A., and W. Leslie Robinette, 1939, "A Study of the Range Habits of the Elk on the Selway Game Preserve," *Univ. of Idaho Bull.*, Vol. 34, No. 16.

6

Farm Game and Its Management

The ecological opportunities for farm game are great indeed, and to list all the types utilized by various farm game species would be a major undertaking. Table 6.1, however, summarizes the principal vegetation types or species used by farm game.

Farm Practices and Changed Conditions. Although we are primarily interested in management operations, nevertheless the great changes that occurred in the conversion of virgin country to farm lands are worth more than a moment's consideration; moreover, it is the results of these changes with which we work. The forest, the swamp, the marsh, and the prairie of virgin days disappeared, to be replaced by cities and towns, cultivated fields, and pastures. It is not surprising that such profound changes in the environment should result in equally profound changes in the wildlife, changes that were beneficial to some species and harmful to others.

Song and insectivorous birds of brush meadows and the woods margins have benefited most. Not only have they increased in numbers in the ancestral range but they have also extended their ranges in many instances. Yet to many species the changes that resulted from settlement of the land have been detrimental. The species inhabiting the deep forest have suffered from its removal, and settlement has had harmful effects upon range animals, waterfowl, and many shore birds. It is not for us here to wonder at changes or to decry excesses; rather it is for us to build and to produce.

Farm practices differ in various areas no less than they differ in their changing of conditions. Wheat farming is probably the most extensive of all farm operations, truck gardening the most intensive. The "slick and clean" farming of rich dairy lands is perhaps the most detri-

TABLE 6.1

USE OF FOOD AND COVER TYPES BY FARM GAME

(Adapted from Grange and McAtee, 1934)

Cover Type	Bob-white	Ring-Necked Pheasant	Hungarian Partridge	Wilson Snipe	Cotton-tail
Ungrazed woodlots:					
Second-growth hardwood	CF	CF	..	..	CF
Mature hardwood	c	c	..	..	c
Swamp hardwood	cf	cf	..	..	cf
Hardwood-conifer	cf	cf	..	..	cf
Tamarack and spruce	..	..	..	..	cf
Young pine and spruce	..	..	..	..	cf
Mature pine and spruce	..	..	..	..	..
Aspen	.	..	..	..	cf
Windbreaks, hedges, and fence rows:					
Osage orange (untrimmed)	C	C	C	..	C
Prickly ash	C	c	C	..	C
Wild plum, hawthorn	CF	CF	cf	..	CF
Cherries, mountain ash	cF	cF	cf	..	cf
Young pine and spruce	C	C	C	..	C
Mature pine and spruce	c	c	..	..	c
Arborvitae (untrimmed)	c	c	c	..	c
Red cedar	CF	CF	c	..	C
Dogwood, serviceberry	cF	cF	cf	..	cf
Sumac	CF	CF	F	..	CF
Briers and berries	CF	CF	cF	..	CF
Grassy fence rows	CF	CF	CF	..	CF
Vines with other cover:					
Wild grapes	CF	CF	C	..	CF
Bittersweet	CF	CF	c	..	CF
Virginia creeper	CF	cf	c	..	Cf
Greenbrier	CF	cF	c	..	CF
Cultivated crops, etc.:					
Standing corn	CF	CF	CF	..	CF
Shocked corn	cF	cF	cF	..	cF
Standing small grain	CF	CF	CF	..	CF
Small-grain stubble	cF	Cf	CF	..	F
Ragweed, etc.	CF	CF	CF	..	CF
Fallow fields	f	f	F	..	..
Orchards	CF	CF	c	..	CF

Farm Practices and Changed Conditions

TABLE 6.1. *(Continued)*

USE OF FOOD AND COVER TYPES BY FARM GAME

(Adapted from Grange and McAtee, 1934)

Cover Type	Bob-white	Ring-Necked Pheasant	Hungarian Partridge	Wilson Snipe	Cotton-tail
Cultivated crops, etc.: *(Continued)*					
Berry patches	CF	CF	CF	..	CF
Red and white clover, alfalfa	CF	CF	CF	..	CF
Sweet clover	c	c	c	..	CF
Ungrazed marshes:					
Cattail	..	C	..	c	c
Sedges	c	CF	c	c	f
Potholes	f	cf	c	c	f
Grassy marshes	cf	Cf	..	CF	cf
Unclassified cover:					
Brush heaps and untrimmed tree tops	C	C	c	..	C
Large thorny roses	C	CF	c	..	Cf
Hollow logs	..	..	..	..	C
Hollow trees (butt hollows)	..	..	..	..	C
Stone walls	c	c	..	..	C
Straw stacks	c	c	c	..	c
Wire entanglements	C	C	c	..	C
Culverts and tiles	..	..	..	..	C
Rail fences	C	C	..	..	C

c—used for cover.
f—used for food.
Capital letter—indicates high degree of use.

mental to farm game, save for some cotton lands and summer fallows. The wire fence has eliminated hedges and stone walls and, consequently, the organisms finding haven there; the wire fence gives a narrow fence row at most, and clean fence rows offer little cover for game. Although great store is put by clean fence rows and clean roadsides, it is probable that the benefit derived is too frequently less than the effort expended. Many roadsides are still conscientiously cut or burned yearly, but it is likely that the purpose of roadside maintenance would be served well in most regions if cutting or burning occurred but once every four or five years, if at all. The forward march of ecological succession will eliminate weeds permanently; annual burning and cutting holds the succession back. The saving in bird habitat would be substantial, and the saving of public funds might also be great.

The protection that can be given to farm game from the more destructive farm practices depends chiefly upon the interest of the farmer himself. No amount of technology can balance lack of application.

FIG. 6.1. A grazed-out Wisconsin woodlot with little cover for most farm game species.

Among the simple practices which have been found helpful is the use of a flushing device for the prevention of destruction of hayfield nests. The flushing device is merely a rod, chain, or combination that fastens to the mowing machine, binder, combine, or plow (or is suspended from the horses or tractor) in such a way as to drag a few feet ahead of the cutter bar or plow. It causes the birds to flush from nests before the machinery hits the bird and nest. The operator, being warned of the nest, is able to lift his implement and to straddle the nest on the next trip around the field. The importance of the flushing bar should not be overrated, however.

Game Food and Cover 95

The regulation of grazing of woodlots can protect game from harm and even benefit it. The grazing of woodlots is usually destructive of game cover (Fig. 6.1) and sometimes harmful to the timber; it also yields little pasturage.

Game Food and Cover. Withholding action is sometimes as important as dynamic operations, and nice judgment is required to decide where, when, and what measures to apply.

It is generally possible to increase the amount of game food and cover on farms without materially interfering with crop production.

Fig. 6.2. The difference between grazed and ungrazed woodlots shows clearly in this picture from Tennessee.

Only a minority of American farms are literally 100 per cent tillable, and most possess some waste land, eroded gullies, fence rows, fence corners, roadsides, creek banks, orchards, woodlots, or windbreaks that are usable for the production of some of the cover that is needed by game species. Not only the quality but also the distribution of cover is an important consideration. For example, brush travel lanes, along fence rows, greatly enhance the value of otherwise isolated blocks of cover.

Fencing (Fig. 6.2) to prevent stock from destroying nesting and winter cover, as well as food-bearing plants, materially increases production of food and cover. Underplantings and brush piles, as we shall see presently, do much toward strengthening the cover in grazed-out woodlots.

Essential cover can be supplied in the fields of grain by cutting the stubble high instead of close to the ground; stubble so cut will provide shelter for birds using weed seed and waste grain. A swath left uncut around the outside of the field will also find ready takers during the winter. Shocked and standing corn, too, will find users during the winter; indeed, corn is still the number one winter food for upland game birds.

The plowing of stubble will affect birds less if it is deferred until spring, when winter use is ended, but plowing should not be deferred until nesting begins. The mowing of weeds can also be postponed until spring in order to give birds a chance to obtain weed seed during winter. The seeds left through the winter seem to have little real effect upon the amount of weeds actually produced, and in any event the weed seed already present in the soil is universally sufficient to assure a crop of weeds when tillage is poorly done.

Building Cover. Many techniques have been used to increase both food and cover, but though standard practices may apply nearly everywhere, nothing after all, will substitute for ingenuity in solving the problems of local areas.

Brush Piles. Brush piles are useful structures where cover is deficient and where game species need cover for resting or escape. Brush piles may also form connecting game ways between plots of cover (Fig. 6.3) or between cover and feeders and food patches. For connecting quail cover they should be not more than about 25 feet apart. They are useful in fence corners, along roadsides, and in grazed woodlots; three to five brush piles to the acre is the suggested minimum number in grazed woodlots. Most feeding stations and food patches need emergency escape cover, and brush piles will supply it for them.

Though brush piles are constructed in diverse ways, all successful ones have open area underneath. The needed open area is formed by piling brush over frames, or by putting the largest limbs at the bottom and piling small material on top, or by piling over a stump.

Brush piles fall into several standard forms, of which the most usual are the bonfire, tepee, ridgepole, and platform types (Fig. 6.4). The bonfire type, as the name implies, is constructed by simply throwing the brush together loosely and without any frame. The tepee pile, on the other hand, differs from the bonfire pile in that poles are first put together in a tepee fashion and the brush then thrown over them. The ridgepole pile is made by laying a large pole against or across one or more stumps or other support and piling brush over it. The platform pile requires three or more supports, across which poles are placed to form a platform supporting the brush. Straw, grass, cornstalks, and

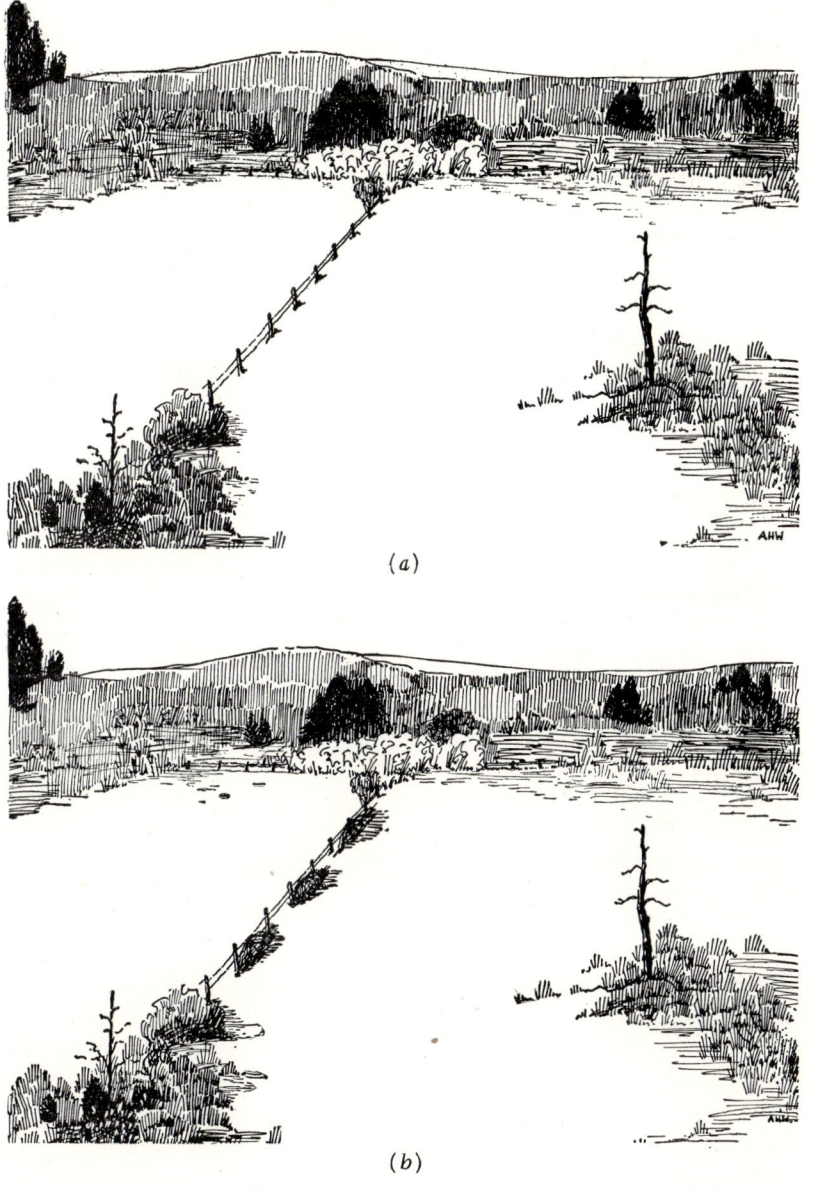

Fig. 6.3. (a) A "lethal" opening where goshawks caught several bobwhites crossing along the fence line from one woodlot to the other. (b) The opening of (a) strengthened by the addition of a few brush piles. No more losses of bobwhites occurred all winter because of an hour's work with brush.

conifer branches are sometimes thrown over loose brush piles to keep out snow, rain, and wind.

Escape Tangles. Escape tangles differ from brush piles in that they are composed of thickets or of live vines or tangling shrubs, which also form thickets and tangles of a permanent nature. Grape (*Vitis*) is one of the best tangle-making vines; the chief shrubs are *Crataegus*,

Fig. 6.4. Frame of poles over which brush will be piled to form a ridgepole shelter. Posts or stumps may be used for supporting the ridgepole.

prickly ash, and several species of willow and dogwood. Vines make satisfactory escape tangles when trained over small trees, and trees already covered with vines can be felled to form ready-made tangles. Bushes and limbs are sometimes lopped or half-cut so that they swing to the ground but stay attached to the trunk and continue to live for many years; vines trained over the lopped branch form an impenetrable and lasting tangle. In the same manner vines are also trained over brush piles and arbors, as well as over close-growing shrubs.

Other Escape Cover. The variety of escape cover that can be constructed is again limited only by the ingenuity of the operator. Poles and logs are easily piled together for rabbit escape cover. Culverts or tunnels have been constructed of stones and sewer pipe for rabbits,

Winter Feeding

but such tunnels need a bend in the middle so that hunters cannot poke out hiding rabbits. Stones piled in such a way that openings are left serve the same purpose. Christmas trees, after they have been used in the house, make temporary escape cover around feeding stations.

Permanent Escape Cover. Permanent escape cover is formed by planting small clumps of shrubs or conifers where needed, as in grazed-out woodlots, fence rows, fence corners, roadsides, or at a point adjacent to permanent feeding stations. Conifers tend to outgrow useful size; hence they are dwarfed by lopping the leader at a height of 10 to 15 feet.

Winter Feeding. Snow inaugurates a new phase in game food supply because it causes a general shrinkage in the accessibility of food. Ice and prolonged cold, singly or in combination with snow, are serious factors in the lives of grain-feeding birds and to some extent even in the lives of their compatriots, rabbits. Farm game birds feed throughout the winter on grain and seeds, for the most part, while rabbits depend upon available herbage. Where food becomes disproportionately scarce during cold weather, it is difficult to winter an adequate breeding population without supplementing the natural food.

Natural food is generally available during the fall, but winter feeding when used should be started early in order to acquaint game with the location of the feeders before the critical period begins. Since birds depend more and more upon the feeder with the coming of snow, the feeder should not be neglected; otherwise the birds will suffer. The most serious scarcity of food may occur late in the winter just before the spring production of new food. This is especially true in the snowless country; in the snow country the disappearance of snow in the spring is likely to uncover some "stored" food for wildlife. It must be remembered that heavy fall feeding by game and non-game species, combined with the loss occasioned by winter, may bring out a late-winter scarcity.

There are four principal methods of winter feeding, and though one alone is usually adequate, the common practice is to combine two or more. These methods are: crop remnants, food patches, scattered grains, and feeding stations.

The major objectives of winter feeding have been described as: to hold birds from wandering (especially in the fall); to prevent starvation during winter snows; to put birds in breeding conditions for spring; and to supply food economically.

Crop Remnants. Crop remnants which are normally available to game birds most often consist of waste grains. Corn husked on the stalk leaves considerable waste grain behind.

The amount of crop remnants and weed seeds left in fall varies greatly, and few figures are available to indicate the amount. The waste rice of the rice fields along the Gulf Coast is estimated to total 15 million pounds. The amounts once found in Wisconsin fields were as follows:

Sample of Remnants Left after the Harvest

	(Pounds per Acre)
Foxtail	50–450
Barnyard grass	Up to 300
Ragweed	80 to 130
Soybeans	150
Tick trefoil	10

Food Patches. Food patches offer many advantages and possibilities in winter feeding and, where usable, are frequently the preferred method of supplying food artificially. They hold birds well during the early fall, although less well after heavy snow has fallen. The food patch requires less work than the feeding station because it does not need many visits in winter, and for that reason, the food patch is desirable in remote areas or in those difficult to visit, especially during inclement weather.

The success of a food patch depends upon a number of essentials of which the chief ones are: suitable soil; suitable preparation; proper plant species or varieties; protection from domestic stock; accessibility for intended wildlife species; sufficient protective cover; and lasting of good foods.

The size of the food patch depends less upon the species and number of game birds feeding there than upon the expected length of the use. In general a patch may be smaller if it is meant only for fall feeding than if it is meant for all-winter feeding. Songbirds will use a patch along with the intended game species; to be successful, therefore, a good patch must be large enough to supply food for all the songbirds that come to it because the food available to game species will, in reality, be only the food left uneaten by the songbirds. A small patch probably will be cleaned out early in the fall by migrating songbirds. Although occasionally larger, food patches for farm game usually are fractional acres. A dozen game birds is about all that a single patch should be expected to carry; if there are more birds than this, more patches should be planted.

Food Patches

The soil for a food patch receives the same treatment as that for a cultivated crop; it must be well plowed and well harrowed; otherwise its food production will be low. In the fall some additional work may be needed to shock grains that are likely to be broken or lodged by heavy snow, such as buckwheat and millet. Broadcast sowings require little attention other than spring planting and possibly fall shocking, although wide-row grains may require cultivation.

TABLE 6.2

FOOD PATCH VARIETIES

(Data from Leopold, Moore, Sowls, 1939)

Variety	Fall	Winter	Exhausted	Used by	Sowing Method	Pounds an Acre
Feterita	Good	None	November 15	Songbirds, game birds	Drill in 3-foot rows	6
Dwarf yellow milo	Good	None	December 1	Songbirds, game birds	Drill in 3-foot rows	5
Early amber sorghum	Poor	Good	April 1	Songbirds, game birds	Drill in 3-foot rows	6
Wheatland milo	Poor	Fair	?	Some game birds	Drill in 2½-foot rows	5
Hegari	Good	None	November 11	Songbirds	Drill in 3-foot rows	4
Sudan grass	Poor	Poor	March 25	Songbirds, game birds in spring	Broadcast	30
Common millet	Good	None	September 30	Songbirds	Broadcast	20
German millet	Poor	Poor	April 1	Songbirds	Broadcast	20
Soybeans	Good	Good	April 1	Game birds	Drill in 2½-foot rows	50
Corn	Good	Good	April 1	Songbirds, game birds	Drill in 3-foot rows	7
Buckwheat	Good	Good (shocked)	November 1 (unless shocked)	Songbirds, game birds	Broadcast	50
Sunflower	Good	None	November 1	Songbirds	Drill in 3-foot rows	5

Food patches should be placed near adequate cover, or artificial cover should be supplied where adequate cover is lacking. The utilization of a patch is usually increased when a few brush piles are added, yet little cover is necessary in the patch planted to varieties that have a rank growth. The addition of a brushy gameway allows users of an exposed patch to come and go in safety.

Although a single grain can be used for a patch, it is usually better to plant in mixtures. Stiff-stemmed grains resist breaking by snow and ice and thus keep their grain above the snow during the winter. For that reason they may advantageously be combined with palatable weak-stemmed grains. Since species of low palatability are not eaten in the fall, they are left to become available during the pinch of late winter or early spring. Late-shattering grains prevent considerable covering by snow in mid-winter; nevertheless, grains that shatter with the arrival of snow are uncovered with its disappearance, a point to remember in planting for late-winter feeding. Corn, the "number one" food plant, makes ideal food patches when supplemented by weeds, such as ragweed (Table 6.2). In many regions mixtures sowed broadcast at the rate of 20 pounds or so to the acre are successful. The mixtures usually include several of the following:

Amber cane	Kaffir corn
Buckwheat	Hageri
Cow peas	Soybeans
Hemp	Feterita
Corn	Milo
Millet	Sudan grass
Proso	Sunflower

Feeding Stations. Winter feed for game birds may be scattered on the ground in the open or under a shelter to form a *scatter station*, or it may be put into a *hopper* that supplies food for several weeks. Hoppers ordinarily have a shelter, usually a structure of poles and brush, to protect them from the weather. There are many variations of feeding stations (Figs. 6.5 and 6.6).

The feeding hopper offers so many advantages for most game species that it is used more than others. Because the hopper is automatic, it requires sufficient capacity for at least three weeks of operation, which means about a bushel of grain. Hoppers should be visited at least once every three weeks in winter in order to discover whether the food is exhausted or the feeder clogged. Rabbits and pheasants will waste grain, but the waste can be reduced by a 2-inch netting placed over the hopper opening.

The elaborateness of the hopper will vary not only with the needs and desires of the operator but also with the amount of carrying of

Feeding Stations

food and hopper required. Lightness of construction and simplicity of design will be appreciated by the man who packs the hopper in on his back. Because hoppers will be used for more than a single season, light construction is not economical. A compromise between size, sturdiness, durability, and weight is the ultimate solution.

The feeding shelter that gives the most general satisfaction for farm-game species is a lean-to structure built of poles covered with brush. The front of the shelter is open and faces the sun, usually facing away

Fig. 6.5. A standard feeding station consisting of a feeding hopper protected by a shelter. Corn on the cob, impaled on spikes at this station, supplies some additional food.

from the prevailing winds; to face the sun and away from the wind generally means that the shelter faces east, south, or southeast. Open spaces, 18 to 24 inches high, are left around the bottom of the shelter to allow users of the feeding station to escape in any direction upon the real or imagined approach of enemies. As previously mentioned, escape cover of thickets, brush piles, or tangles provides additional protection, as well as resting places.

Grit put out with the food is a welcome addition to a feeding station. Stirring the soil under a shelter or building a shelter over some bare ground provides grit with less effort, but either practice increases the danger of spreading infectious diseases by soil contamination.

Both rack and platform feeders hold ears of corn impaled upon spikes, but the platform feeder also serves for the feeding of loose grain. In places where squirrels tend to raid the feeding stations, tins around the supporting posts of the platform feeder prevent squirrels from reaching the grain and wasting it (Fig. 6.6). Pheasants, bobwhites, Hungarian partridges, prairie chickens, sharp-tailed grouse,

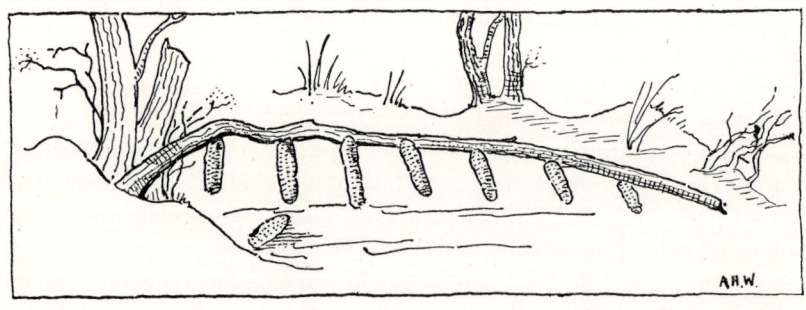

FIG. 6.6. Upper, rack with corn impaled upon spikes. Middle, platform used to hold ear corn. It may also hold a hopper or scattered grain. The metal guards prevent tree squirrels from robbing the platform. Lower, ears of corn impaled upon spikes and twigs.

and mourning doves use platform feeders. Wire baskets also are suitable for holding ear corn. Another method of keeping ear corn above the snow and wet ground is to string it on binder twine and drape it over stumps and brush piles or around the base of trees. Corn impaled on sticks will serve also.

The kinds of grain used at feeding stations are innumerable, but corn is "standard," although other grains—for example, wheat, buckwheat, and scratch feeds—are almost as valuable. A number of factors control the amount of grain used, but for the sake of brevity, the chief ones can be listed as:

Palatability	Accessibility of other foods
Weather	Amount of other foods
Familiarity	Time of beginning of feeding
Accessibility of the feeding station	Protection offered by feeding stations

Food consumption, which is by no means uniform throughout the winter, fluctuates with the weather and with availability of other foods; an approximation of the weekly amount consumed by various species is listed in the table.

Species	Weekly Amount Needed for Each Individual
Bobwhite	½ pound
Hungarian partridge	1 pound
Ring-necked pheasant	1–2 pounds
Prairie chicken	1–2 pounds
Sharp-tailed grouse	½ pound
Fox and gray squirrel	2 pounds
Cotton-tailed rabbit	1–2½ pounds
Others	5–20 pounds (monthly at station)

Using corn for comparison, palatability has been rated thus:

Palatability of Grains (after Hawkins)

Corn	100	Oats	−2
Scratch feed	75	Amber sorghum	−12
Buckwheat	25	Wheatland millet	−20
Wheat	15	Barley	−22

SUGGESTED READING

Allen, Durward L., 1938, "Ecological Studies on the Vertebrate Fauna of a 500-acre Farm in Kalamazoo County, Michigan," *Ecol. Monographs*, 8:347–436.

Allen, Durward L., 1949, *The Farmer and Wildlife*, Wildlife Management Inst., Washington, D. C.

Baumgras, Philip S., 1943, "Winter Food Productivity of Agricultural Land for Seed-eating Birds and Mammals," *Jour. Wildlife Management,* 7:13–18.

Bennett, Hugh Hammond, 1939, *Soil Conservation,* McGraw-Hill Book Co., New York.

Dambach, Charles A., 1948, *A Study of the Ecology and Economic Value of Crop Field Borders,* Ohio State Univ., Graduate School Studies.

Davison, Verne E., 1941, "Wildlife Borders—an Innovation in Farm Management," *Jour. Wildlife Management,* 5:390–394.

Davison, Verne E., 1945, "Wildlife Values of the Lespedezas," *Jour. Wildlife Management,* 9:1–9.

Edminster, Frank C., 1941, "Wildlife Management Through Soil Conservation on Farms in the Northeast," *U.S.D.A. Farmers' Bull.* 1868.

Gerstell, Richard, 1942, "The Place of Winter Feeding in Practical Wildlife Management," *Penn. Game Comm. Res. Bull.* 3.

Glading, Ben., 1947, "Game Watering Devices for the Arid Southwest," *Trans. Twelfth N. A. Wildlife Conf.:* 286–292.

Graham, Edward H., 1944, *Natural Principles of Land Use,* Oxford University Press, New York.

Graham, Edward H., 1947, *The Land and Wildlife,* Oxford University Press, New York.

Grange, Wallace B., 1937, "Feeding Wildlife in Winter," *U.S.D.A. Farmers' Bull.* 1783.

Grange, Wallace B., 1949, *The Way to Game Abundance with an Explanation of Game Cycles,* Charles Scribner's Sons, New York.

Holt, Ernest G., and William R. Van Dersal, 1942, "Wildlife and Land Use Patterns," *U.S.D.A. Misc. Publ.* 444.

King, Ralph T., 1938, "The Essentials of Wildlife Range," *Jour. Forestry,* 36:457–464.

Leopold, Aldo, 1933, *Game Management,* Charles Scribner's Sons, New York.

Leopold, Aldo, Elwood B. Moore, and Lyle K. Sowls, 1939, "Wildlife Food Patches in Southern Wisconsin," *Jour. Wildlife Management,* 3:60–69.

Miller, J. Paul, and Burwell B. Powell, 1942, "Game and Wild-fur Production and Utilization on Agricultural Land," *U.S.D.A. Circ.* 636.

Stoddard, Herbert L., 1939, *The Use of Controlled Fire in Southeastern Game Management,* Coop. Quail Study Assn.

Trippensee, Reuben Edwin, 1948, *Wildlife Management,* McGraw-Hill Book Co., New York.

Van Dersal, William R., 1938, "Native Woody Plants of the United States, Their Erosion Control and Wildlife Values," *U.S.D.A. Misc. Publ.* 303.

7

Farm Game Birds and Mammals

The major small-game hunting pressure falls upon the farm game species, particularly upon the cottontails and the pheasants in the more thoroughly farmed areas. The quails largely absorb the pressure of hunting south of the principal pheasant range, though the mourning dove, regarded elsewhere as a songbird, is heavily hunted.

The increase in hunters has resulted in some extensions of regular hunting to animals not ordinarily classified as "game." Thus, near population centers of the West (and sometimes in rural areas), ground squirrels are heavily hunted, though seldom taken home and eaten. Road hunting is especially practiced on ground squirrels, in spite of the fact that road hunting and even possessing loaded guns in automobiles is illegal in practically all states. It must be confessed that ground squirrel hunting comments upon the declining quality of game, a game that an earlier generation of hunters would surely have disdained. In parts of the Northeast, another rodent, the woodchuck or ground hog, is hunted by some as a game animal in testimony also to declining game values.

Table 7.1 gives condensed biological data for farm game.

Hungarian Partridge (*Perdix perdix*). The Hungarian partridge is an exotic game bird whose introduction from Europe has been successful only in regions combining medium to low rainfall and humidity. Cold does not seriously limit the Hungarian partridge, but it is rarely successful in regions where the depth of snow exceeds 6 to 12 inches for any length of time. In fact, whether it is or is not successful in any region seems a little difficult to determine, for even in areas where apparent success has been obtained the birds have later declined for no readily explainable reasons. The Hungarian partridge is more

TABLE 7.1

BIOLOGY TABLE FOR FARM GAME

Species	Range	Weight (grams)	Mating	Normal Limit of Sex Ratio	Breeding Season	Parturition or Hatching Season	Gestation or Incubation Period	Number of Eggs or Young	Food	Environment
Bobwhite (*Colinus virginianus*)	Eastern North America	140–200	Mon.	1:1	April–July	May–August	20–24 *	8–18 (11)	Seeds, fruits, insects	Brushy areas
Ring-necked pheasant (*Phasianus* sp.)	Exotic	750–1250	Pol.	1:3	April–June	May–August	20–23 *	6–15 (10)	Seeds, fruits	Brushy areas
Hungarian partridge (*Perdix perdix*)	Exotic	300–400	Mon.	1:1	April–June	May–July	21–25 *	8–15 (10)	Seeds, herbage	Open areas
Valley quail (*Lophortyx californica*)	Southern Pacific Coast region	150–220	Mon.	1:1	March–June	March–July	20–24 *	8–18 (10)	Seeds, herbage	Brushy areas
Cottontail (*Sylvilagus* sp.)	North to southern Canada	800–1500	Pol.	?	March–July	April–August	4–5 †	3–7	Herbage	Brushy areas

* Days.
† Weeks.

exacting in its preferences than the pheasant; consequently, stocking efforts have succeeded less often.

Although the Hungarian partridge inhabits open area, especially cultivated or stubble fields, still it is sometimes found in grass lands or in areas having but little cultivated land. The Hungarian partridge is reported to live only at low altitudes, usually below 3000 feet, but this statement seems erroneous.

Habits. The successful establishment of the Hungarian partridge has occurred only on superior soils, for the species does not seem to thrive in areas of gravel, sand, or peat. It shows preference for medium to heavy soils, especially lake-bottom clays, rich glacial drift, and loess.

The density of Hungarian partridges has been known to reach one to 4 acres, but ordinarily one to 10 acres should be considered a high density. One to 15 or 20 acres is probably the more usual density to be expected.

The bird is monogamous, and a one-to-one sex ratio is the rule.

In the fall the birds gather into coveys, which generally stay in the open fields. The coveys roost like quail on the ground during the night in stubble, under grass, and under low bushes. Normally the covey wanders in winter within a radius less than one-half to three-quarters of a mile. The principal winter cover consists of standing corn, tall stubble, tall grass, cover crops, fence rows, and roadsides.

Nests are placed on the ground in grass or similar cover of open fields or edges.

Nests, nesting sites, and nesting cover can be preserved by protection from fire and needless destruction of fence rows, roadsides, ditch banks, stubble fields, and waste corners, and they can also be saved by flushing bars and other devices for protection from farm machinery and animals.

The Hungarian partridge suffers little from predators, even though it is largely an inhabitant of open fields. Nests are destroyed, to some extent, by the tramping of domestic stock and by enemies when exposed by loss of protective cover from overgrazing. Domestic dogs and cats are the most destructive predators.

Food Habits. The Hungarian partridge is a granivorous bird, but in addition to grains it feeds upon weed seeds, insects, some herbage, and fruit, as well as the seeds of a number of shrubs and trees. It consumes more green food than the pheasant in the dry Palouse region, but elsewhere it appears to consume less. The food sources available to Hungarian partridges during the winter may be listed as seeds and fruits of weeds, shrubs, and trees, corn on the stalk and shock, crop remnants, food patches, and feeding stations.

The birds come readily to food patches but less readily to feeding stations. The stations must be in the open because Hungarian partridges do not penetrate heavy thickets to any extent. Like pheasants and quail, they quickly learn to open unhusked corn in order to get at the kernels.

The young feed upon insects during the first few weeks of life, later turning to seeds and some herbage.

The Hungarian partridge seems to thrive without access to standing water. Dew, succulence, insects, and soft fruits seem able to supply all the water needed.

Census Methods. Although not caught so easily as pheasants, Hungarian partridges can be trapped in funnel and "bob-wire" traps.

The several census methods used for the Hungarian partridge may be enumerated as: drives with men or with dogs, track counts, transect counts, covey flush counts, nest censuses.

Bobwhite (*Colinus virginianus*). The bobwhite, commonly known as quail, can be found in eastern and southern North America from northern Mexico to Canada and from the Atlantic west to South Dakota, Colorado, and New Mexico. Some range extension as the result of settlement has occurred at northern and western edges of the ancestral range. The range of the bobwhite has been artificially extended by a number of western states that have tried, with little success, to introduce the bird.

The bobwhite inhabits brush lands, open woodlots, swales, fence rows, and edges of cultivated fields.

Habitat Requirements. All quails are birds of low mobility, and the bobwhite is no exception. During its entire life it rarely ranges more than a mile or more from its place of hatching. It is a bird of the light-snow country because it is unable to withstand a combination of strong winds, intense cold, and deep snow. A series of mild winters allows the population to build up.

The combination of wind, temperature, and snow determines the northern limits of the bobwhite range and, in addition, limits the population or even causes severe winter losses. A "hardness" test for the severity of winters graphs the daily temperature against depth of snow (in equal units for degrees of temperature and inches of snow). The amount of "lethal weather" is represented by the area subtended on the graph by the snow and minimum daily temperature curve

(Fig. 7.1). The numerical index of hardness can be obtained by measuring the subtended area with a planimeter or by applying the formula for the area of a polygon as given in any geometry book:

Area $= \frac{1}{2}[x(y_2 - y_n) + x(y_3 - y_1) \cdots x_{n-1}(y_{n-1} - y_{n-2}) + x_n(y_1 - y_{n-1})]$

A similar index for *drought intensity* is given as half the sum of the squares of the intervals in days between days having more than 0.05 inch of rainfall during the growing season. Thus a 6-day rainless period would contribute 18 to the seasonal index, and a 12-day one would

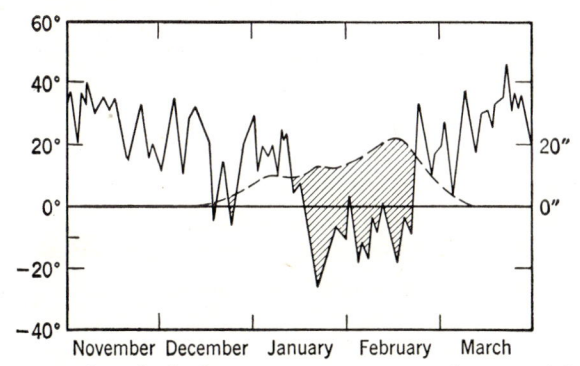

Fig. 7.1. Suggested method of testing winter severity for ground-feeding birds. The shaded area between the snow line (broken line) and the minimum daily temperature in degrees Fahrenheit measures the "hardness" of winter. (After Leopold, *American Midland Naturalist*, 1937.)

contribute 72. The drought index, which is not restricted in its application to bobwhite studies, can be used in study of plants as well as most animals.

The bobwhite takes up an individual territory only during the breeding season; the covey itself, on the other hand, occupies a definite covey range only during fall and winter. Although the size of the covey range may be but a few acres, the usual size is probably 40 acres or more. The density varies likewise. Its maximum appears to be a bird to 1 or 2 acres, but the density most frequently found is less than one bird to 6 to 12 acres.

Quail, like other animals, require several types of cover, and we can list the chief ones as: (*a*) travel cover, (*b*) resting cover, (*c*) roosting cover, (*d*) feeding cover, and (*e*) nesting cover. A tangle or thicket where quail are safe from predators, real or imaginary, where they can be in the warm sunshine, and where they can move quickly to food makes good resting cover in winter. Quail generally roost in small circles on the ground under vegetation, such as grass, forbs, or brush, and require protected places for night roosting during the winter in order that snow will not drift over them. Nesting cover is dry low cover, which may be grass, forbs, or small woody shrubs. Nests are usually located along the edges of woods, brush, and fence rows, but rarely in the open far from cover.

Coveys break up early in the spring when pairing takes place. Unmated or "bachelor" cocks that attach themselves to family groups may annoy paired birds so much that nesting and incubating are hampered. Since males generally cease calling as soon as they are mated, calling during the summer usually indicates unmated cocks.

Food Habits. The bobwhite is a granivorous bird that feeds upon fruits, herbage, and insects in addition to seeds, yet the selection of food taken by the bobwhite seems almost unlimited. Like most farm-game birds, the bobwhite leans heavily upon legumes for its food.

Many summaries have been published for the food species eaten in various localities, and it seems best to omit any detailed discussion here, for the student can find such summaries with little effort. There are usually but a few important food species in any region, but generally speaking the bobwhite depends upon the following foods:

Foxtail	Smartweed
Corn	Other weed seeds
Small grains	Berries
Legume seeds	Mast
Ragweed seeds	Insects

Improving Food and Cover. The techniques of general application in improving food and cover conditions for farm game have been covered in the preceding sections. The greatest returns for the effort applied result from improving potential habitat, but nevertheless improvement of occupied ranges should not be overlooked.

Dew, succulent vegetation, and many moist foods probably supply sufficient water in normal times, but periods of drought may cause distress or even mortality. Some benefit will be derived by the quail if green foods or plants that bear moist fruit ripening late in the summer are added to the environment.

Dusting places, though often plentiful enough, are sometimes insufficient in number or accessibility. This deficiency can be remedied by throwing up small mounds with shovels or by adding cover where needed. Mounds thus thrown up dry quickly after rains (Fig. 7.2).

The ashes that result from burning brush piles are sometimes suitable for dusting if adequate cover is adjacent. These will perhaps supply needed grit.

Protection. In some parts of the country the bobwhite is justifiably classified as a song and insectivorous bird and is thereby entitled to year-around protection. Winter conditions are severe in the North, where the bobwhite already lives near its margin of existence, and general hunting in some places is inadvisable lest the continued existence of the bird be endangered. In general the allowable kill

Fig. 7.2. A dusting mound thrown up by hand.

seems not to exceed 20 per cent of the fall population, except in years of unusual abundance.

Though the bobwhite has many natural enemies, few of them are of sufficient importance to justify widespread control measures. Predator suppression has rarely proved successful in the past as a method of increasing quail populations. Studies indicate that it may have some local value when combined with other measures, though most efforts used in control operations are more advantageously employed when turned to operations that strengthen the environment.

Census Methods. Snow is an invaluable ally to the census taker; in fact many coveys can be counted from tracks, without the observer even seeing a bird. Quail are censused by several different methods, of which the chief ones follow:

Covey counts	Calling males
Flush counts	Trapping
Track counts	Roost counts
Drives (with and without dogs)	Nest counts

Practiced field men can get complete sex counts of flushed coveys with considerable success.

Valley Quail (*Lophortyx californica*). The valley quail lives in the lower altitudes of the Pacific region from southern Oregon to lower California, and originally it may have ranged east to Nevada. The valley quail has been introduced in many parts of the West, as far north as British Columbia, and as far east as Utah and Wyoming.

Habitat Requirements. The valley quail range includes both partly humid coast region and the dry interiors below 5000 feet altitude. It is a bird of the light-snow country, and, as a rule of thumb, it can be said not to live higher or farther north than the line where 4 inches of snow remains for any extended period. It is rather tolerant of human disturbance and of changes in the environment. Despite some break-up of the primitive environment and its conversion to cultivated fields, the valley quail has been able to maintain itself with much success in its original range.

In some measure the valley quail is similar to the bobwhite of the East in its choice of cover and in its general habits; in fact in many ways it might be considered as a western counterpart of the bobwhite. Like the bobwhite the valley quail is a bird of the brush land. Unlike the bobwhite, however, it rarely nests farther than a half mile from water and tends to concentrate around watering places in late summer and early fall, at least in the dry interior. The reduction of brush fires in the foothills of California has permitted stands of brush too dense for the valley quail.

The travel radius of the valley quail is low, for it rarely travels more than a few hundred yards a day. On the whole its daily movements probably fluctuate between a hundred feet and a quarter of a mile, although they may be more at times. The usual yearly travel radius is probably less than 1 mile and certainly less than 2 miles.

The birds possess little individual territory in the nesting season, but during the winter they gather into large coveys which occupy covey territories. When the covey breaks up with the coming of spring, the covey territory ceases to exist. Some shifting of birds from one territory to another occurs, yet a covey may exist as a fixed unit and repel outsiders. It is probable that the minimum number of birds required for an independent covey is 10, and coveys reduced to fewer birds presumably merge with others. Valley quail coveys are larger than those of the bobwhite.

The nest of the valley quail usually consists of a lined depression placed near shrubs. Probably 50 to 60 per cent of the nests are normally unsuccessful.

Valley quail roost in bushes and trees, and it appears that they seldom roost on the ground like bobwhites. (The young roost on the ground, of course, until they are able to fly to trees and bushes.) The roosting site is in dense foliage and varies in height from a few inches to 35 feet, depending upon the type of cover. The birds seem to prefer, however, a site 10 to 15 feet above the ground.

Food Habits. Like all gallinaceous birds, valley quail feed shortly after leaving the roost and again before going to roost at dusk. Desultory feeding occurs throughout the day, but again as in other Galliformes, there are two feeding maxima, one at about 9:00 A.M., and another between 4:00 P.M. and dusk.

Grains, seeds, fruits, herbage, and insects constitute the principal articles of diet. Legumes, which comprise a third of the diet of the quail, are the most important food plants; cultivated greens rank next. Among the fruits eaten, *Crataegus*, *Ribes*, and *Amelanchier* should be mentioned. Green vegetation seasonally supplies both important nutritive requirements and moisture. Drought during the breeding season may cause a failure of green vegetation and in turn a disturbance of quail reproduction.

The number of different foods usually varies from 8 to 10 per meal, but the number of individual items may reach 1000. The size of the food particles varies from $\frac{1}{32}$ to $\frac{3}{16}$ inch in diameter.

The amount of grit contained in the gizzard fluctuates between $\frac{1}{3}$ and $\frac{1}{2}$ cubic centimeter. The size of the pieces of grit generally lies within the range of the food particles, but it averages more than the usual size of the food particles. The valley quail thus follows the general rule among game birds that the size of the grit, though within the size range of the food, averages more than that of the food particles.

During winter the birds may not go to standing water even though it is available. Their use of standing water increases when hot weather advances and greens turn brown; broods may travel to water two or three times daily during the heat of the summer. The amount of water taken by a bird at one visit is not known, although it has been recorded that a 10-day chick carried more than a cubic centimeter of water in its crop.

Improving Food and Cover. Valley quail avoid both wide-open areas and those covered by dense vegetation. Methods for increasing interspersion include opening the range by cutting operations in thickets and "timber," forming openings in grass and brush with disk harrows and brush cutters, and using controlled burning. The timber in the area inhabited by the valley quail is generally of little commercial value, and so its destruction need cause little concern. Narrow open strips run through the brush and chaparral at intervals of a quarter of a mile have proved valuable. One hunting club in California feeds the birds along wagon roads by blowing scratch food into the brush with a power blower mounted on a truck.

The live-oak woods of California supply fire wood but not much saw timber. A short rotation and clear cutting in scattered blocks is recommended for these woods.

Overgrazing has proved to be destructive of habitat; consequently, the reduction of overgrazing benefits the quail.

Food patches are rather useless in dry regions and in areas where little or no snow falls. However, food patches are probably helpful where quail have been introduced farther north or where food patch plants can be grown without irrigation. Disturbance of the soil by plowing or disking encourages the growth of many valuable native food plants and must be considered at present as the best that can be offered in the way of a food patch.

Because water is important in the life of the quail in arid areas during dry weather, the improvement of springs, water holes, and reservoirs sometimes constitutes the most valuable management technique. It is sometimes possible to pipe water from high springs to low levels and to bring underground water to the surface. Because quail do not go far from cover, exposed springs need cover planting for maximum service. Barrel tanks that automatically supply water to covered troughs or from "nipple valves" are useful. Several other forms of "gallinaceous guzzler" have proved of great value, among them concrete tanks or cisterns below catchment aprons that fill during rainy periods and feed out the water continuously. The supplying of water enables many quail to breed in areas formerly vacant. Shade may be as necessary an adjunct of watering and feeding sites in the dry lands as escape cover is elsewhere.

Protection. Predator control is ineffective as a management technique for valley quail despite its popularity among sportsmen and laymen. Strengthening the environment is the cheapest and easiest solution to the predation problem.

Although hawks and owls catch some quail on insecure ranges, they benefit quail, with few exceptions, by destroying competitors, such as ground squirrels and pack rats, that eat foods suitable for quail. Coyotes and wildcats are not important predators of quail; on the contrary, they are beneficial in that they are two of the most important controllers of ground squirrels.

Throughout much of the West, poisoning of rodents is an important governmental and farm activity. Though the reduction of rodents is beneficial to quail on experimental areas, the use of thallium kills so many birds that it offsets any general good that rodent poisoning might do. Grain soaked in phosphorus poisons have also been widely used for ground squirrel poisoning; such poisons are harmful to game birds, especially late in the spring after belated snowfalls.

Census Methods. Census methods for valley quail are still inadequate. The birds of the more arid part of the range live near water holes, streams, and springs, a circumstance that simplifies the work of finding them. California reports success in open country with a "horseback census." Three men, mounted on horses, ride back and forth across the census area, keeping 200 feet apart; three riders can cover 750 acres a day by this method. The center man keeps the record for all three. The accuracy of the count is reported as approximately 90 per cent when conditions are favorable.

Pheasant (*Phasianus* sp.). The pheasant is an exotic whose native home is Asia. It has been established successfully in a number of regions of medium to low humidity and rainfall. Although cold does not seem to restrict pheasants, deep snow, on the other hand, restricts their distribution and abundance. Pheasants have not been established successfully in northern regions where the snow blanket exceeds 12 inches for any length of time or in southern ones of high humidity and temperature.

The pheasant utilizes more open range than the bobwhite, but it seems to prefer swales, open and brushy woods, grassy draws, and brushy fence rows, though it lives successfully in areas of rank vegetation, such as forbs and coarse grass. Probably this rank vegetation is the ecological equivalent of brush. The areas of successful introduction seem to be determined by climate; within climatic limits the pheasant is associated with crop land, especially where corn and small grains are likely to be available during winter.

Habitat Requirements. The pheasant is more mobile than the bobwhite and cottontail, but whether it is more mobile than the Hungarian partridge, in all areas, is not certain. During the winter it generally moves into winter concentration areas, usually ungrazed or lightly grazed draws, swales, and brush patches. The winter movement may cover several miles in the more rolling western pheasant areas, but it is usually less than a mile in the East and Midwest.

Pheasants in many areas nest earlier than bobwhites and for that reason have greater need for nesting cover left from the previous year. When they lack adequate nesting cover, pheasants will resort to hay, stubble, and grain fields, where nest losses are bound to occur; some will do so even when cover is of the best. Roadsides and brushy fence rows, if unburned or ungrazed, supply excellent nesting cover early in the spring.

The male establishes a "crowing ground," generally in or near a clump of brush. Some males remain unmated because crowing-ground cover is too remote from the type of nesting cover preferred by females.

The pheasant is quite polygamous, and an uneven sex ratio is therefore possible. It is probable that a sex ratio of one cock to three hens is normal, although under favorable circumstances a ratio of one cock to five hens works successfully or even one to eight hens where the population is heavy. The density of pheasants is variable, although a maximum density of one pheasant to 1 or 2 acres is probably rarely reached; a density of one bird to 15 or 20 acres should be considered satisfactory.

Food and cover supplied for quail are also suitable for pheasants. Although pheasants will use a more open range than that of the bobwhite, still the requirements of both differ mainly in degree, except for the need of crowing grounds on the part of the male pheasant. In habitat choice the pheasant is intermediate between the bobwhite and the Hungarian partridge.

Food Habits. The pheasant is classed as a granivorous bird, even though rather omnivorous in its feeding habits, for it eats seeds, fruits, insects, and some herbage. It depends almost entirely upon seeds and fruits during the winter, when it requires nearly a quarter of a pound of food per day. During the first four weeks of life the young pheasant lives almost wholly upon insects, which supply 87 per cent of the food for the first week. Pheasants readily use feeding stations and food patches in winter. They prefer corn to other artificial foods and can obtain kernels from the unhusked ear by their own efforts. The amount of grit contained in the stomach varies from 2.20 grams in mid-winter to 5.50 during the spring. The pheasant, like most birds, requires more grit when eating herbage than when eating grain.

Protection. In place of attempts to increase pheasants by control of predators, efforts should be directed towards strengthening the environment because predation losses are slight on secure ranges.

Pheasants take to hay fields when nesting cover is inadequate. Losses owing to mowing of hay sometimes can be reduced slightly by using flushing bars. It is seldom that the time of farming operations can be adjusted to avoid nest destruction, although some adjustment, especially the time of burning or plowing stubble, can reduce losses.

The hunting season for pheasants is usually set for mid-fall, after late young have almost reached maturity and before the losses of winter begin. The permissible amount of hunting and the number of pheasants bagged depends, naturally, upon the biological surplus present. This surplus varies between areas and may reach as high as 75 per cent or as low as 5 per cent. Sometimes there may be no surplus. Inasmuch as the pheasant is polygamous, differential sex hunting is allowable. The proportion of hen and cock birds making up the bag depends upon the desired sex ratio, which varies to some extent with the density of the population. One hen to two or three males forms the usual bag proportions when a season is open on hens, but studies indicate that more pheasants can be raised (and taken by hunters) when *no* hens are hunted.

Trapping and Censusing. There are a number of trapping methods, but most of them require snow to work efficiently. Pheasants are easily trapped in funnel or bob-wire traps constructed of 2-inch netting. Because the birds tend to injure themselves by dashing against the netting, traps made of fish nets or tennis netting are preferred by some trappers. Brush thrown over the tops of the traps, however, is effective in keeping the birds from beating their heads against the top netting, or the interior of the trap can be draped with burlap.

Usable census or index methods are:

Direct counts	Track counts
Drives by men	Nesting censuses
Counts with dogs	Crowing-ground censuses
Counts at feeding stations	Roadside surveys

Cottontail (*Sylvilagus* sp.). The cottontail rabbit, the most widely distributed of all farm game animals, is found wherever suitable conditions occur from southern Canada to Panama. Within this region the cottontail breaks up into at least three species, each of which consists of a number of subspecies. The eastern cottontail (*Sylvilagus floridanus*) inhabits eastern North America from the Atlantic to the great plains and foothills of the Rockies, and from Canada south to Panama. The Rocky Mountain cottontail (*Sylvilagus nuttalii*) lives in the northwestern states and Nevada, Utah, and the northern Rockies. The western cottontail (*Sylvilagus auduboni*) overlaps the Rocky Mountain species in the Rockies and extends through the Southwest to central Mexico. The cottontail has increased its range in some parts of the country in the wake of forest cutting and break-up of the grass lands. The eastern cottontail has been transplanted to parts of western North America outside its original range; the western cottontail likewise has been transplanted to some parts of the East.

The cottontail inhabits brush lands, open woodlands containing ground cover, fence rows, roadsides, swales, dry marshes, and some grass areas. Rank-growing plants often provide suitable conditions for the cottontail, and in this respect they serve the same functions as brush. The two western species use grasslands more than the eastern form does.

Habitat Requirements. Cottontails, because of sedentary habits, rarely move more than a mile from the place of birth. The individual rabbit has a home range that can hardly be called a territory because it is not held to the exclusion of others; on the contrary, much overlapping of individual home ranges occurs. The home range of the rabbit varies from 1 to 10 acres, and it seems probable that a home range of 6 acres would be average. The density of rabbits is variable. The maximum density to be expected is probably 2 to an acre, though this density is rarely reached.

Rabbits use "forms" oriented to the winds, and each rabbit has one or more forms that are individual property regularly used by the same animal (Fig. 7.3). Cottontails build nests in dry, open, grassy places where the young remain for about three weeks. Although burrows are used as retreats during the winter months, they are rarely used for nesting or resting in summer. Burrows may be constructed by the rabbits themselves, but more often rabbits will use abandoned holes of woodchucks and other animals. In supplying burrows the woodchuck is an important animal to cottontails. Cottontails also settle in recesses formed by rocks and fallen trees, hollow logs, and butts of hollow trees.

The cover problem for the cottontail should cause the game manager little worry in summer when the rabbits use any thick vegetation. With the approach of winter, however, rabbits move to heavy thickets composed of shrubs or mixed shrubs and grasses, especially thickets that have adequate numbers of satisfactory burrows. The animals keep trails clear in summer by nibbling vines and other vegetation that tends to block their paths; continual use keeps trails open in winter when snow tends to fill them.

Food Habits. The cottontail feeds at some time or other upon almost any vegetation found in its environment. The diet includes leaves of annuals and perennials, whole plants, bark, fruits, and seeds. In some regions the favored foods are the legumes, such as clovers and lespedeza. Rabbits often eat the bark of stems and twigs during winter,

Fig. 7.3. The forms of rabbits may give some indication of rabbit abundance.

especially when snow is deep. Among these woody plants should be mentioned smooth sumac, *Crataegus*, blackberries, and raspberries. Considerable damage may occur at times when rabbits girdle trees and shrubs while feeding, but this is partly compensated in some instances by the thinning that results from girdling.

Rabbits do not need free water, although they will frequently resort to surface water for drinking. Dew and succulent vegetation provide sufficient moisture, except in times of prolonged drought when rabbits that do not have access to water may suffer.

Management Operations. The management techniques devised for other farm game invariably work successfully for cottontails; in fact management operations for farm game have been known to work successfully only for rabbits.

Though they do not provide appreciable amounts of food, conifers nevertheless offer superior shelter, and sometimes clumps of conifers may be considered the basic permanent cover in rabbit management. Fewer burrows are required where conifer clumps are heavy because drooping lower branches covered by snow provide retreats that are equivalent in some respects to burrows. The same applies to heavy thickets and vegetation. Burrows in the open, unless constant use by the animals keeps them open, frequently become closed by deep snow; in contrast to this, conifer clumps and heavy thickets prevent snow from filling burrows.

Rabbit damage to trees and shrubs is usually associated with rabbit populations of high density. Control measures generally consist of reduction in the population by shooting and trapping. Deterrents (such as screening orchard trees) have met with considerable success. Several useful chemical repellents are available in the commercial markets. Plugging all burrows and removing protective cover (wood piles, brush piles, brier patches, and covered fence rows) evict rabbits from orchards.

Trapping and Censusing. Rabbits can be caught easily in box traps of the "figure 4" type, with corn, carrots, and apples as bait. Properly set snares are effective in runways.

Rabbits are marked by tattooing numbers in the ears either with commercial tattooing devices or with carbon ink and a sharp needle. Ear punching and notching and most ear tags are not suitable because the marks heal over rapidly and ear tags tend to tear out.

There is no adequate census method for cottontails. Census or index methods that are indicative, however, are:

Drives	Track counts
Transects	Form counts
Random counts	Feces counts
Trap nights	Roadside counts
Trapping and marking	

SUGGESTED READING

Bent, Arthur Cleveland, 1932, "Life Histories of North American Gallinaceous Birds," *U. S. Nat. Mus. Bull.* 162.

Buss, Irven O., 1946, "Wisconsin Pheasant Populations," *Wisc. Cons. Dept. Publ.* 326.

Conklin, W. Gard, and James N. Morton, 1936, "More Food for Upland Game," *Penn. Game Comm. Bull.* 11.

Suggested Reading

Dalke, Paul D., 1942, "The Cottontail Rabbits in Connecticut," *Conn. State Geol. and Natur. Hist. Surv. Bull.* 65.

Emlen, John T., Jr., and Ben Glading, 1945, "Increasing Valley Quail in California," *Calif. Agric. Exp. Stat. Bull.* 695.

Errington, Paul L., 1933, "The Nesting and Life Equation of the Wisconsin Bob-white," *Wilson Bull.*, 45:122–132.

Errington, Paul L., 1934, "Vulnerability of Bob-white Populations to Predation," *Ecology*, 15:110–127.

Errington, Paul L., and F. N. Hamerstrom, Jr., 1937, "The Evaluation of Nesting Losses and Juvenile Mortality of the Ring-necked Pheasant," *Jour. Wildlife Management*, 1:3–20.

Gorsuch, David M., 1934, "Life History of the Gambel Quail in Arizona," *Univ. Arizona Bull.* Vol. 5, No. 4.

Grange, Wallace B., 1949, *The Way to Game Abundance with an Explanation of Game Cycles*, Charles Scribner's Sons, New York.

Hickie, Paul, 1940, *Cottontails in Michigan*, Mich. Dept. Cons.

Lay, Daniel W., 1940, "Bob-white Population as Affected by Woodland Management in Eastern Texas," *Texas Agric. Exp. Stat. Bull.* 592.

Lehman, Valgene W., 1939, "Habitat Improvements for Quail," *Texas Game, Fish, and Oyster Comm. Bull.* 17.

Leopold, Aldo, 1933, *Game Management*, Charles Scribner's Sons, New York.

McAtee, W. L. (Editor), 1945, *The Ring-necked Pheasant and Its Management in North America*, American Wildlife Institute, Washington, D. C.

McCabe, Robert A., and Arthur S. Hawkins, 1946, "The Hungarian Partridge in Wisconsin," *Am. Midland Naturalist*, 36:1–75.

Seton, Ernest Thompson, 1925–1929, *Lives of Game Animals*, 4 vols., Doubleday, Doran and Co., Garden City, N. Y.

Stoddard, Herbert L., 1931, *The Bob-white Quail*, Charles Scribner's Sons, New York.

Trippensee, Reuben Edwin, 1948, *Wildlife Management*, McGraw-Hill Book Co., New York.

Yeatter, Ralph E., 1934, "The Hungarian Partridge in the Great Lakes Region," *Univ. Mich., School For. and Cons. Bull.* 5.

Yocom, Charles F., 1943, "The Hungarian Partridge (*Perdix perdix* Linn.) in the Palouse Region, Washington," *Ecol. Monographs*, 13:167–202.

8

Forests and Forest Wildlife Management

The wildlife that will be considered here as *forest wildlife* includes those vertebrates that are adapted for a forest life, that spend the major portion of their lives there, and that obtain the major portion of their wants from the forest. Yet it must be recognized that individual opinion will differ on any classification of animals as forest or non-forest species. A study made for this book shows that, of the 2368 species of vertebrate animals in the United States and Canada, there are 527 (22.26 per cent) wholly or partially dependent upon the forest; of the 239 species that are called *game*, 67 (28.03 per cent) are likewise wholly or partially dependent upon the forest (Table 8.1).

In addition to these *dependent* species we have others that are *aided* by forest conditions. Some fish, for example, are able to use streams because shade from the forest canopy keeps the water cool or because the forest steadies the runoff. Secondary and even tertiary benefits accrue to aquatic wildlife from the forest; among them may be cited the beneficial effects to aquatic habitat from the work of beavers, which themselves depend so heavily upon the forest.

Wildlife Relations to the Forest. That wildlife needs the forest is a well-known truism, for the wildlife within the forest is supported and protected by the forest during its entire life, from birth to death. The forest, like other environment, supplies three distinct needs of its wildlife: places to breed in safety, places of refuge, and an adequate food supply.

Many species of wildlife have become adapted to forest conditions through a long evolutionary process, during which some species have become more narrowly specialized for life only within the forest. Perhaps the most striking example of such narrow specialization in our

TABLE 8.1

NUMBER OF ANIMAL SPECIES WHOLLY OR PARTIALLY DEPENDENT UPON THE FOREST (UNITED STATES AND CANADA)

Animal Group	Approximate Number of Species	Wholly Forest Species Approximate Number	Per Cent	Partially Forest Species Approximate Number	Per Cent	Total Wholly or Partially Dependent upon the Forest Approximate Number	Per Cent
Freshwater fishes	600	?		?		?	
Game	88						
Amphibians	138	33	23.9	15	10.9	48	34.8
Game (none)							
Reptiles	149	11	7.4	17	11.4	28	18.8
Game (none)							
Birds	811	209	25.8	80	9.9	289	35.6
Game	69	12	17.4	13	18.8	25	36.2
Mammals	670	109	16.3	53	7.9	162	24.2
Game	82	28	34.2	14	17.1	42	51.2
Total	2368	362	15.3	165	7.0	527	22.3
Game	239	40	59.8	27	11.3	67	28.0

forest birds is the large ivory-billed woodpecker, which possesses a bill especially adapted for scaling off the bark of dead cypress trees under which beetles live in quantities sufficient for so large a bird. On the other hand, a species like the downy woodpecker, not so narrowly specialized, can find food in crevices in the bark as well as extract insects and larvae from wood or even pithy weed stems; it can feed upon seeds and fruits, if necessary, and may even feed in weed patches. The difference in success of the two species is great: the downy woodpecker inhabits almost the whole of North America; the ivory-billed woodpecker, if not already extinct, is restricted to a small remnant in the South.

Forests themselves need wildlife, though not to the degree that wildlife needs the forest. During eons of evolutionary time the plant and animal life of the forest has become an ecological unit. Insectivorous birds glean insects from the trees the year round; migratory insect feeders (and resident insect feeders too) operate during the period when the insect population is expanding or most active, that is, during the spring, summer, and early fall; resident insectivorous birds remain during the winter and search the trees for hibernating insects and insect eggs. A tree harboring a family of red-eyed vireos is freer of insects than the tree that lacks such protection. The vireos, which require large quantities of insects, search the branches and leaves assiduously; one pair of vireos alone can account for hundreds of insect larvae daily. Especially is this true during the period of nestlings.

The white-headed woodpeckers also render an important service in maintaining the health of the trees in the pine forests of the West where they work ceaselessly at their appointed task of gathering insects, insect eggs, and insect larvae. This species is not able to excavate in live wood because of the inadequacy of its drilling apparatus; therefore, it must have dead limbs in which it can make holes for nesting. If all the dead material in its home forests were removed, the white-headed woodpeckers would disappear in one generation.

If they have seeds not adapted for distribution by wind or other physical agents, reproduction without the help of animals is impossible in those tree species that are "good stepmothers but poor mothers." The wildlife feeding upon the seeds and fruits of these species invariably carry many of the seeds some distance from the parent tree, where they may bury or otherwise cache them and by so doing assure some degree of planting.

The uphill movement of heavy seeds and the uphill spread of the species producing them is not possible by the force of gravity alone because gravity tends to move them downhill only. "Uphill planters" of the forest, such as woodpeckers, jays, and tree squirrels, carry seeds in all directions for storage. Without the help of the uphill planters, heavy-seeded species would not spread up steep slopes because the force of gravity would be against such spread. For this reason the forest must produce some mast yearly in order to support a population of the animal species that are able to move the heavy seeds uphill. It may be that only once in several centuries will the services of the uphill planters be needed in reproducing the parent trees, but the absence of the uphill planters at the critical time would make it less likely that a heavy-seeded tree would succeed itself. Extending the trees' range on steep slopes would of course be impossible.

The well-being of forest soils depends upon the accumulation of animal bodies and of materials that animals may have stored in the soil, together with the workings of animals, especially in burrowing. Wild animals, particularly the rodents, are significantly important in preventing runoff, erosion, and flooding. The work of the beaver in this respect is very well known; yet in addition to helping to prevent excessive runoff, the beaver is an important aid in fire control in those areas where beaver ponds are extensive and numerous.

To the untrained observer evidence of damage is always more obvious than good service, and therefore the damage receives disproportionate attention, with the result that the factor of damage to the forest by wildlife is universally overrated. Damage by wildlife, except under abnormal conditions, may be almost wholly ignored as far as the forest is concerned. Under normal conditions wildlife, especially songbirds and deer, are "dainty" feeders and rarely concentrate on one bush or one spot for any length of time. Deer may nibble leaves and the ends of branches, and thus they leave little permanent injury or evidence of their work.

Still another forest-wildlife relationship is the control of the spread or regeneration of palatable plants by the feeding habits of deer or snowshoe rabbits. Even the grasses of the original prairie were influenced by herds of buffalo.

Pristine Numbers. As has been mentioned many times, pristine forests of North America did not teem with birds and mammals, despite statements to the contrary. The great herds of ungulates lived on the prairies, where rodent colonies also lived. Concentrations of birds, except for such as the passenger pigeon, generally occurred in association with marshes or waterbodies. Perhaps ruffed grouse and snowshoe rabbits reached high densities during cycle highs in pre-Columbian days, but since virgin forests of today produce fewer individual animals and a smaller mass total than developmental stages, such as cut-over lands, it is doubtful that primeval virgin timber produced any greater concentrations of animal life.

Animal life expanded rapidly with the cutting of timber by man, particularly the mixed-habitat animals like robins, song sparrows, and cottontail rabbits. Exclusively forest dwellers have declined.

The occurrence of big game species in the forests of pre-Columbian days is indicated by the abundance of Indian villages, earthworks, and trails. These sites coincide rather remarkably with good soils and good farming land today, except for those of salmon- and other fish-culture tribes. Evidently even in virgin areas it took good soil to produce good vegetation for support of deer and other species upon which Indians depended.

Correlation of Forestry and Wildlife Management. The principle of multiple use means that all resources of the forest should be given consideration in accordance with the importance of the respective resources, though of course none must be allowed to degenerate or disappear. It has been stated that "game management within forest areas looks to the production of the largest possible annual crops of game consistent with the preservation and management of the forest itself, and it is the business of the forester to see that this resource, as well as others, is brought to its fullest utility." While this view may be true of forests managed intensively for timber crops, it is not true of the forest areas where timber cannot be a major product.

The general modifications and changes in forest practices recommended in the best interests of both wildlife management and forestry fall into five groups:

1. Timber production should be practiced only on first-class sites; other areas should be left for wildlife—and scenery. Many of our forest areas are not good timberlands anyway. In areas where recreational demand is high (or potentially high), timber production should be subordinated to recreational use.

2. Concentrated grazing by domestic stock is inimical to the interests of wildlife and should be reduced where injurious. Big-game winter range should be protected from stock.

3. Silvicultural practices and activities that are unnecessarily destructive to food and cover should be modified, reduced, or eliminated. It is not so much a matter of *what*, as of *how much* and *where*.

4. The forest should not be planted or allowed to grow to single species; natural openings should be preserved; conifer plantations should be in small blocks or otherwise broken up.

5. Where economically feasible, cutting operations should be in small units well distributed over the forest. Frequent light cuts are generally better for wildlife than infrequent heavy cuts.

The problem of administering forests for wildlife is complicated by the newness of wildlife management technology. Most practicing foresters lack training in wildlife management, for only younger foresters from a few schools have received training in the subject. Few of them as yet occupy executive positions. In a like manner few wildlife-trained people have had forestry training.

Forest Area. The future does not indicate that all forest areas will pay the costs of management, a point of especial interest owing to the increasing use of wood substitutes and better utilization of forest products through technological advances. It is obvious, therefore, that there is little logic in practicing silviculture on *poor* sites or sites where a continued sustained deficit is more likely than a future sustained yield. Not all forest areas will produce lumber in the future, just as not all had saw logs before the white man's arrival.

The original forested area of the United States totaled about 822 million acres, or about 40 per cent of the total area, of which some 615 million acres remain in forest. Some imagination, however, may be needed to regard as forested much of the 108.7 million acres of desert scrub and alpine area. About 55 million acres in eastern United States are better suited to forest than to crops and may in time return to forest.

A future status recommended for forestry shapes up as follows:

	Acres
(1) Intensive timber management	100,000,000
(2) Extensive timber management	338,900,000
(3) Protection land not favorable to timber management	69,700,000
(4) Cleared timberland and reserved areas	52,000,000
(5) Chiefly valuable for purposes other than timber production	108,700,000
	669,300,000

There seems to be little likelihood that the 108.7 million acres of non-timbered "forest land" will ever become valuable for lumber production. To this may very properly be added the 69.7 million acres of protection land not favorable for timber, giving a total of 178.4 million acres of land, the affairs of which could most profitably be administered directly by wildlife managers. Much of the remaining forest lands could be handled cooperatively with wildlife managers, or much of it even could be supervised by them and still produce fully as many timber products. The state conservation departments seem to be the logical future land-management agencies for most wild lands other than national parks and monuments and possibly first-class timber lands.

Winter feeding grounds (and also water-holes and stream sides) should be managed and guarded carefully for the benefit of wildlife. Such critical areas may be of small size, but their importance is disproportionately great because they supply important elements in wildlife ecology for larger areas during the pinch part of the year.

One point—and a most important one—should be kept in mind. Many areas have so great a value for timber production that these values should predominate over wildlife values. On many areas, however, the value for wildlife is so much greater than for forestry purposes that in those places wildlife value should predominate. Similarly, there are many areas where the relative values are more nearly equal, and a balance of interests is thereby indicated.

General Considerations. Forest operations, depending upon the species and the locality as well as on the nature of the work, usually can benefit wildlife; indeed it is probable that few forest operations, when properly conducted, cannot be made to benefit wildlife in some way.

On most forests, both hardwood and conifer, are many large hollow trees which serve as dens for den users like raccoons, squirrels, wildcats, and owls. Though den trees may be considered worthless or even detrimental by the forester, they are of critical importance to these species. One den tree left to the acre is recommended for New England. Dead trees or limbs can be left for woodpeckers, which usually are reluctant, or even unable, to drill holes in hard, live wood. Standing "snags" are looked upon freely as fire hazards, yet their value to wildlife is generally great enough to outweigh the small fire hazard in all but the most unusual instances.

Mast trees, of which the best known are beech, oaks, and hickories, provide abundant supplies of food for wildlife, and, though the number to leave for maximum benefit to wildlife and the forest is debatable, it is presumed that 5 mast trees an acre is a reasonable number. Since mast trees are benefited by increased space, those (and other food trees) that grow in the interior of the forest produce less than those that grow in the open or along the forest margin. On steep slopes the higher trees tend to be exposed on the downhill side, which thus increases their mast production. Cutting some of the surrounding trees gives them more space and light.

Wildlife uses the interior of the forest less than the margin, where the maximum wildlife utilization occurs. Small openings scattered through the forest to increase the "edge effect" may vary in size from those left by the removal of single trees to openings of several acres.

It is probable that the maximum benefit for small birds and mammals occurs from openings less than 2 acres in size. A good rule of thumb is that the minimum diameter of openings should approximate the height of tall trees.

Natural openings and those left by logging roads, camps, and clearings should be maintained. Some openings are formed by normal forest operations, namely, logging, the construction of fire lanes, and camp sites.

Inasmuch as an adequate supply of grit usually is obtainable from exposed soil, gallinaceous birds are seldom troubled by the problem of obtaining grit in the woods, except in the winter. Uprooted trees often expose dirt that wildlife can use; occasionally dirt held above the snow by upturned roots supplies grit for several winters. Grit is exposed along steep slopes, cliffs, river banks, and trails, and around animal burrows and ant hills.

Birds and mammals use exposed soil for dust baths, as well as for grit, and frequently the sources of grit are also suitable for dusting. Small mounds can be thrown up very quickly with a shovel to supply dusting places in the woods. The mounds should be elevated a few inches above the surrounding forest floor to allow for drainage; if properly constructed the mounds will dry quickly in wet weather.

Food-bearing shrubs and trees should be encouraged whenever possible. Though many will grow under dense stands, shrubs are usually hindered by shade and by competition with the trees for water. Improved shrub conditions quickly follow openings created by blowdowns, roads, clearings, or fires.

Because the trees help to keep the water of streams cool and supply protection from the sun to fish and other aquatic life, the cutting of timber along streams should not expose a stream unduly. Narrow strips of timber left along streams serve both for seed trees and for shade (provided, of course, that they are not injured by wind damage).

One of the eastern states has devised some efficient management methods for the heavily hunted pine areas that might well serve as a model. Fire lanes, which are needed more in conifer areas than elsewhere, and roadways divide the forest into 400-acre units with "safety strips" along each side of the fire lane or roadway; the outer border of each safety strip is a food border 25 to 50 feet wide. The blocks are again broken into smaller units by openings, while all old fields are retained in an open condition rather than allowed to revert to timber. Clearings that vary in size to 2 acres are made at various intervals along the safety stretches through the woods. Various species of food-bearing plants are planted along the strips and in the clearings by direct seeding with seed gathered from native plants and sowed by hand. Among the recommended plants are partridge pea, tick trefoil, lespedeza, goat's rue, wild indigo, panic grass, and paspolium grass. Escape cover—of tangles, brush piles, and thickets placed at intervals along the strips, edges of the fields, and clearings—provides safety. Breaks of this sort need to be jagged in order to reduce possibility for development of "firing lines."

Silvicultural Practices. Silvicultural practices that are good for wildlife are usually good forestry; silvicultural practices that are harmful to wildlife are often poor forestry. Many management practices for forest wildlife are but modified silviculture. Even so drastic an operation as burning to provide mineral soil for the seeds of the Douglas fir benefits animal life by shifting succession back to early stages, even though it may require a few years for brush to come in on the mineral soil.

Interspersing. The value to wildlife of any forest area is measurable in general terms by the miles of edges between plant types, plus an allowance for the general composition of the forest. Maximum edge effect is obtained only by maximum interspersion of plant types. The greater abundance of wildlife (in number and species) in the well-interspersed forest reflects the value of interspersion; hence the use of large blocks of single-tree species of one age class should be avoided whenever possible because insufficient interspersion results. All-age classes and the use of conifers in small blocks scattered among hardwoods makes possible a maximum wildlife stand in the area. Wildlife uses principally the area near the edge of conifer plantations, and few signs of ruffed grouse are found farther than 300 feet from their edges.

The carrying capacity of the forest is related to age class, and the age class that supplies the food and cover needed by the wildlife will determine, for the most part, the carrying capacity of the whole forest. The living of wildlife on the portion of the forest having the proper age class means that the amount in the whole area is supported and limited by this portion of the forest.

Distributing the cut over many small areas may increase the cost of the cut, but tractor and truck logging generally makes such distribution feasible on "going" forests. The adaptability of truck logging usually makes it possible to shift operations from one small area to another without materially increasing the cost of cutting the timber. Maximum representation of age classes is best for wildlife, and this is brought about by distributing each year's cut in small blocks.

Release Cutting. Timber stand improvement work should give consideration to the saving of food-bearing trees; many valuable food-bearing trees are cut as "weeds" because they interfere with timber-producing trees. Among the food trees often listed as weeds are blue beech, pin cherry, crab apple, hawthorn, dogwood, holly, magnolia, mountain ash, birch, sassafras, service berry, and ironwood. Because it is not economical to practice weeding on a very extensive scale in the present stage of forestry, food-bearing trees appear to be safe from general and widespread destruction.

The release of mast trees from competition has already been mentioned. Some species, such as the aspen, can be cut for deer food when too large to produce browse within reach, and the stumps will put out a sprout growth which increases the amount of available food. Coppice cutting is frequently used to advantage in older forests.

Thinning. Thick growth produces little food; thinning of such areas materially increases browse. Thinning of hardwoods is best done in the winter when it will supply browse for deer. Thinning can be used to produce stocky growth, as well as to increase the amount of edges. Of the sharp-tailed grouse, ruffed grouse, and prairie chicken, Franklin Schmidt (*Wilson Bulletin* 48:186–203) writes:

> Budding grouse of all species prefer trees that are at the edge of a thicket, standing alone, or in small groups. A dense stand of white birch or aspen is of little use as a bud supply except for a few trees around the edge. It is not known whether the buds are larger or better on trees in the open, but it is apparent that a stocky, brushy tree has more buds and is easier to climb around on than a slim tree in a dense thicket. Budding trees which meet these specifications can be provided either by planting isolated trees, or by thinning thickets which are too dense, either by cutting or pasturing.

Brush Piles and Slash Disposal. Just as they do elsewhere, brush piles supply valuable safety cover for wildlife in the forest, especially in the open woods. Slash should be left piled rather than burned unless the fire hazard dictates its destruction. The fire hazard is low in hardwood slash because the wood decomposes rapidly yet burns slowly; coniferous slash, on the other hand, decomposes slowly yet burns rapidly. Fortunately the need for brush piles as safety cover is less in coniferous stands, where the fire hazard is high, because the branches of conifers themselves supply good cover (except in old or pruned stands). Although more wildlife is present in hardwood forests, they supply less cover than coniferous forests; consequently the need for brush piles is greater in the hardwood forests.

Controlled Burning. It has been demonstrated that the exclusion of fire is not always advantageous and that controlled burning may be a valuable silvicultural practice as well as a valuable game practice, especially in the southern states. Burning is a means of reproducing plant species that have seeds requiring mineral soil in which to germinate, and it is also effective in preventing too dense a cover or the dominance of less desirable plants. The value of controlled burning is becoming recognized, but a clear distinction should be made between *controlled* and *uncontrolled* burning. Only controlled fire is recommended here. It should be made clear also that controlled burning should not be applied just anywhere. The thesis that all forest fires should be religiously suppressed is still supreme, and so great care must be exercised in recommending controlled burning lest misunderstanding occur. The belief that prevention of all fires automatically increases desirable game species or even is best for the forest itself, however, is not universally correct.

Controlled burning has been practiced with success in the Southeast, where it is recommended for bobwhites and turkeys, provided the burning can be done at the right time, in the right amount, and with the proper frequency. Quail and turkeys decline under the rigid fire exclusion in pine stands owing to increased pine straw, wire grass, and broom sedge. Controlled burning also has been found to increase forage and to preserve organic material in the soil in southern pines. In Georgia the proper season for burning is from mid-February to April, depending upon the season and the plants that live in the area. The season in other areas would be correspondingly later. Native perennial legumes are not hurt if burning takes place as late as May first, but other plants may be damaged by burning if germination has started. If the burning is done too soon, the seeds of some species may germinate so early that they will be subject to frost injury. Care must be taken, however, to burn sufficiently early to prevent injury to nesting birds.

The frequency of burning depends upon the cover that is present and the amount of food it produces. Some areas can be burned every year, whereas others need burning not more often than every 2 to 4 years. Burning must be done at longer intervals if the plants in the area do not produce food the first year after a fire, but if they do produce food in the year of the fire, it is safe to burn annually. Frequent light burnings are better than infrequent heavy ones.

Burning is often done in blocks, with unburned areas between, and the operations are shifted from year to year so that areas are burned in rotation. Burning is confined to definite blocks by means of fire breaks. Spot burning has the advantage of opening small areas at intervals throughout the woods; burning a large area, on the other hand, is not recommended because it leaves little variation in cover.

The time of the day for burning varies. Burning at night is favored unless there is a wind likely to extend the fire beyond the desired limits. The dampness of night in the South causes fire to burn slowly and to die out before morning. Yet, if the burning is attempted too early in the evening, the fire is likely to burn more vigorously and faster than can be controlled. Although burning immediately after rains may be the safest time, it may not be possible.

Because controlled fire sometimes gets out of control, shovels, pumps, and an adequate crew must be at hand to suppress escaped fire. If the chance of a runaway fire is averted, the practice of controlled burning is economical and beneficial on areas to which it is adapted.

Domestic Grazing. Conflicts between hunters and stockmen occur more often on forest ranges than elsewhere; hence this is an appropriate time for discussion of grazing and wildlife. The principle of multiple use calls for grazing as one of the methods of utilizing forest resources, yet grazing needs rigid regulation, not only from the standpoint of forest reproduction but also from the standpoint of wildlife. In some areas grazing is a higher form of use than hunting, but in others hunting is a higher form and entitled to prior consideration. It is impossible for wildlife to compete successfully with domestic stock under ordinary circumstances because of the aid given to the domestic stock by man. In the West stock runs on the range in the summer and moves to the lowlands during the critical winter period, whereas wildlife must find whatever it can in the depleted range. Ranchers have pre-empted lowland areas constituting the ancestral wintering grounds for elk and other big game in many mountainous sections of the West, with the result that the carrying capacity of the entire big game range has been reduced.

Overgrazing, and damage to the forest as well as to the wildlife range, has generally been underemphasized because of the economic factors involved in the stock industry. Reduction in grazing is needed in many areas, not only for the sake of the wildlife but also as a measure of protection of the range and an aid in its rehabilitation. But statements of harmful effects of grazing on the game in one area must not be automatically applied everywhere. In the "brush-land" section of Texas, for example, white-tailed deer have increased enormously because overgrazing by stock has destroyed the grasses and favored growth of brush. The increased brush markedly benefits the browsing deer.

Overgrazing may induce an increase of jack rabbits and rodents, with the attending problems of rodent damage to grazing lands and forest reproduction. Such animals have been termed "animal weeds" because their excess numbers are the resultant of maladjustment, just as undesirable plant species grow on disturbed soil. Proper regulation of grazing may solve the problem, and conservative range management is the obvious method for handling the problem of rodent damage where overgrazing is the direct or contributing cause.

Wild animals are more capable than domestic stock of caring for themselves on ranges with a large predator population, such as cougars, wolves, grizzlies, and coyotes. Because of this fact, predator protection can accomplish indirectly a reduction in stock that will benefit wildlife, a reduction that may not be obtainable by ordinary sportsman efforts. Sportsmen who insist upon rigid predator control should remember that they are helping domestic stock at the expense of game species, in which the sportsmen themselves are interested.

Recreation Use of the Forest. Forest lands supply some of our leading outdoor recreation areas. It is not at all possible to list the total forest recreation acreage. Public areas vary from a fractional acre, providing shade for a roadside table maintained by the highway department, to great national parks. To this we must add summer-home areas, camps, dude ranches, and all other private or commercial recreation areas, probably in total acreage as great as or even greater than public areas. The total runs into scores of millions of acres within the United States and Canada.

Organized forest land, such as that under administration of the various states or federal forest agencies, have become yearly more important in outdoor recreation. Foresters have become rather more recreational-minded, in line with forestry principles of making the widest possible use of forest land consistent with sound policy. This is more true of foresters in land administration than of range or other land administrators who are not professional foresters. On the whole foresters have become more cooperative with game departments and park officials than they formerly were. In many states of course game, forests, and parks are all parts of a unified conservation department, which thus promotes cooperation. Foresters, because of their year-around familiarity with their forests, have been able to recognize needs of game management well in advance of others, even regular game department officials. This is particularly true of deer-problem areas, where foresters have called attention to the development of an overpopulation problem long before others were aware of it, sometimes even a decade ahead of its actual occurrence.

Because the state sets the various seasons and regulations for the hunter while the foresters administer the land, the most cordial relations are essential between the game officials representing the regulatory agency and the foresters representing the landholders. In some states game officials and foresters (usually of the Forest Service) determine the forage available in the forest and the populations of big game present in order to arrive at a recommendation for the fall hunting season. A hunting policy may then be agreed upon that will divide the forage between domestic stock and wild game on a formula basis, such as 50 per cent for each. Often the foresters carry on the surveys themselves, but cooperative effort is becoming common. The game departments are generally showing a willingness to employ competent personnel to do such work, and foresters tend to leave much of the work to them when possible. The increase in competent personnel in the game departments has made it possible for foresters to devote to other matters the time they formerly spent in game matters, and so the number of foresters engaged in game work has declined.

Many areas have been set aside within the national and state forests for wilderness wildlife or other preservation. Conflicting use or entrance of disturbing elements are prohibited. The areas so designated within the national forests are termed as follows:

Natural areas.
　Small areas (largest only 10 square miles) to preserve representative local flora and fauna.

Primitive areas.
　Areas of varying size wherein only primitive conditions of travel or living are permitted.

Roadless areas.
　Areas where permanent roads are excluded though "temporary" ones are permitted for economic exploitation.

Vanishing-species area.
　Land reserved for preservation and protection of rare or threatened flora or fauna.

Wild areas.
　Small areas (5000 to 100,000 acres) with primitive conditions wherein all commercial uses, summer homes, and motor transportation are excluded.

Wilderness areas.
　Same as for *wild areas* but larger than 100,000 acres.

138 Forests and Forest Wildlife Management

Improvements for Hunters. Public forest lands rarely require fees from hunters or others for use of the land, but some private forest operations lease hunting rights or establish other charges in order to increase the forest income, carry taxes, and pay for other fixed expenditures on the land. Few improvements are needed for hunters, though private forests may erect or authorize the erection of hunting camps or lodges.

As a general rule the quality of the hunting declines with ease of access to hunting areas, particularly to big-game lands. Roads make it convenient for hunters to reach the heart of game lands, sometimes almost to the target area, at little expense to them. But pack animals are usually available to transport hunting parties at a low cost, universally lower than road construction and maintenance, though such road expense must be paid for by the public treasury rather than by the individual, as with pack-animal hire.

SUGGESTED READING

Adams, C. C., 1926, "The Economic and Social Importance of Animals in Forestry, with Special Reference to Wild Life," *Roosevelt Wildlife Bull.*, 3:509–676.

Chapman, Herman H., 1936, "Forestry and Game Management," *Jour. Forestry*, 34:104–106.

Curtis, James D., 1941, "The Silvicultural Significance of the Porcupine," *Jour. Forestry*, 39:583–594.

Davenport, L. A., 1941, "Timber vs. Wildlife," *Jour. Forestry*, 39:661–666.

Forest Service, 1933, "A National Plan for American Forestry," 2 vols. *Senate Doc. 12, Seventy-third Cong., First Session.*

Grange, Wallace B., 1949, *The Way to Game Abundance with an Explanation of Game Cycles*, Charles Scribner's Sons, New York.

Grinnell, Joseph, 1924, "Wild Animal Life as a Product and as a Necessity of National Forests," *Jour. Forestry*, 22:837–845.

Grinnell, Joseph, 1936, "Uphill Planters," *Condor*, 38:80–82.

Hamilton, W. J., Jr., and David B. Cook, 1940, "Small Mammals and the Forest," *Jour. Forestry*, 38:468–473.

Hawley, Ralph C., 1946, *The Practice of Silviculture*, John Wiley & Sons, New York.

Hawley, Ralph C., and Paul W. Stickel, 1948, *Forest Protection*, John Wiley & Sons, New York.

Hosley, Neil, 1946, "The Status of Federal Agencies in Forest-Wildlife Management," *Jour. Forestry*, 44:897–902.

King, Ralph T., 1938, "The Essentials of Wildlife Range," *Jour. Forestry*, 36:457–464.

Lutz, Harold J., and Robert F. Chandler, Jr., 1946, *Forest Soils*, John Wiley & Sons, New York.

Suggested Reading

McAtee, W. L., 1947, "Distribution of Seeds by Birds," *Am. Midland Naturalist,* 38:214–223.

Moore, E. B., 1940, "Forest and Wildlife Management in the South Jersey Pine Barrens," *Jour. Forestry,* 38:27–30.

Pearce, John, 1947, "Identifying Injury by Wildlife to Trees and Shrubs in Northeastern Forests," *Fish and Wildlife Serv. Research Rept. 13.*

Smith, Clarence F., and Shaler E. Aldous, 1947, "The Influence of Mammals and Birds in Retarding Artificial and Natural Reseeding of Conifers in the United States," *Jour. Forestry,* 45:361–369.

Stoddard, Herbert L., 1939, *The Use of Controlled Fire in Southeastern Game Management,* Coop. Quail Study Assn.

Trippensee, Reuben Edwin, 1948, *Wildlife Management,* McGraw-Hill Book Co., New York.

Toumey, James W., and Clarence F. Korstian, 1947, *Foundations of Silviculture,* John Wiley & Sons, New York.

Westveld, R. H., 1949, *Applied Silviculture in the United States,* John Wiley & Sons, New York.

9

Game Birds of the Forest

Forest game birds, like animal life as a whole, are not evenly distributed, nor do they inhabit all stretches of the forest. Their life requirements are such that only certain sections of the forest offer these essentials within traveling distance; consequently only those sections of the forest that satisfy their instinctive needs will be occupied. Some game birds, like the spruce grouse, are narrowly adjusted to specific forest types or the mixture of several forest types and thus are restricted closely to the parts of the forest containing these types. Topography plays an important part in the distribution of game birds because of its influence on vegetation types. The general and environmental types and the game birds that use them are shown in Table 9.1. The reader should not interpret the table as implying that the sections listed are used exclusively but only that they are used enough to justify separate recognition.

Forest game birds are essentially non-migratory (or but slightly migratory), with the exception of the woodcock, which performs long north and south migrations each year. The turkey formerly migrated considerable distances in the northern part of its range. Seasonal movements may take place among other game birds, though they are usually altitudinal; or movements from one type of cover to another may also occur, but for only a few miles at most.

Forest game birds tend to be solitary or to join together in small or temporary flocks; large flocks are unknown. The whole life of most forest game birds often is spent in limited areas, and few birds, other than woodcocks, are known to die farther than 5 or 10 miles from the place of hatching.

The biological requirements and attributes of the forest game birds are varied. The major ones are summarized briefly in Table 9.2.

There are many species of game birds, such as the bobwhite, that inhabit brushy forest borders or even penetrate far into open woods,

Game Birds of the Forest

TABLE 9.1

USE OF THE FOREST BY GAME BIRDS

(Adapted in part from Grange and McAtee, 1934)

Cover Type	Blue Grouse	Spruce and Franklin Grouse	Ruffed Grouse	Turkey	Wood-cock
Virgin timber:					
Pine	cf	cf	..	cf	..
Spruce	c	CF	..	..	..
Fir	CF	cf	c	..	..
Hardwood	..	..	cf	cF	c
Mixed hardwood-conifer	..	..	cf	cf	c
Hardwood swamp	..	..	cf	cf	c
Chaparral	..	..	..	c	..
Woodlots:					
Second-growth hardwood	..	..	CF	cf	c
Mature hardwood (open stand)	..	..	cf	CF	c
Swamp hardwood	..	..	CF	cf	C
Mixed hardwood-conifer	..	..	CF	cf	c
Tamarack and spruce	cf	cf	cf	..	c
Young conifers	CF	CF	c	..	c
Mature conifers	CF	CF	c	..	c
Aspen	f	..	cF	..	c
Box elder and cottonwood	..	..	c	..	..
Vines:					
Grape	..	..	CF	cf	..
Bittersweet	..	..	cf	cf	..
Virginia creeper	..	..	cf	cf	..
Greenbrier	..	..	f	F	..

c—used for cover.
f—used for food.
Capital letter—indicates high degree of use.

but because they live in farm habitats, for the most part, they will be treated as farm game birds. Ptarmigan, on the other hand, live above timber line and in the open tundra; they are considered here as birds of the Northland.

The family Tetraonidae includes the major game birds of the forest. The family arose in North America, perhaps as early as late Cretaceous

TABLE 9.2
BIOLOGY TABLE FOR FOREST GAME BIRDS

Species	Range	Weight (grams)	Mating*	Sex Ratio	Nesting Season	Number of Eggs	Incubation (days)	Food	Environment
Blue grouse (*Dendragapus obscurus*)	Western North America	900–1500	Pol.	?	April–June	6–10	18–24	Berries, buds, conifer needles	Coniferous forests
Spruce grouse (*Canachites canadensis*)	Northern U. S. northward	400–550	Pol. ?	1:1?	May–June	10–14	17–20	Conifer needles, berries	Coniferous forests
Franklin grouse (*Canachites franklini*)	Northwestern U. S. and southwestern Canada	400–550	Pol. ?	1:1?	May–June	10–12	17–20	Conifer needles, berries	Coniferous forests
Ruffed grouse (*Bonasa umbellus*)	Northern North America	450–675	Pol. ?	1:1?	April–June	9–14	21–24	Berries, buds, leaves	Hardwood, mixed hardwood forests
Mountain quail (*Oreortyx picta*)	Pacific Coast region		Mon.	1:1	May–June	7–16 (10)	20–21	Berries, seeds	Brush and timber
Turkey (*Meleagris gallapavo*)	Eastern part of the U. S., northern Mexico	5500–11,000	Pol.	1:4	Feb.–June	8–14	28–29	Insects, mast, berries	Hardwood and mixed forests, brush lands
Woodcock (*Philohela minor*)	Eastern U. S. and Canada	150–275	Mon.	1:1	April–June	3–5 (4)	20–21	Earthworms	Damp woods and thickets

* *Mon.* means monogamous; *Pol.* means polygamous.

times but certainly by the Tertiary, and has spread throughout the northern hemisphere. The prairie grouse and tundra grouse (ptarmigan) groups have moved from the forest into open country. The black grouse (*Lyrurus*) of Europe is a forest grouse with strong tendencies to use open areas like some of our prairie grouse. Probably the absence of birds of pheasant habits made it possible for this forest family to expand thus into the open.

Blue Grouse (*Dendragapus obscurus*). The blue grouse inhabit the western mountains and forests from New Mexico to southern Alaska and Yukon Territory, east to Wyoming and the Black Hills. The blue grouse is associated with coniferous forests and is widely distributed throughout the fir belt (*Pseudotsuga* and *Abies*) of the West. It has been aptly called "the coniferous counterpart of the ruffed grouse." The blue grouse was formerly common in the coniferous forests but has disappeared from many of its former haunts and is becoming scarce in others.

Habitat Requirements. In the spring the blue grouse migrate from the higher ridges to lower altitudes to nest; they gradually work back to winter range in the higher altitudes in late summer and fall. This movement is the reverse of usual migrations of mountain dwellers from higher to lower altitudes at the approach of winter and back with the coming of spring. The reason for the reversal is not clear, but it appears to be related to the difference between the food habits of the birds in summer and winter. Most of their journey up and down the mountain is on foot.

Blue grouse are found throughout the lower parts of their range during the nesting season, although they nest sparingly in the heavy timber or in dry areas far from water. Nests are placed in open pine forests, in timbered draws and the vicinity of open water courses, in thickets, along the edges of meadows, and in the border between sagebrush and timber. Dry situations are used for nesting, usually with adequate cover, although they are sometimes wholly exposed.

The blue grouse and spruce grouse are tree-dwellers, particularly in winter. Most gallinaceous birds alight on the ground when frightened by an intruder, but these two take to the trees for safety.

Food Habits. During winter blue grouse subsist for the most part upon the leaves of coniferous trees; they prefer the needles of fir to those of pine, spruce, and hemlock. When snow lies deep upon the ground, the birds spend most of their time in the trees, though they may descend and walk about on the snow with the aid of the "snowshoes" characteristic of all grouse. The diet changes to larch needles,

144 Game Birds of the Forest

deciduous leaves, berries, buds, seeds, and insects with the coming of summer and return to the lowlands (Fig. 9.1). Seeds and fruits of the blueberry, service berry, manzanite, gooseberry, currant, strawberry, buffalo berry, elder, salal, and mountain ash are eaten during the summer. Fall foods include any of these fruits that are available and also needles of *Larix, Pseudotsuga,* and *Abies.*

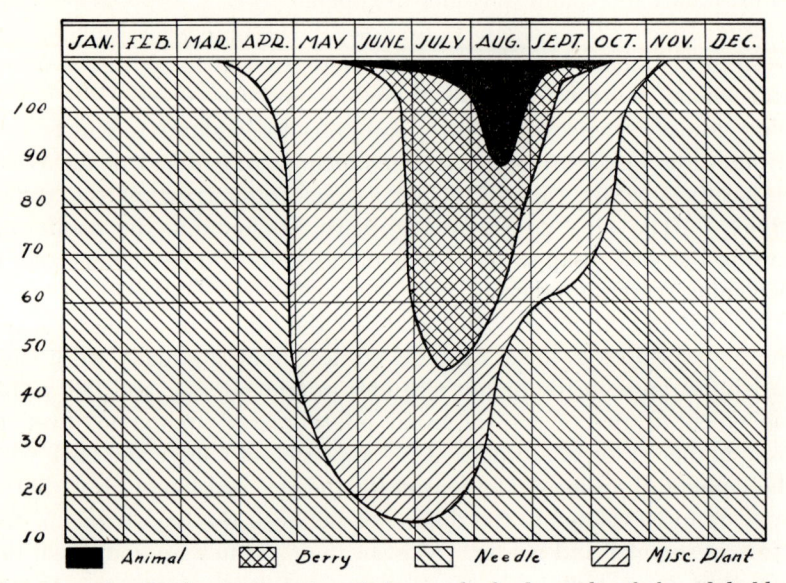

Fig. 9.1. Graphical representation of the yearly food supply of the adult blue grouse. The figures are percentages of the total food eaten. (Data from James Beer.)

Improving Food and Cover. Care should be exercised in forest work, of course, to protect berry-producing shrubs and to encourage them wherever possible. If needed, such shrubs can be planted in the breeding areas. Along moist draws, many non-producing shrubs can be removed and replaced with berry producers.

The grouse use fir (*Abies* and *Pseudotsuga*) and some pine trees (*Pinus albicaulis*) for wintering. The preferred winter trees are of dense foliage, either alone or in combination with others, especially dwarf fir trees along the tops of ridges and near timber line. "Topping" conifers is an excellent method of providing the dense low growth preferred by the birds. It is obvious that a 2- or 3-pound bird will not only receive protection from wind and enemies in the dense stocky growth but will also be able to obtain needles more easily. Since the trees in the high areas where the grouse winter produce little if any lumber or pulp, there is no loss to lumber and pulp interests when the trees are pruned for grouse.

Water is an important need on dry range, and many springs and water holes can be improved by cleaning, planting, fencing, digging, damming, or piping. Mechanical water devices may be useful also.

Although it seems that neither has been tried, it is likely that controlled burning and controlled grazing can improve the breeding range.

Protection. Blue grouse are hunted excessively near settlements and in areas of easy access from population centers; greater protection is needed for areas of high hunting pressure. The natural enemies of the blue grouse are unimportant and affect the population little, so far as known, but parasites, on the other hand, may be significant in juvenile mortality in concentration areas. Sheep and cattle cause eviction of blue grouse by overgrazing and consequent destruction of cover and food-producing shrubs, as well as by trampling nests. The relation of grazing to grouse, however, is not yet fully understood.

The blue grouse populations in much of the West rise and fall in cycles of undetermined nature. There has been a general decline on all ranges where water sources now disappear before midsummer, unless quantities of berries are present.

Spruce Grouse (*Canachites canadensis*) **and Franklin Grouse** (*Canachites franklini*). The two closely related grouse, perhaps of but one species, adapted to the spruce forest inhabit northern North America from Labrador to Alaska and south to the northern states. The Franklin grouse is found in the Pacific Northwest from southern Alaska south to northern Oregon and east to Montana and Alberta. The spruce grouse inhabits the country from Alaska and central British Columbia eastward to Labrador and southward to Maine, New York, Michigan, Wisconsin, and Minnesota.

They are non-migratory and inhabit the northern coniferous forests and swamps, in both second-growth and virgin timber. The range of the two species conforms substantially to that of the spruce upon which they depend for food. The spruce grouse rarely leaves the thick spruce trees wherein it finds both food and protection throughout the winter; it is probable that the Franklin grouse does likewise.

The nests of the spruce and Franklin grouse are placed on the ground in dry situations—at the edge of bogs, among thin stands of jack and lodgepole pines, along the edge of timbered draws, and around the edges of openings in the forest.

Food Habits. Both grouse feed upon buds and needles of spruce and also, to some extent, the needles of fir and balsam during the winter. In the summer they eat the needles of spruce, fir, larch, pine, and arbor vitae, as well as the leaves of ferns, hardwood trees, and shrubs. Their summer food includes large quantities of berries, such as blueberries, blackberries, raspberries, and elderberries, as well as insects.

Protection. Both the spruce grouse and Franklin grouse are known throughout their range as "fool hens," a name derived from their unsuspicious nature and lack of timidity. Unlike other species, they acquire little fear of man, and therefore they are easily killed with guns and even sticks or nooses. It is sometimes possible for a hunter to wipe out an entire group, one at a time, because the birds may not fly even after several members of the group have been killed. Spruce grouse have been extirpated in some parts of the range and regularly retreat from settled areas and areas of disturbance. Forbearance on the part of hunters and woodsmen is needed in order that the birds may maintain themselves in the more settled portions of the range. Few Franklin grouse are now found in the low altitudes.

Ruffed Grouse (*Bonasa umbellus*). The ruffed grouse is a species whose population tends to fluctuate, from time to time, in cycles as great as or greater than those of the blue grouse. The fluctuations interfere with yearly expectation based upon past experience, but the regularity of the cycles makes it possible to predict the trends of future years with some certainty. Such predictions are accurate enough to be useful in determining years when birds can be expected in numbers that warrant open seasons.

Ruffed grouse have maximum densities, which, though fluctuating from area to area, seem to average one bird to 4 or 5 acres; the saturation point, however, seems to be about one bird to 3 acres.

Range and Habitat. Ruffed grouse are found throughout the timbered parts of North America from Alaska to Labrador, and south, at least in the mountains, to North Carolina, Tennessee, Missouri, Colorado, Utah, and California. They inhabit virgin timber, second growth, cut-over lands, mixed hardwood forests, and woodland swamps. In the virgin timber they are found along creeks, around woodland swamps, alder swamps, natural openings, and to a less extent in the heavy timber itself. A wider choice of habitat occurs in cut-over, second-growth, and farming areas. The ruffed grouse is generally associated with hardwoods and may be expected to occupy any suitable hardwood area of sufficient size within the limits of its range.

Habitat Requirements. Ruffed grouse appear to occupy definite territories during the breeding season. These territories require cover ranging upwards from 15 to 30 inches in height. The necessary cover divides into five classes: drumming, nesting, brooding, molting, and wintering.

Because the ruffed grouse requires drumming logs, which are essential parts of the habitat during the breeding season, no area will be occupied if drumming logs (or suitable substitutes) are lacking. Drumming logs need some cover, for the birds tend to avoid exposed logs, but the amount of cover required around a drumming log varies; indeed grouse will occasionally use logs that have no cover at all.

The nesting sites selected by ruffed grouse vary, though usually the nest is near the base of a tree, stump, log, or clump of shrubbery. Nests are frequently placed along the edge of openings, where the sitting bird has opportunity for observation of the approaches to its nest.

Closely related to the nesting cover is the need for brood cover of low-growing vegetation adjacent to openings where the female takes the young to feed. The openings provide both insects and fruits, the insects being essential to the young during the first few weeks of life. The brood retires to the brood cover for resting, at least until the young are able to fly and perch in trees. Molting cover is used from the middle of July to September, when birds retire to thickets during the critical molting period.

Winter cover, which is extremely important, consists of clumps or thick branches of balsam, arborvitae, red cedar, spruce, and fir, as well as hardwood thickets. Because protection from wind is all-important in winter, the branches of pine are too open to furnish very good winter cover except when the trees are small. The birds regularly take advantage of dense grape tangles for winter roosting where available. During the period of deep snow in the northern part of the range, ruffed grouse burrow or plunge into the snow for night roosting; sometimes they remain under the snow throughout the day. They may even thus hole up during a storm of several days duration.

Food Habits. The food habits of the ruffed grouse have been extensively studied, and since many excellent reports are available for various localities, it seems best to omit a detailed summary here. Staple winter foods consist of buds from aspen, birch, hazel, willow, and alder. In addition ruffed grouse feed extensively upon the catkins of the canoe birch and also pick birch seeds from the snow in winter. Sometimes the birds fly against the branches to cause the seeds to shell out and fall to the snow below. During other seasons of the year they feed upon available mast, fruits, seeds, foliage, and insects.

Improving the Food and Cover. Interspersion is of prime importance in ruffed grouse management, just as it is for other birds, and the degree of interspersion controls the number of grouse that can utilize an area. To obtain a density of one grouse to 5 acres requires a higher degree of interspersion than to obtain a density of one grouse to 100 acres. There are normal factors of interspersion in many forests—such as blow-downs, rocky outcrops, and steep slopes—but man-

Fig. 9.2. A ruffed grouse drumming log around which cover has been planted.

agement operations can add materially to the amount of interspersion. Openings are of paramount importance in ruffed grouse management.

It is sometimes advisable to underplant in grazed-out or open wood lots in order to provide food and shelter for grouse. Such underplantings are best made in clumps rather than scattered as individual shrubs. Balsam, spruce, and cedar form excellent winter cover when planted in clumps, and they also offer protection for drumming logs. The obvious forest-game practices of using vines for escape tangles, lopping limbs, and dwarfing conifers can be employed where suitable for improving ruffed grouse range. Solid block plantings of conifers seem to be rarely used; few signs of ruffed grouse farther than a hundred yards from the edge have been reported.

Drumming logs seem to be so important in the life of the ruffed grouse that it may be worthwhile at times to make the drumming logs more desirable by planting cover around them (Fig. 9.2). Where other conditions are suitable but drumming logs absent, the capacity of the ruffed grouse range is increased if drumming logs are supplied by felling standing snags and trees or even by hauling in logs. It may be worthwhile to shift existing logs to more suitable positions or move them from concentrated areas to areas deficient in logs.

Ruffed grouse use a great deal of grit, especially during the period when they feed upon buds and herbage; indeed the need for grit is greatest in all birds during the period of feeding upon rough "forage." Grit is not so important on range supplying hard seeds as it is elsewhere.

Fig. 9.3. Planting permanent food plants for wildlife.

Soft foods, foliage, succulent plants, and dew supply the water needs of ruffed grouse, which do not ordinarily require open water for drinking purposes. Openings planted to clover, strawberries, or other vegetation that keeps green throughout the winter offer sufficient moisture in early spring as well as late summer. The increase of ruffed grouse observed along roads during late summer may reflect their attraction to succulent plants rather than indicate population increase.

Artificial feeding is unnecessary or unimportant at the present time so far as ruffed grouse are concerned; feeding stations do not attract them much. The birds rarely suffer from insufficient quantities of food during winter, a period when an adequate supply of buds is available. Berry-producing shrubs, however, should be planted, protected, or encouraged wherever possible for they are eaten extensively in summer and fall, and they supplement the bud diet in winter (Fig. 9.3). Food-producing trees should be given extra space in order to make the stocky form best for grouse. Food-producing trees, shrubs, and herbs which are used by ruffed grouse and are tolerant or moderately tolerant of shade are listed as follows:

Moderately Shade Tolerant	Shade Tolerant
Holly	Laurel
Greenbrier	Wintergreen
Virginia creeper	Blueberry
Euonymus	Huckleberry
Alder	Viburnum
Cherry	Birch
Amelanchier	Arbutus
Hazelnut	Witchhazel
Maple	Spicebush
Poplar	Beech
Blackberry	Oak
Rose	Trefoil
Elderberry	Thimbleberry
Grape	Dogwood
	Bittersweet
	Ironwood

Berries of low palatability or those buried under the snow are valuable food sources because they are not eaten early but are left until spring when food is most needed. (Contrary to popular opinion, the food shortage for birds is frequently most acute in late winter or early spring rather than in midwinter.) In New England apple trees are found throughout the forest that has grown up on abandoned farms; the production of buds and fruit can be increased by release cuttings favoring the apple trees.

Enemies. As mentioned earlier, cold and starvation are probably unimportant threats to the life of the ruffed grouse because the food supply is generally abundant throughout the winter. Grouse have been known, however, to be trapped in the snow by crusts that form after the birds have burrowed in for the night. Some flying grouse are killed by striking objects. The nest destruction by predators seems to be less than 3 per cent; pilfering of eggs by chipmunks and red squirrels in Minnesota caused 5 per cent loss of the eggs, although it occurred in 30 per cent of the nests. Studies show that predator control has little effect in increasing grouse populations, and predators, such as owls, goshawks, and weasels, cause little real loss, even though they are popularly supposed to be serious enemies of ruffed grouse.

The juvenile mortality may reach 75 per cent, and most of it occurs during the first 60 days after hatching. Some of the mortality is chargeable to enemies, some to disease, and some to chilling. Chicks are lost if they get tangled in vegetation or fall into steep-sided depressions deeper than 2 or 3 inches. Many chicks die from low vitality, the cause of which is unknown.

Many parasites and diseases attack ruffed grouse, although none appears to be of great importance in affecting the populations. *Leucocytozoan bonasa* has been found responsible for much loss of chicks in Ontario. Coccidiosis occurs regularly, and tularemia is also reported. Various parasites, such as ticks, cestodes, and nematodes, are repeatedly found infecting the birds, but, as far as we now know, they do not cause a problem of very great significance to management.

Protection. The ruffed grouse is fairly tolerant of disturbance and will live close to man if given adequate protection. Hunting takes its greatest toll near settlements and in the parts of the woods readily accessible from highways. Grouse hunting is rarely an important factor at distances greater than 2 or 3 miles from highways, except where big game is also hunted. Refuges, other than as a means of preventing extirpation near centers of human population, have little value in ruffed grouse management.

Whether more liberal seasons and bags can be authorized at the peak of the cycle is not clear. Some biologists maintain that more grouse may be taken because the birds face a decline anyway, but others hold that it is these older age classes that must be carried over for the recovery phase of the cycle.

Census Methods. There are several possible ways of determining grouse populations, each based upon a sample count rather than upon an enumeration of all the birds present. Drumming birds have been counted and the population estimated as twice the number of drummers, but this is not satisfactory because the sex ratio may not be even.

The number of breeders on an area is determined by counting the females that feign injury, as feigning indicates young or nests nearby. Regular cruising in the brood season can give counts of broods and measure their decline in number and size.

The King method of censusing (based upon the flushing distance) is the best census method to date for ruffed grouse.

Trapping and Marking. Ruffed grouse are difficult to attract to traps, but some success in catching birds has resulted from use of funnel and portable bobwire traps baited with grapes and grain. Special means can be used at various times of the year; for example, males are caught at drumming logs by "cock and hen" traps, by extended jaw traps, and in steel traps with padded jaws. (It is sometimes necessary to place a small block between the jaws of the trap to keep them from closing too tightly.) The birds may be decoyed on their logs by mirrors. It is possible to catch incubating females at the nest, but because desertion may result, catching incubating females is not recommended, except where intensive scientific studies are being made.

There is still no sure way of telling the sex of live birds, either in the hand or the bush, though the terminal band of the tail tends to be less broken in the male than in the female. Day-old chicks can be sexed by the genital eminence.

Wild Turkey (*Meleagris gallopavo*). The wild turkey lives principally in the hardwood or mixed hardwood country. Its original range extended from Maine to Colorado and Arizona and south to Florida and northern Mexico. The wild turkey has been extirpated over much of this ancestral range and is found today only in the more undisturbed or wilder sections.

The wild turkey occupies a wide variety of habitats, perhaps the widest of any game birds. It lives in mountains and in swamps, on dry ridges and in wet bogs; it inhabits upland and lowland, hardwood and mixed hardwood-conifer forests; it is at home in virgin timber, in cut-over lands, in forests, and in brush; and it dwells in the piny woods as well as in the open pine lands.

Local Migrations. The turkey formerly migrated on foot in the northern and central parts of the range, where it crossed rivers by flying and then continued its journey on foot. It is doubtful, however, that extensive migrations take place today; probably the maximum migration is from ridge tops to lower valleys. Turkeys normally are wide ranging and wander many miles during the year; even daily movement is sometimes 3 or 4 miles.

Habitat Requirements. Reasonably large areas are required for adequate turkey management; 10,000 to 15,000 acres is probably the minimum size to try to manage; 100,000 acres is better, though a township is a convenient unit. Successful turkey management can be practiced in areas having as much as 50 per cent of the land in cultivation. The best turkey areas today seem to be the large Texas ranches.

Wild Turkey 153

The turkey nests in dry situations, and the sites selected range from open and exposed sites to deep cover.

In the late fall turkeys generally congregate in flocks, which break up into small bands with the approach of spring. Young males often band by themselves during the second year. In the wild males breed at 2 years of age, females at 1.

Food Habits. Turkeys eat a wide variety of nuts, fruits, seeds, and berries. They feed extensively upon mast of oak and beech, upon the fruits of blueberry, huckleberry, dogwood, blackberry, grape, dewberry, and strawberry and upon the seeds of *Lespedeza* and *Desmodium.* The young are fed insects, especially grasshoppers, obtained in openings and around the edges of the forest.

Improving Food and Cover. In the Southeast, controlled burning, at longer intervals than those necessary for the bobwhite, is recommended as a method of improving food and cover for the wild turkey.

Food patches ranging in size from 1 to 4 acres are useful, yet because of the possibility of soil contamination, food patches must be shifted from time to time. Turkeys are rather susceptible to disease. Turkeys in the South eat greens in winter, which can be supplied where needed by fall planting of wheat, rye, or other green crops. Other desirable food-patch plants include maize, millets, soybean, cow pea, sorghum, and chufa. Though food patches may be placed wherever turkeys will use them, it is advisable to locate them far enough from habitations to prevent domestic poultry from running upon the food patches and to eliminate the attendant danger of spreading diseases to the wild turkeys. It is sometimes necessary to fence food patches in order to keep out domestic stock, especially hogs.

Artificial feeding in the winter is useful, at least in the northern part of the turkey range and probably elsewhere. Grain is fed from feeders or scattered directly upon the ground; moving the feeding areas from time to time reduces the possibility of disease.

Various food-bearing shrubs and trees, such as dogwood, grape, smilax, ironwood, ash, chinquapin, oak, beech, and gums, are much used by turkeys. Silvicultural operations, especially release cuttings, which favor these species are recommended.

Though turkeys may regularly resort to standing water, even traveling 2 or 3 miles daily to obtain it, they occasionally inhabit dry range. Young and adults obtain considerable water from dew, insects, and standing water, as well as from fruits and succulent vegetation. The water supply on the turkey range can be increased by the construction of "tanks" (using check dams or scooping depressions in the soil).

Protection. Predation has little effect upon the population; it has not yet proved to be significant in wild turkey management; in fact it may be beneficial. Throughout the turkey country illegal kill (together with trapping and unethical hunting) and farm operations are the most serious current obstacles to turkey management. Turkeys are preyed upon by dogs, especially in the South where hunting dogs and hunting-dog blood predominates.

Wild turkeys readily cross with domestic strains, which reduces the "wildness" of the stock. Farmers and ranchers living in the turkey country could well refrain from raising domestic turkeys by the free-range method in the interests of better wild turkeys and better wild turkey hunting.

Livestock, especially hogs, eat the mast of the forest, often before turkeys have a chance to get at it. Carefully controlling domestic stock on the turkey forest range would be advantageous, but such control is not possible, at least in those states that lack fence laws. Food-patch fences of rails or strands of barbwire permit turkeys to use the patches but prevent stock from entering.

Censusing. Familiarity with the area and the birds is the best present means of obtaining information on the size of the turkey population. Turkeys that gather in flocks at food patches and feeding stations allow counting from blinds erected for the purpose. Sometimes the birds are counted at roosts or as they go to roost. In spring the breeding population is located and determined by counting the gobbling males and allowing for females according to the observed sex ratio.

Restocking. It is difficult to obtain good *wild turkey stock;* all available commercial stock is heavily mixed with domestic strains, and birds of this inheritance lack the wildness that makes for choice birds. Unless the turkey stock is pure, it is best to defer restocking until good wild stock can be obtained. Turkeys tame easily and if handled too much—or if lacking the essential inherited wildness—game farm releases will make themselves at home in the nearest farmyard instead of going wild.

Turkeys are restocked by straight liberation or by liberation in 20- to 40-acre breeding paddocks under semiwild conditions. As soon as the young are able to fly and partially care for themselves, the wire along one side of the fence is lifted to allow the broods to scatter. When there are wild gobblers in the region, the hens can be retained in these breeding fields, and ramps placed around the outside to enable the gobblers to cross the fence.

Mountain Quail (*Oreortyx picta*). The mountain quail inhabits the western United States from southern Washington south to lower California, and from the Pacific coast to eastern Oregon. Because the bird has been introduced extensively, it is not known whether the birds of extreme eastern Oregon, eastern Washington, and western Idaho are native or introduced. Evidence indicates that the quail was introduced north of the Columbia River about 1860. The mountain quail, which is the largest of the true quails, inhabits both the forested humid coast region and the open forests and draws of the dry interior. As its name implies, it is a bird of the mountains and ranges to 10,000 feet altitude.

Habitat Requirements. The habits of the mountain quail are not well known, despite the fact that it is a rather common bird in some parts of its range. It inhabits both brush and timber, but is found in greatest abundance along the edge between them. Clearings, cutover, and burned-over areas of the western mountains that have grown to brush are frequented, especially when these regions have grown to berry-producers, such as salal (*Gaultheria shallon*) and blackberries (*Rubus*).

Little is known of the bird's need for water; in the lower altitudes of the dry interior it is restricted to draws, gulches, and canyons; it ranges throughout the forest in the humid belt and in higher altitudes. Apparently water is not so important in the life of the mountain quail as it is in the life of the valley quail. The difference in the need for water is presumably due to the difference in habitat, for the mountain quail lives chiefly in the timber, which is a moister environment than the open country used by the valley quail.

The birds of the high altitudes perform an altitudinal migration on foot. In late summer and autumn the birds of the high ridges move down to lower valleys and foothills for the winter; some, however, are sedentary in the lower altitudes.

The mountain quail is presumed to have extended its range northward as a result of logging operations. The number of birds in logged-off areas has also increased and is frequently many times the number that lived there before logging operations took place.

Although little is known of their roosting habits, it seems probable that the birds generally roost in trees rather than on the ground. Roosting seems to be confined to conifers and thick deciduous growth.

The bird chooses a dry nesting site and builds a nest on the ground in a depression lined with grass and pine needles. The nest is placed under conifer slash or fallen tree tops and occasionally under bushes, small trees, or logs.

Food Habits. The young live upon insects for the first 2 or 3 weeks, and gradually change to the adult diet, which consists of berries and seeds of shrubs, forbs, and grasses. Quantities of herbage are eaten, especially in spring and during periods of drought.

Improvement and Protection. Because little or no management research has been undertaken, it is impossible even to suggest management techniques other than provisions for water on dry ranges. Likewise the enemies of the mountain quail and the need for protection from enemies and human beings are quite unknown; presumably they are unimportant.

Woodcock (*Philohela minor*). The woodcock is a migratory species ranging over the forested region of eastern North America and breeding from the Atlantic east to Manitoba south into the Gulf states. It winters chiefly in the Gulf states, but stragglers are sometimes found farther north where suitable conditions exist around protected springs, in draws, and in other moist, open places.

The woodcock, a bird of the hardwoods, rarely utilizes coniferous stands. The reason becomes obvious when one examines the food habits of the species; the woodcock depends upon earthworms, which are absent or rare in coniferous stands. It prefers timbered woodlands and boggy thickets, it lives in wet and brush pastures, and it dwells in moist glens. The woodcock in migration uses coverts like those of the breeding season and appears in many unexpected places as well.

Migrations. The woodcock moves northward with the advance of spring and arrives in the northern states between the middle of March and the middle of April. Its departure in the fall is somewhat prolonged but usually takes place in the northern portion of its range during October and November, though some birds may remain well into December.

Habitat Requirements. The singing ground of the male woodcock is certainly as essential as the crowing ground of the cock pheasant or the drumming log of the ruffed grouse. A small clearing or open space in the woods, of a minimum size of about one chain square, is selected for the singing or courting ground.

The site selected for nesting is generally among the hardwood leaves of the open woods where there is little undergrowth. The woodcock builds no nest structure but lays its eggs in a slight depression in the forest floor, usually within 100 or 150 yards of the singing ground.

Nests are located in a variety of places among the hardwoods, especially near the edges of hardwood swamps and moist thickets, though they often appear along the edges of woods and fields. Woodcocks will occasionally nest at the edge of coniferous plantations, but they rarely penetrate far into the edge.

Food Habits. Approximately 95 per cent of the woodcock's food consists of animal matter, and of this earthworms and soft-bodied larvae compose 75 to 90 per cent. The woodcock is one of the most voracious eaters among birds and can daily consume its weight in earthworms. It gets food by probing in soft mud—the probe holes being commonly known as "borings"—and on occasion it may probe for food in decaying stumps and logs. During drought woodcocks turn to fruits and insects and even resort to dry situations not otherwise used.

Improving Food and Cover. The dependence of woodcocks upon earthworms restricts them to humus soils because earthworms are most abundant in rich soils. Any operation that enriches or changes the soil in favor of earthworms could benefit woodcocks. Changing the plant composition—for example, by mixing conifers with hardwoods—is a procedure that aids woodcocks by increasing the number of earthworms.

The number of earthworms in an area can be determined rather rapidly by clearing the surface of a sample plot (one square foot or more) and applying a strong irritant, such as a solution of lye or mercuric chloride, which causes the earthworms to squirm out and away.

Because woodcocks prefer moist habitats, water diverted and caused to seep through the soil may form suitable food and nesting coverts for them. Similarly the maintenance of springs is especially desirable, and it may be possible sometimes to prevent the drying of spring holes, draws, or hillside bogs by placing impervious cores across the flow of water. Naturally the return of vegetation, especially forest, to the catchment area of springs will aid in maintaining water flow during dry weather.

Because the singing ground is a necessity and limits the territory inhabited by woodcocks, it is sometimes possible to increase the woodcock population by providing artificial singing grounds through clearing or cutting the timber and brush near grounds frequented by the birds.

Protection and Enemies. A number of native predators, including possibly the red squirrel, are potential enemies of the woodcock, but until more information is secured regarding them, they must be dismissed as insignificant. Woodcocks often suffer from adverse weather conditions, and those that migrate north early are sometimes beset by sudden cold snaps which freeze the ground, so that they are unable to obtain food. Drought also makes it difficult for the woodcocks to find food because it forces the earthworms to deeper levels. When woodcocks are found away from normal habitat, unfavorable changes may be safely assumed. Excessive rain causes some loss of young by chilling, and floods may evict adults from lowlands.

Census Methods. There are no methods for censusing woodcocks with a high degree of accuracy, but random sampling, which will give a rough indication of abundance, is especially useful as a quick method for determining relative changes. The drive method has been tried with little success because woodcocks flush reluctantly even though beaters pass close to them. Counting singing birds in the early evening has been done with some success both in America and in Europe. The number of males is determined by counting occupied singing grounds, and the total population can be computed as twice that of the singing males. Though the count of singing males is the most satisfactory method so far devised, it does not give accurate information because the number of singing males is not a true indicator of the number of mated birds; furthermore the sex ratio may not be even.

Trapping and Banding. A number of methods have been used for catching woodcocks for banding, but perhaps the one used with the greatest success is "night lighting." In night lighting the birds are sought on known feeding grounds and located by reflection of light from their eyes; they are then caught with hand or clap nets. Females can be caught at nests by means of hand nets or throw nets, but this is not recommended except for special investigations, as it may cause desertion. A mounted woodcock and even a mirror have proved successful on singing grounds as a means of decoying males into traps formed of netting over extended-jaw traps.

Sex Determination. The length of the bill is a relatively useful index for sex determination. It may be assumed safely that birds having bills longer than 72 mm are females; birds with bills shorter than 64 mm are probably males, as are 95 per cent of those with bills shorter than 66 mm.

SUGGESTED READING

Beer, James, 1943, "Food Habits of Blue Grouse," *Jour. Wildlife Management,* 7:32–44.

Suggested Reading

Bent, Arthur Cleveland, 1927, "Life Histories of North American Shore Birds (Pt. 1)," *U. S. Nat. Mus. Bull.* 142.

Bent, Arthur Cleveland, 1932, "Life Histories of North American Gallinaceous Birds," *U. S. Nat. Mus. Bull.* 162.

Edminster, Frank C., 1947, *The Ruffed Grouse, Its Life History, Ecology, and Management,* The Macmillan Co., New York.

Grange, Wallace B., 1949a, *The Way to Game Abundance with an Explanation of Cycles,* Charles Scribner's Sons, New York.

Grange, Wallace, B., 1949b, *Wisconsin Grouse Problems,* Wisc. Cons. Dept., Madison.

Grinnell, Joseph, Harold Child Bryant, and Tracy Irwin Storer, 1918, *The Game Birds of California,* University of California Press, Berkeley.

King, Ralph T., 1937, "Ruffed Grouse Management," *Jour. Forestry,* 35:523–532.

Ligon, J. Stokley, 1946, *History and Management of Merriam's Wild Turkey,* New Mexico Game Comm.

Mendall, Howard L., and Clarence M. Aldous, 1943, *Ecology and Management of the American Woodcock,* Univ. Maine, Maine Coop. Wildlife Res. Unit.

Neff, Johnson A., 1947, "Habits, Food and Economic Status of the Band-tailed Pigeon," *N. A. Fauna* 58.

Pettingill, Olin Sewall, Jr., 1936, "The American Woodcock," *Mem.* 9, *Boston Soc. Nat. Hist.*

Trippensee, Reuben Edwin, 1948, *Wildlife Management,* McGraw-Hill Book Co., New York.

10

Forest Game Mammal Management

Many game mammals inhabit the forest, but this discussion, as in the previous chapter on forest game birds, will be limited to several of those that depend upon the forest for the majority of their life requirements. Forage is often the major factor in range preference of forest game mammals. As it is sometimes difficult to separate habitat preference from forage preference, many species that use the forest in part of their life cycle will not be considered here as forest game mammals.

The members of the deer family (Cervidae) are generally gregarious, at least during part of the year, but most mammals of the forest (both game and non-game species) are solitary or only slightly gregarious. Even the deer of the forest are less gregarious than their relatives of the open, although deer may concentrate together in winter or in some habitats. Gregarious species perform extensive migrations more than solitary ones; in fact few solitary animals move much seasonally. The travel radius of forest game mammals tends to be less than that of game mammals of the open range. Even individuals of a species inhabiting both the forest and other habitats tend to move less in the forest. In the high mountains, however, deer and elk have learned to move distances that are comparatively long, for deer, in order to take advantage of summer range in the mountains and winter range in the valleys.

Timber type has an important bearing upon occupation of the forest by game mammals, for game mammals, like all wildlife, find suitable or optimum condition only in parts of the forest. Table 10.1 lists the game mammals of the forest that extensively use the major forest types, but these designations should not be understood as exclusive, because detailed types are not listed. Neither does the list include all the habitats that might be named, for to list all the timber types relied upon by forest game mammals would require a remarkable tabulation.

TABLE 10.1

USE OF FOREST BY GAME MAMMALS

(Adapted in part from Grange and McAtee, 1934)

Cover Type	Black Bear	Fox and Gray Squirrels	Snowshoe Rabbit	Columbia Black-Tailed Deer	Mule Deer	White-Tailed Deer	Moose
Virgin timber:							
Pine	c	..	c	..	c	c	c
Spruce	c	..	fc	c	c	c	c
Fir	c	..	..	c	c	c	c
Hardwood	c	fc	fc	..	..	fc	fc
Mixed hardwood-conifer	c	fc	fc	..	..	fc	fc
Hardwood swamp	c	fc	fc	..	..	FC	..
Chaparral	..	..	..	..	fc	..	..
Woodlots:							
Second-growth hardwood	c	FC	fc	..	..	FC	fc
Mature hardwood (open stand)	c	FC	fc	..	..	fC	fc
Swamp hardwood	c	FC	fc	..	..	FC	fc
Mixed hardwood-conifer	c	fc	fc	..	..	FC	fc
Tamarack and spruce	..	..	FC	..	..	c	c
Young conifers	..	..	FC	..	..	c	c
Mature conifers	..	..	fc	..	..	c	c
Aspen	..	..	Fc	..	..	Fc	Fc
Box elder and cottonwood	..	..	..	..	..	fc	..
Vines:							
Grape	f	fC	..	..	..	f	..
Bittersweet	..	fC	..	..	..	f	..
Virginia creeper	..	fc	..	..	..	f	..
Greenbrier	..	c	..	..	..	..	..

c—used for cover.
f—used for food.
Capital letter—indicates high degree of use.

TABLE 10.2

BIOLOGY TABLE FOR FOREST GAME MAMMALS

Species	Range	Weight	Mating*	Normal Limit of Sex Ratio	Breeding Season	Parturition Season	Gestation Period (weeks)	Number of Young	Food	Environment
Black bear (*Ursus americana*)	Most of North America	200–400 lb	Mon.	1:1	June–July	January–February	28–30	1–3 (2)	Meat, berries, herbage	Hardwoods, mixed coniferous forests, sometimes found in the open
Grizzly bear (*Ursus horribilis*)	Western North America	300–800 lb	Mon.	1:1	June–July	January–February	30	1–4 (2)	Meat, berries, herbage	Heavy timber, cut-over areas, sometimes found in the open
Brown bear (*Urus gyas*)	Northwestern North America	1000–1600 lb	Mon.	1:1	July	January–February	30	1–4 (2)	Meat, berries, herbage	Heavy timber, shore, open country

Fox squirrel (*Sciurus niger*)	Eastern and southern states	600–800 grams	Mon.	1:1	December–April	February–May	4	2–5 (3)	Nuts, berries	Hardwood forests
Gray squirrel (*Sciurus carolinensis*)	Eastern and southern states	450–600 grams	?	?	December–April	February–May	4	2–5 (3)	Nuts, berries	Hardwood forests
Elk (wapiti) (*Cervus canadensis*)	Western North America (formerly the East)	500–800 lb	Pol.	1:5	September–October	May–June	33–36	2–3	Browse, herbage	Mountains, foothills, plains
Mule and black-tailed deer (*Odocoileus hemionus*)	Western U. S.	125–300 lb	Pol.	1:5	October–December	May–June	32–38	1–3	Browse, herbage	Heavy and open timber
White-tailed deer (*Odocoileus virginianus*)	North America	100–225 lb	Pol.	1:5	October–December	May–June	28–32	1–3	Browse, herbage	Hardwood, mixed, and coniferous forests
Moose (*Alces americana*)	Northern North America south to northern states	900–1500 lb	Pol.	1:3 ?	September–November	May–June	32–40	1–3	Browse, herbage, aquatic vegetation	Hardwoods, mixed, and coniferous forests

* *Mon.* means monogamous; *Pol.* means polygamous.

Table 10.2 gives in brief form the general biology of forest game mammals.

Formulas for converting dressed weight to live weight are valuable for local studies at checking stations because the weight of animals, when properly interpreted, may be useful in administrative and biological work. Animals on rich forage may have a different dressed weight-live weight ratio from those on poorer range because of the greater fat content in the tissue.

For deer the respective ratios have been given as follows, though how widely they may be applied is not known. They may be somewhat similar, however, for other big game mammals.

Dressed weight	78.8% of live weight
Meat weight	65.5% of live weight
Live weight	126.8% of dressed weight
Live weight	152.7% of meat weight

SMALL GAME OF THE FOREST

Although this chapter treats in detail but a few of the small game mammals of the forest, several additional ones might be mentioned. The raccoon, for example, is hunted by many people, and "'coon hunting" is a recognized high sport in some regions, especially in the South. But it seems best to consider such animals of dual status as fur mammals.

The gentle flying squirrels inhabit a large part of forested North America, as far north as the Limit of Trees, and are indeed worthy of any forester's attention. They nest in holes, such as woodpecker holes, and have used nest boxes provided for them. The western gray squirrel has the same general life pattern as its eastern relatives. The tufted-ear squirrels are protected largely because they are showy; they add yet another unique touch to the Southwest.

Gray Squirrel and Fox Squirrel (*Sciurus carolinensis, Sciurus niger*). The ranges of the gray and the fox squirrels correspond more or less with the distribution of the oak-hickory forest, although the gray squirrel goes farther north than the fox squirrel. The two species inhabit eastern North America from about central Texas to Florida, north to southern Canada.

The squirrels are found throughout the deciduous forests, principally where oaks and hickories grow, rarely in brush or recently cut-over lands. It is stated that the gray squirrel is more a bottom land dweller and the fox squirrel more a dweller of the dry woods, yet this is not a universal rule, for gray squirrels often are found on mountain ridges and fox squirrels in bottom lands. The gray squirrel has a somewhat wider range of habitat selection than the fox squirrel, for it will inhabit maple forests and may move into aspen-birch reproduction 20 years after a forest fire. The fox squirrels, on the other hand, stays close to the oak-hickory forests.

Habitat Requirements. The habitat requirements of squirrels are related to their special food preferences. The density may reach two to the acre, although one squirrel for 1 to 3 acres is the more normal maximum density. Isolated woodlots of less than 5 to 10 acres probably are unable to maintain many squirrels.

Both gray and fox squirrels have two types of habitations, tree dens and tree nests. Woodpecker holes or cavities resulting from broken limbs and subsequent decay supply den holes. The recommended minimum number of den trees for squirrels is one for each acre, though it is generally advisable to have more. Ninety per cent of the young are born in den nests and transferred to leaf nests later. Squirrels live in the dens almost exclusively in winter and may use them at other times for escape retreats and for storage of food. Dens are generally located in trees more than 15 inches in diameter. They may be within 15 feet of the ground or as high as 100 feet above ground, but the average height of the den is probably 35 feet. The usual cavity measures 5 to 8 inches inside diameter and 1 to 2 feet in depth; larger cavities, although they may be used, seem unsatisfactory. The entrance varies from 3 to 4 inches in diameter.

It is probable that every squirrel has at least one leaf nest in addition to a den nest; gray squirrels use leaf nests more than fox squirrels do. Leaf nests are of two types, permanent and temporary. The permanent nests are usually constructed of sticks and leaves and located close to the trunk in trees exceeding 8 inches in diameter. Squirrels keep their permanent nests in good repair because they occupy them for more than one season. Because temporary nests are used only during a brief period in summer, they are made almost wholly of leaves and are fragile. The temporary nests are sometimes placed in vines, but more often they are found in the tops of small trees or far out in the branches of larger ones. Leaf nests, both temporary and permanent, range from 20 to 75 feet above the ground.

Food Habits. Soft-shelled pecan or hickory nuts seem to be preferred food among the squirrels, but other nuts, particularly acorns and beechnuts, are also eaten regularly. Squirrels feed upon many soft fruits and seeds, as well as vegetative parts of plants. They also take kindly to many cultivated crops. The destruction of the chestnut (*Castanea americana*) by blight has been a factor in the reduction of squirrel population in parts of the East and Southeast. Table 10.3 lists the most important foods of the fox and gray squirrels.

TABLE 10.3

FOODS REGULARLY EATEN BY GRAY AND FOX SQUIRRELS

Mast	*Fleshy Fruits*	*Seeds*	*Vegetation*
Hickory nuts	Grapes	Maple	Fungi
Acorns	Blackberries	Elm	Maple buds
Chestnuts	Raspberries	Box elder	Elm buds
Beechnuts	Cherries	Corn	Aspen buds
Walnuts	Plums	*Euonymus*	Willow buds
Butternuts	Mulberries	Basswood	Sprouts
Buckeyes	Dogwood	Bittersweet	
Hazelnuts	Sour gum		
	Huckleberries		
	Blueberries		

Squirrel emigrations that seem to be associated with failure of the mast crop have been reported. Hordes of passenger pigeons formerly consumed much of the mast crop, which sometimes resulted in a squirrel exodus. Sometimes the grackle consumes much of today's acorn crop.

Squirrels require water, which they get from many sources, such as succulent vegetation and water that accumulates in limb depressions, stump hollows, and ground pools. In winter squirrels take water from snow and the drip of icicles, and on occasion from sap which they obtain from broken twigs or by nicking the bark themselves.

Improving the Food and Cover. Squirrels prefer a forest of mixed species containing all age classes, and they tend to avoid even-aged and single-species stands. Mast trees require space for best mast production, and such trees are aided by release cutting and thinning. The mast-producing species of trees, such as oak, walnut, hickory, and beech, should be favored in silvicultural operations. Special attention also should be given to the preservation and increase of fruit trees, shrubs, and vines which squirrels utilize for food and cover. Grape vines need space in order to produce satisfactory grape tangles, and removal of competition favors them.

Selective logging is possibly more beneficial to squirrels than other forms of logging; clear cutting is the most harmful. Shelter-wood cutting improves squirrel range when not more than 20 to 25 per cent of the timber is removed at each cut. Because they are vital in the lives of squirrels, den trees should be left standing where squirrels are desired, even though they may be considered "wolf" trees by the foresters' code. Overmature stems make the best den trees; in any event they rarely pay the cost of harvesting.

From 6 to 30 years are required to produce a satisfactory den when rotting wood must be removed by squirrels themselves. Squirrels tend to hollow out holes begun by decay where limbs break off, and they regularly nick the bark to keep cavities from healing over. Paradoxical though it seems, a substantial squirrel population must be present in order to prevent the healing over of cavities and the consequent elimination of dens and reduction of the squirrel population. In the South the gum trees often form hollows and supply the major portion of den trees; in the North den trees usually are oak.

Limbs may be girdled artificially in order to induce decay and cavity formation, but this requires a number of years and has not proved satisfactory. Den facilities can be provided where holes are absent by nest boxes of boards, kegs, or sections of hollow limbs similar to those used for birds. The interior should be from 12 to 20 inches deep and preferably not more than 6 by 8 inches in diameter; the opening should be about 3½ inches across. Squirrels normally gnaw the edges of natural openings to prevent closure, and they ruin nesting boxes by continuing the habit; surrounding the opening with metal, however, may keep the squirrels from gnawing the wood. For best results nest boxes should be placed in or near the trunks of trees. Excelsior can be supplied for artificial nesting material if the area lacks a natural supply.

Lightly grazed woodlots support heavier squirrel populations than heavily grazed woodlots. It is probable that light grazing keeps the ground cover open so that the squirrels are better able (or perhaps less reluctant) to travel on the ground. Heavy grazing not only removes much ground cover but also may injure trees.

Because squirrels tend to waste food by storage, feeding stations are not very satisfactory, yet a lack of winter food makes artificial feeding welcome. Nuts and acorns can be gathered where plentiful and taken to woodlots that are deficient in food. Corn and grains are good winter foods, and food patches have been used with some success for squirrels.

Protection. Squirrels increase under protection and probably reach the maximum possible density in 5 years when given complete protection. The proper time for an open season on squirrels, when one is feasible, is in the fall when the young are quite full grown; open seasons in the summer or breeding season should be avoided. The length of the season necessarily will vary in different localities, but a season probably should not exceed 15 to 30 days in length, with daily bag limits ranging from two to five, depending upon abundance of squirrels and hunting pressure.

In some parts of the country hunters thoughtlessly cut hollow trees in which squirrels take refuge, in order to drive them out. This practice is contrary to good management as it reduces the carrying capacity by destruction of valuable den trees.

Where allowed to range freely, hogs conflict with squirrels by feeding extensively upon mast.

Predation is an insignificant drain upon squirrel populations and can be largely overlooked in squirrel management. Squirrels themselves occasionally prey upon song and insectivorous birds by destruction of nests and eggs. It is, therefore, advisable to exercise caution in increasing the density of squirrels in order to prevent them from doing harm to the normal bird population of an area. Careful studies of the bird population are needed to determine whether an increase in the number of squirrels would be harmful to birds.

Census Methods. Undoubtedly the most accurate means of counting the population of squirrels is the time-consuming method of trapping and marking all the individuals on an area. *Spot counting* by time and area has been tried. From a fixed position, all the squirrels within the range of visibility during a 30-minute period at the time of day when squirrels are most active are counted. The area covered is then determined by the distance at which squirrels were observed, and the squirrel population is calculated from this unit of area.

The number of used nests is a good index to the number of squirrels present, because this number averages slightly more than one per squirrel. Considerable experience is required, however, to determine whether or not nests are being used. The squirrel population can be determined to some extent by counting all squirrels on a transect or quadrat, but, as in all methods that depend upon observation, this one is hampered by the squirrel's habit of remaining inactive or hiding.

Snowshoe Rabbit (Snowshoe or Varying Hare) (*Lepus americanus, L. washingtonii,* and *L. bairdii.*). The snowshoe rabbit (taxonomically three species) inhabits the northern part of North America from Alaska to Labrador, extending farther south in the mountains. It is found in the Appalachian Mountains south to Pennsylvania and West Virginia and in the Rocky Mountains to New Mexico, and it reaches California in the Sierra Nevadas. At the present time the snowshoe rabbit oc-

Snowshoe Rabbit (Snowshoe or Varying Hare) 169

cupies practically all the original range, having been extirpated only from a narrow fringe along its southern edge. This is because it lives in the mountains and northern forests, mostly beyond farm limits. It ranges from sea level to timber line and sometimes higher.

The snowshoe rabbit inhabits both virgin timber and second growth; it lives in spruce, cedar, and tamarack swamps of virgin areas, as well as along the edges of "beaver meadows," river banks, and similar places where the vegetation is low and heavy and cut up with small openings. The rabbit occupies a wide range of habitats in second growth, being found in swamps as well as high land. In fact it can be said to occupy practically any type of boreal forest where the canopy is not too high or too open. There are noticeable variations between the types of range carrying heavy populations during the high of the rabbit cycles and during the low of the cycles. The rabbit is found chiefly in coniferous swamps, willow and alder thickets, jack pine, and denser second-growth reproduction during the low; often it will be found only in the swamps during this period. At the high, on the other hand, the population expands to occupy in force much of the cut-over lands, second-growth forests, and coniferous reproduction.

The snowshoe rabbit is a "forage animal" of the northern forest and is preyed upon by many predators, both bird and mammal. It is basic in the food chain of several fur bearers.

Habitat Requirements. The snowshoe rabbit lives a sedentary life; the individual normally stays in a restricted area throughout its whole life. A few emigrations have been noted by reliable observers, but such movements must be considered exceptional. The home ranges of individual rabbits overlap so that "territories" have the appearance of communal range, though they are individual as far as each animal is concerned.

Burrows are seldom used by these animals, although they frequently utilize depressions in the snow or retreats under cover called *forms*, which appear to be individual property. Each rabbit has one or more forms, usually several oriented with the prevailing winds, making it possible to face into the wind by shifting forms when necessary. The rabbits regularly resort to brush piles, fallen tree tops, and thick natural cover for resting. Runways, which become well-beaten trails, are probably used indiscriminately by many rabbits.

The snowshoe rabbit uses dust baths that may be considered as "communal," because more than one rabbit uses each dusting area.

The dust baths are generally located in openings where the soil is exposed to the sun.

Few nests of the snowshoe rabbit have been seen; presumably it rarely constructs even the simplest of nests for the young.

Food Habits. The snowshoe rabbit feeds upon bark, browse, and herbage, and probably it eats almost any plant growth, though it does show definite preferences. It prefers aspen, willow, alder, birch, serviceberry, jack pine, lodgepole pine, white cedar, spruce, grass, and ferns. It also feeds upon many low shrubs, such as blueberry.

Populations. The snowshoe rabbit population is characterized by several violent cycles, the principal one being about 9 years long. The population may range from 3400 to the section (640 acres) to about zero between the highs and lows of the cycles. Rabbits can be considered abundant when the population reaches 1000 to a square mile and scarce when the population drops to but 50 to a square mile. At times the population may even reach 10,000 to the square mile. It is probable that a "normal" population in the accepted sense of the word does not occur. Should it be possible to speak of a normal population for snowshoe rabbits, however, the figure would presumably approximate 200 to a square mile.

Improving the Range. There are areas where it is desirable to increase the population. Because the snowshoe rabbit population tends to persist in greatest strength in the swamps during the low of the cycle, such areas should be preserved from drainage or overgrazing, as well as from "outgrowing" the rabbits. In both swamps and high land youthful stages of vegetation succession benefit rabbits more than mature stages do, and it is desirable to keep these areas from becoming too mature. Timber that has passed its useful stage can be cut or girdled to leave room for younger growth. Likewise openings in the forest encourage thickets, and brush piles and fallen tops provide cover. When winter food is scarce, felling aspen or other saplings allows the rabbits to feed upon the tender bark of the tops.

Control of Populations. The snowshoe rabbit sometimes injures forest reproduction—especially newly established plantations or areas under intensive silviculture—but ordinarily it does no other damage to man's interests. The rabbits feed upon tender vegetation and for this reason may attack seedling pine and spruce or girdle trees, though they rarely injure anything larger than saplings. The snowshoe rabbit can perform a valuable service to forestry by thinning dense stands, especially jack pine and lodgepole pine that reproduce in dense stands after fires. Since crowding tends to make them stunted, the drastic

Snowshoe Rabbit (Snowshoe or Varying Hare) 171

thinning by the rabbits makes for satisfactory growth by freeing trees from stagnation.

In some areas injury to plantations by snowshoe rabbits constitutes a serious problem. Delaying planting operations until the low of the rabbit cycle has passed reduces such injury. Seedlings planted with more than customary space provide less available cover for rabbits and, therefore, result in lower populations.

Rabbits can be controlled where necessary by snaring in the runways or by shooting and trapping. Drives are not very successful in controlling snowshoe rabbits because of the habitat in which they live, their tendency to stay close to the home range, and their tendency to hide, particularly in the swamps. The use of poisons is open to serious objections because it is unselective and likely to destroy other species of wildlife. Several states have prohibited such practice. Control of the natural predators (great horned owl, goshawk, coyote, and wildcat) should not be permitted in regions where serious rabbit injury occurs. In fact it may be desirable actively to encourage such predators.

Census Methods. The methods of censusing snowshoe rabbits fall into four classes: trapping, driving, counts, and transect counts.

Trapping gives the number found on the sample plots (usually of 2 or more acres), but the figures may include influx animals. The plots can be laid out arbitrarily or, preferably, to correspond with vegetation types. The results of trapping can be expressed in absolute abundance, the exact number of rabbits living on the sample areas, or in relative abundance, usually expressed in terms of number of rabbits per trap night. Snares are most effective devices for "dead trapping" snowshoe rabbits. They are set in the runways, which, though easy to locate in winter, are hard to find in summer except in swamps. Live traps of various designs are baited with fruits, alfalfa, and aspen.

In dropping counts it is necessary to count the number on sample quadrats, usually a square yard each. It is said that an average of 9.5 scats a square meter (8 a square yard) indicates a rabbit population of 1000 per square mile.

In the transect-count method the number of rabbits observed on the line of travel indicates the population. The population varies with the square because the transect is a linear measurement, whereas area is a square measurement. Six animals observed on the line to 50 miles of walking is said to indicate 1000 rabbits to the square mile. Three observed would indicate about 250 to the square mile, which seems too small a sample for judging such large numbers. Because the snowshoe rabbit does not "flush" readily, use of flushing distances is ordinarily not feasible.

Marking. Snowshoe rabbits are marked the same as cottontails.

SUGGESTED READING

Allen, Durward L., 1943, *Michigan Fox Squirrel Management,* Michigan Department of Conservation, Lansing.

Cahalane, Victor H., 1947, *Mammals of North America,* The Macmillan Co., New York.

Goodrum, Phil, 1940, "A Population Study of the Gray Squirrel in Eastern Texas," *Texas Agric. Exp. Station Bull.* 591.

Grange, Wallace B., 1949, *The Way to Game Abundance with an Explanation of Game Cycles,* Charles Scribner's Sons, New York.

Green, R. G., and C. A. Evans, 1940, "Studies on a Population Cycle of Snowshoe Hares on the Lake Alexander Area," *Jour. Wildlife Management,* 4:220–238, 267–278, 347–358.

Grinnell, Joseph, Joseph S. Dixon, and Jean M. Linsdale, 1937, *Fur-Bearing Mammals of California; their Natural History, Systematic Status, and Relations to Man,* 2 vols., University of California Press, Berkeley.

Hamilton, W. J., Jr., 1939, *American Mammals,* McGraw-Hill Book Co., New York.

MacLulich, D. A., 1937, *Fluctuations in the Numbers of the Varying Hare (Lepus americanus),* University of Toronto Studies, Biol. Ser. 43.

Seton, Ernest Thompson, 1925–1929, *Lives of Game Animals,* 4 vols., Doubleday, Doran and Co., Garden City, N. Y.

Trippensee, Reuben Edwin, 1948, *Wildlife Management,* McGraw-Hill Book Co., New York.

11

Forest Game Mammal Management (Continued)

FOREST BIG GAME

The big game mammals of the forest are largely members of the deer family (Cervidae) or the larger carnivores. Most of the hunting pressure, however, falls upon the cervids. The white-tailed deer alone, for example, outnumbers today all the other cervids put together and accordingly absorbs a major share of the big game hunter's attention.

Black Bear (*Ursus americanus*). The black bear originally inhabited most of North America between the Atlantic and Pacific Oceans, from Labrador to Alaska, south to Florida and the highlands of Central Mexico. Though absent from the settled central portion, it occupies nevertheless the major outline of its ancestral range.

The black bear occupies a wide range of habitat, but it usually frequents forested and brushy areas; it may, however, wander into the open. It lives in mountains as well as lowlands, occupies virgin, cut-over, brush, and second-growth areas, and is at home in hardwoods and mixed hardwood-conifers, as well as in pure conifer forests.

Habitat Requirements. The habitat requirements of the black bear and the individual space needed by each animal are varied. A single bear may roam over 200 square miles, though 10 is perhaps the usual range. The density may reach one to a square mile, but one to 3 square miles is probably the normal maximum density. This does not indicate the true space requirements, however, because individual ranges overlap when populations are high. The highest known density seems to have been reached in the central hardwoods, where black bear environment was presumably optimum. In the often cited Ohio hunt of 1818, 21 black bears were killed on 25 square miles of virgin timber, and no doubt some escaped through the line of hunters. A density of one to a square mile seems probable. (The area of the Ohio hunt was an "island" of timber in pioneer farmland and may, therefore, have been a special concentration.)

Because of persistent pursuit, the black bear today has somewhat more exacting requirements for successful survival than it had under pristine conditions. Good black bear range includes rough or rocky terrain, thick timber, or cover to which the animals may retreat when closely pursued. Increased protection is the best alternative to such retreats.

It is likely that black bears hibernate to some extent in all parts of their range. Regular hibernation or cessation of activity takes place in the North, where they spend the winter in caves, among large rocks, in hollow logs, in hollow trees, and in windfalls, always in dry situations. They have been known to use thickets and even large brush piles.

Bears frequently have wallows similar to those of elk, yet such wallows apparently are a "luxury item" rather than an essential part of the environment.

The breeding habits are not clearly known. The females breed in their third year of life and probably in alternate years thereafter. They may live 20 years. The black bear may practice a monogamy of sorts.

Food Habits. The bear is one of the most omnivorous of animals. It digs roots in all seasons when it is about, especially upon emerging from hibernation; in fact, the need for bogs having bulbs may govern the choice of bear range in some areas. It feeds extensively upon berries (raspberries, blackberries, and blueberries) and consumes quantities of mast. Bears are well known for their habits of tearing logs and stumps apart and overturning stones in their search for ants. The black bear will feed upon meat when available but rarely becomes a consistent predator, although it will dig rodents and catch fish. It will eat carrion when other foods are not available but can subsist upon herbage alone for an indefinite period.

Protection. If given reasonable protection, the black bear will inhabit rough lands fairly close to settlements. In order to prevent excess drain upon bear populations, rigid protection must be offered throughout the year, with only a short open season when warranted; the season should coincide with the deer season. Some westerners maintain that bear seasons should be in March. Because the bear is more valuable as a game animal, trapping is generally discouraged.

The bear rarely does damage to human property, but occasionally individual animals will become "renegades" and acquire a taste for hogs or sheep. Individual bears may also become habitual camp robbers, fruit raiders, or honey thieves. When a bear turns renegade, it is necessary to eliminate him, but incidents of this kind should not serve as excuses for campaigns of extermination. It is to be expected that, given an opportunity, an otherwise well-behaved bear may seize a sheep or raid a camp; isolated cases, however, do not indicate renegades. Unless provoked, the black bear is harmless to man, and authentic reports of groundless attacks upon human beings are rare. Nevertheless bears are dangerous animals, even though, like other animals, they prefer to run when man is around.

Censuses. Familiarity with the region, combined with an ability to see and read sign, is essential in estimating successfully the number of bears present. Bears generally detect man first; no matter how numerous they may be, even the experienced woodsman may seldom observe them. Their presence is indicated by tracks in trails, soft earth, and freshly exposed soil. They also leave such evidence as claw marks on trees, overturned stones, torn logs, food leavings, and feces.

Elk, Wapiti (*Cervus canadensis*). The original range of the elk included the central portion of North America in a belt reaching from the Piedmont along the Atlantic to the shores of the Pacific. It reached Canada on the north, and down to the Carolinas, Missouri, and New Mexico on the south. It is now extirpated over most of this great range and today is restricted almost entirely to the mountainous parts of the West.

The elk is a rather plastic animal as far as environmental tolerance is concerned, and it originally used a wide selection of habitat. It lived in the forest, brush, and prairie park land; it lived on the plains as well as on the mountain slopes; its original range touched arid, semiarid, and humid lands. This discussion of the elk might with some justification be assigned to the chapter on open-range game, for the elk in some areas occupied open range about as much as forest. In the early days, at least, the elk was very much a prairie animal in the prairie country.

Habitat Requirements. The elk is a migratory species, moving in the fall from the higher altitudes, where it summers, to the lower valleys, where it winters. The evidence indicates that no distinct migration occurred in the low eastern forests or on the plains formerly inhabited by the elk. It is probable, however, that elk concentrated during severe weather in sheltered areas, such as prairie groves and river bottoms.

Elk are classified as mobile animals, not only because they migrate annually but also because of their ordinary wanderings. Normal movements may cover 10 miles in a single day, yet elk sometimes spend the entire summer in circumscribed areas of a few hundred acres; range conditions and insects probably control the amount of movement. Elk may migrate as much as 50 miles, but the migration is generally less, and, like mule deer, they tend to follow the same paths annually.

Valleys and foothills offering protection from wind and deep snow now compose the favored winter range. The preferred cover consists of heavy brush mixed with some conifers.

As the snow melts the elk move back to spend the summer in the thin timber, open slopes, and mountain meadows of the higher altitudes.

Population density depends upon the conditions of the range and fluctuates from area to area. Presumably it may reach a maximum of 10 to the square mile under favorable conditions. Early explorers, however, reported elk herds on the prairies that rivaled bison herds in size.

Bulls wallow in mud holes in the breeding season, but an elk wallow, like a bear wallow, must be considered a luxury rather than a necessity.

Food Habits. Of all American members of the deer family, elk graze most. Elk eat grasses, sedges, and browse in early summer but shift to greater proportions of browse as the summer progresses. Among the important browse species are maple, aspen, buck brush, willow, elderberry, mountain mahogany, and mountain ash. Data for summer palatability and browse intensity in the Selway range of Idaho show that the key species there are *Salix* spp., *Acer glabrum, Bromus carinatus, Elymus glaucus,* and *Carex geveri.*

Management Activities. Provisions for adequate winter range are extremely important in making possible the full utilization of summer range. Winter range for the elk, as for other big game species, is less abundant than summer range. Valley bottoms, the ancestral winter range of the elk, have been acquired by ranchers throughout much of the present elk country, a fact that makes it difficult or impossible for elk to obtain food and protection during the winter in proportion to summer range. The running of large numbers of domestic stock in the elk summer and winter range is a source of serious competition.

Elk, Wapiti

If adequate stands of elk are to be maintained, a reduction in the domestic stock is necessary, especially on the elk winter range.

Before sound management practices can be devised and put into effect, studies of the production and utilization of forage are needed. Determination of the carrying capacity of elk range requires special study. The elk itself is more destructive to the range than any other of North American big game species. Under conditions of overpopulation, any big game species may eat up the range; elk, however, even when not in excess numbers, may feed intensively on a single bush until it is destroyed. Because the elk is a large animal, it may injure forage by severe trampling during the period in the spring when the ground is exceedingly soft from rain, melting snow, and thawing frost. An elk is an animal of great power and has been known to go through a wire fence (even barbed wire) and tear out several rods of it, fence posts and all.

Various temporary measures have been tried for the relief of starving elk during winter. Browsed-out trees and shrubs have been felled to bring browse within their reach, and hay has been fed to them. Although winter feeding is not a permanent solution to the problem of winter forage, humanitarianism dictates feeding of starving herds, even at the risk of piling up trouble for the future.

Elk often travel 4 or 5 miles for salt and, like cattle, linger around the salt licks. Salt is set out on the range both to prevent concentration at the few natural salt licks and to obtain a better distribution of the elk, which in turn makes for better utilization of the range. Salt can be supplied by pack strings or from airplanes (Fig. 11.1).

Surface water, which appears to be a necessity during the heat of summer, is usually available in the higher mountains but not on dry range. Any improvement in the water supply on dry range is to be recommended.

Regulated hunting has proved useful in breaking up elk concentrations, but other means are as successful, though not without an outlay of funds. On some western ranges elk kill has been purposely overliberalized to reduce the herd, which in turn reduces antagonism of stockmen.

Probably the normal sex ratio can be one bull to five cows. If the sex ratio is unbalanced by excess hunting of bulls, open seasons on cows or closed seasons on bulls are necessary. When the sex ratio is unbalanced, there should be an open season on cows only if the range is used to capacity; otherwise there should be one on neither sex.

178   *Forest Game Mammal Management*

Elk sometimes damage ranch hay stacks in winter where forage is scarce. Heavy fences around the stacks are the remedy. Elk also damage farm fields by heavy stamping in the spring or during open winters. The action that the game manager takes must be governed by the local situation.

Fig. 11.1. Four 50-pound salt blocks on the tipping tray, coming in for an aerial drop. (Photograph by Montana Game Department.)

Censuses. Elk now are usually counted from airplanes (Fig. 4.3), often with the aid of a ground survey party. Sex ratios and calves may be found from ground surveys.

Mule Deer and Black-Tailed Deer (*Odocoileus hemionus*). The black-tailed deer group, which consists of two distinct deer, the mule deer (*O. h. hemionus*) and the Columbian black-tailed deer (*O. h. columbianus*), inhabits the western part of North America from central Alberta south to northern Mexico. It formerly ranged east to Manitoba and Nebraska, but today it is absent from the easternmost portion.

The mule deer are somewhat gregarious, more so then the Columbian black-tails or the white-tailed deer, and are also associated with more open forest. Though now inhabiting the mountains, the foothills, and the valleys, the mule deer formerly reached far out into the open plains near water courses and draws. They are found most frequently in open forest, cut-over lands, and areas which have grown up to brush. Parts of the range of the Columbian black-tailed deer, on the other hand, are as heavily timbered as any of the white-tail range. The range of the black-tailed deer is characterized by varying degrees of aridity, from the dry interior inhabited by the mule deer to the humid coastal area inhabited by the Columbian black-tail. The summer range is now chiefly in the slopes and higher parts of the mountains, and winter range varies from south slopes to lower valleys. The winter and summer ranges are not always distinct, however, for many deer winter and summer where the conditions are favorable in the lower altitudes.

Habitat Requirements. The black-tailed deer regularly migrate in the parts of the range where deep snows and winter storms prevail. The individual deer usually inhabits a single watershed and rarely crosses a divide to another; the area used by the individual animal may be small. It is possible that many deer spend their entire lives within a radius of 5 to 10 miles of the place of birth.

The deer of the higher slopes of the mountains migrate to the foothills and lowlands in early fall to pass the winter in sheltered valleys and on the lower slopes. Like the elk ranges, these areas are small in proportion to the summer range, but they are of great importance.

In those regions of light snowfall the migrating deer generally stop at the first valley encountered on the downward trek. The usual distance of migration of the mule deer averages about 20 miles, but it may reach 50 miles; even longer migration distances are known. The migrating animals tend to follow the same route each season in going between the winter and summer ranges; likewise the winter and summer ranges become relatively fixed, although a little natural shifting from range to range occurs. Tradition and the lie of the land account for this. Heavy hunting or other major disturbance may cause some shifting of winter quarters or migration routes.

Both black-tailed deer, especially the mule deer, generally stay within reasonable distance of water, but adjacent surface water does not seem to be a necessity, for mule deer frequently live on dry ranges where for long periods no surface water occurs. Succulent vegetation probably supplies much moisture, as it does for other animals.

Deer need salt and may travel long distances to salt licks, yet they may ignore salt licks for considerable periods. Salt distributed carefully may lure mule deer from overgrazed areas to less heavily grazed ones and will sometimes hold them on the higher slopes for a longer time in the fall.

Food Habits. The black-tailed deer are browsers, but the mule deer graze more than either the Columbian black-tail or the white-tailed deer. In addition to browse they feed upon such foods as grass,

Fig. 11.2. A browse line or "sky line" resulting from lack of winter deer food. Conifers like this have little value as deer food. (Photograph by Burton Lauckhart.)

herbage, forbs, acorns, fungi, and lichens. In early spring the deer may feed almost exclusively upon grass, for a short period, and then return to browse. They generally avoid pine, spruce, and fir except in emergencies (Fig. 11.2). The variety of plant species eaten is very great indeed—too great to summarize here, except in the general terms already given—and detailed determination must be left for each separate segment of the range.

Improving Food and Cover. Considerable conflict occurs between deer and domestic stock, especially sheep. This conflict is most serious on the winter range because of the relatively small amount of winter territory in proportion to the summer range. Game departments of the West seek now to buy many of the small but highly utilized winter areas. Winter range, being in protected valleys, generally has been pre-empted by ranches, and the lack of winter range is today the chief limiting factor in mule deer management.

Drift fences sometimes will divert mule deer herds from overused ranges to underused ranges or cause them to enter unoccupied winter range. The same device works for other big game.

The grazing capacity of an area, either for stock or deer, alone or together, is definitely limited. Generally it has been exceeded, with consequences evident in the deterioration of the range. The relative grazing intensity on an area is revealed by close check of "key species" of plants, the amount of utilization of the key species indicating the condition of the forage as a whole. Sometimes forests can be opened to allow better growth and abundance of those shrubs and forbs heavily utilized by deer. Where winter food is growing out of reach, drastic cutting must be done to renew the browse at a lower level in the form of brush, reproduction, or coppice growth.

Occasionally deer herds increase beyond the carrying capacity of the range and thereupon cause its deterioration, but apparently no example of deer "irruptions" is associated with virgin conditions. Where only a deer herd is involved or where it is not possible or feasible to remove stock and other conflicting interests, it is necessary to reduce the deer population by regulated killing of one or both sexes. Because the buck population is generally low, increases in the allowable take of bucks will not of itself reduce the herd enough to benefit the range without unbalancing the sex ratio; consequently an open doe season is usually required on overpopulated deer range.

Small plantations of conifers on the winter range provide warm cover, and in summer coves of aspen in the mountains are especially sought by mule deer during the heat of the day.

Protection. The sex ratio for the black-tailed deer probably varies with different areas; a normal sex ratio could undoubtedly fluctuate between 1 to 3 and 1 to 5. In order to maintain the desired sex ratio, differential protection of the does is necessary, but strict adherence to the one-buck system, on the other hand, may cause unbalancing of the sex ratio.

The black-tailed deer are benefited by refuges located along the migration routes where they pass during the hunting season. Unless there is a doe season, the does receive protection everywhere so that refuges aid bucks only.

Though cripple losses are high in some localities, they are often lower than generally believed. Hunters miss a deer completely more often than they wound it, even though a hunter believes that he hits every deer at which he shoots. Wounded deer are often taken within a short time by other hunters, and a number of injured deer may recover completely.

The illegal kill, however, is often higher than commonly thought. Cougars and wolves are usually so scarce that deer losses due to their activities can be passed over without further consideration. The losses in deer herds from coyotes are overestimated. Coyotes, unless they are in packs or pursuing weakened deer, rarely are able to pull down deer. Coyotes occasionally kill fawns, but study shows that the loss from this source is low.

Accidental collisions with cars along the highways can be reduced by signs warning motorists of the danger of deer on the road. Deer crossings, especially, need designation. The brush can be cut away from the sides of deer crossings to form "re-entrants," which increase visibility for deer and motorists.

In parts of the West some fawns and adults are drowned in irrigation ditches that have steep sides up which the deer are unable to crawl. Where irrigation ditches are located in deer country, sloping the banks reduces this loss, as well as loss of domestic stock.

Four methods have been used to control deer damage to private property: deterrents and repellents, fences, live traps, and doe seasons.

Census Methods. The most satisfactory method to date for censusing all deer is the *drive,* but the drive is best suited to relatively smooth terrain and requires considerable manpower. Deer regularly migrate singly or in small groups along well-defined migration routes, and it is sometimes possible to count the animals (or their tracks) as they migrate. It is also possible to count deer on suitable areas by observation from points of vantage. Airplane counts have been made with some success. Winter deer surveys are undertaken by several game departments in order to check the number, sex ratio, and condition of the animals, as well as the condition of the range.

When antlers are present, the sex count is reliable as far as the number of bucks is concerned, but care must be taken to separate does from yearlings. After the antlers are shed, bucks and does can be differentiated to some extent by the thicker neck of the buck and by the udders of the does. Fawns are hidden when young and consequently difficult to count; reports of "dry does" are usually exaggerated.

Forage censuses are sometimes necessary in determining the amount of utilization of the range, and various means are employed. In Arizona the amount of forage needed daily by the mule deer is reported to be 2.35 pounds of air-dried forage for each 100 pounds of deer, a figure slightly higher than that for domestic stock.

Trapping. Deer can be caught in pen traps with drop doors, but the traps must be small in order to prevent the animals from injuring themselves by their struggles. Carrots, apples, alfalfa, and salt have proved satisfactory for bait, alone or in combination with lead-in fences. Salt is sometimes the best bait for summer use. Deer are marked with ear tags similar to those for cattle.

White-Tailed Deer (*Odocoileus virginianus*). The white-tailed deer originally occupied the wooded parts of North America from Florida and Texas north to southern Canada, west to the northern Rockies; it reached the Pacific Ocean at the mouth of the Columbia River. It is now extirpated or reduced throughout the central part of the range, but it has extended its range somewhat to the north since settlement and cutting of timber.

The white-tailed deer occupies forest areas, woodlands, groves, thickets, river bottoms, and similar habitats. It is less abundant in heavy timber than in second growth and cut-over lands, and, generally speaking, it reaches its highest densities in the developmental stages of ecological succession.

Habitat Requirements. The white-tailed deer shows considerable tolerance of man, more than any other wild ungulate. If given protection against severe molestation by men and dogs, it will live in the larger woodlots, swamps, river flats, and bottoms of farming communities; indeed it frequently lives near metropolitan centers. The area required by a single white-tailed deer is small, sometimes but a few acres in extent, but the minimum size of an isolated area that will hold deer is unknown. This deer moves little, at least in comparison with other deer, yet the distance traveled in a single night has been known to exceed 10 miles.

Although the individual may possess a home range, it appears that territory as such is not held to the complete exclusion of others of its kind. Individual areas overlap, and so we can probably think of the *home range* as the area over which an individual deer moves, rather than as a territory held in exclusive possession.

The density of white-tailed deer is subject to wide variation. Michigan reported a population of 219 to the square mile on the Hanson Refuge, a density of one deer to 2.9 acres. The 18,200 square miles of deer country in the Lower Peninsula of Michigan averaged 50 to the square mile (a density of one to 12.9 acres). In the Upper Peninsula, however, the 16,309 square miles of deer country averaged only

18 to the square mile, or a density of one to 35.6 acres; the maximum density for any area in the Upper Peninsula was one to 9.4 acres in the Escanaba River tract. It appears that most or all of these densities were abnormal, for the abundance of deer presented an acute problem in Michigan.

A density of one to 17 acres on the Lebanon State Forest of New Jersey was reported as too great. Other densities of one to 10 acres (New Jersey), one to 21 acres (North Carolina), one to 8 acres (Michigan), and one to 26 acres (Wisconsin) indicate high densities for deer. In the southern Appalachians it is probable that the maximum allowable density is one to 15 acres of cut-over land and one to 30 or 40 acres of old growth. In the North, if snow is not too deep, a density of one to 25 or 30 acres of cut-over and one to 50 or 100 acres of old growth probably represents maximum allowable densities, although local areas always will be capable of maintaining higher densities than the average.

Little seasonal movement takes place in the southern and central parts of the range, but in the North, especially in the deep-snow country, white-tailed deer congregate in winter *yards* located in cedar swamps and also in *concentration areas* located in the summer range.

Deer yard together at the approach of deep snow in cedar swamps, which vary in size from a few acres to hundreds of acres. Continual passage of deer maintains open trails by tramping of the snow as it falls. Deer yards serve definite parts of the summer range and therefore determine its usability because summer range is "unusable" when winter range is inadequate. The movement between summer range and winter yards is usually short, rarely more than 10 miles. White-tailed deer are creatures of habit and return to the same swamps annually, even though they become overbrowsed to such an extent as to cause distress from lack of food. They may even starve in a browsed-out swamp when an unused one is available a short distance away on the other side of a ridge.

Deer require salt in some form (Fig. 11.3), and they also have other requirements, such as windy ridges and water for refuge during the summer fly period. It seems likely, however, that many of their "needs" are not limiting because deer occupy ranges lacking them.

Food Habits. Although the white-tailed deer is primarily a browser, it feeds upon herbage, forbs, lichens, mosses, mast, and berries. The deer "clip" browse with the grinding or back teeth, which requires tipping the head; for this reason deer are unable to clip vegetation

White-Tailed Deer

so closely as cattle and sheep, and thus they are at a disadvantage in competition with domestic stock.

More than 600 plant species have been found to be consumed by white-tailed deer in Missouri, and 53 plant species have been found eaten in winter concentration areas of Wisconsin. Probably most plants growing in a region could be found in the deer diet if enough

FIG. 11.3. The soil has been eaten away for several feet by deer at this natural Michigan salt lick.

study were undertaken. Doubtless the species given in the following list are the general browse species that lead throughout the range:

White cedar (*Thuja occidentalis*)
Willow (*Salix* sp.)
Aspen (*Populus* sp.)
Sweet fern (*Myrica* sp.)
Oak (*Quercus borealis, coccinea, velutina, alba*)
Serviceberry (*Amelanchier* sp.)
Raspberry (*Rubus* sp.)
Cherry (*Prunus* sp.)
Maple (*Acer* sp.)
Dogwood (*Cornus* sp.)
Laurel (*Kalmia* sp.)
Huckleberry (*Gaylussacia* sp.)
Blueberry (*Vaccinium* sp.)

Deer living in northern yards depend upon cedar browse (*Thuja*) almost exclusively during winter and eat other species only occasionally or when the supply of cedar is reduced. Deer eat the browse as high as they can reach, and a well-defined browse line often develops. Cedar browse supplies most of the nutritional needs of the deer, and it alone is sufficient to maintain their weight and strength. The average white-tail requires about 4½ pounds of cedar browse a day.

Improving Food and Cover. The abundance of deer in areas of early plant succession and their scarcity in virgin timber give clues to silvicultural operations. The maintenance of early stages of ecological succession is the goal for which to strive in deer-range improvement.

The reproduction and brush that follow clear-cutting are used by deer, but because clear-cutting results in even-aged stands, it should be done in strips or blocks (with some seed trees left if need be) well spread over the rotation period and the working circle. Group and strip selection are satisfactory methods of harvesting timber from the standpoint of deer unless the area covered at each cut is usually too small. Both the single-tree selection and shelterwood systems are probably of less benefit to deer than group and strip selection or clear-cutting in blocks and strips, which opens areas more drastically and results in a more luxuriant growth of browse a few years after cutting. The shelterwood system is very good for the reproduction of tolerant browse species if the cutting cycle is less than one-third the length of the rotation; otherwise it tends to produce substantially even-aged stands. Small openings are of high value in heavy timber although less so in cut-over areas.

Openings are made also by "stripping" both sides of fire lanes and by keeping old logging roads and camp sites open rather than reseeding them or permitting invasion of trees. Openings are sometimes seeded to legumes, like alsike clover, and maintained for deer, which show a marked preference for alsike clover during spring and fall.

Although winter feeding has not proved successful or feasible on a general scale, it is useful as a humanitarian measure in local problem areas. A concentrated cake has been developed for use in areas where winter food shortage is critical. These cakes, composed of 45 parts of molasses to 55 parts of soybeans, are prepared in tin containers and weigh 25 to 50 pounds each. The tins are stored in deer yards before winter begins or packed in when emergencies arise.

Starving deer are helped in winter yards by cutting overbrowsed cedar in order to make the tops available. Maple, aspen, cherry, and other browse species can be cut in the summer range or concentration areas, and the deer will usually clean up all such cuttings in a short time. It is better to provide browse by frequent cuttings than by a few large-scale operations. Many species of woody plants can be induced to supply browse in the form of sprouts by frequent cutting.

Cedar usually is damaged so heavily in overbrowsed swamps that it is difficult or impossible to obtain satisfactory regeneration in the face of constant browsing. The amount of food produced by seedlings and small cedar trees is less than that produced after the trees attain a larger size. If the deer herd holds down the reproduction, it is advisable to reduce it to a point below the actual carrying capacity of the swamp in order to give the cedar a better opportunity to reach a satisfactory production age. A 25-year rotation has proved satisfactory in furnishing the maximum combination of browse, posts, and wood.

When deer in overbrowsed yards fail to use underbrowsed swamps near by, efforts may be made to lead them to the unused ones in order to relieve pressure on the overbrowsed yards. Deer keep trails open in their home yards by continual passage but hesitate to strike out across deep and soft snow. Attempts to drive them from one swamp to another are usually unsuccessful unless a satisfactory trail is broken through the snow to the new swamp; likewise trails must be broken within the new yard in order to induce deer movement within it. Deer can be baited into the new swamp by hay or cedar browse scattered along a connecting trail, but after they have crossed to the new swamp, means must be taken to prevent their immediate return, usually by blocking the return trail with deep snow or fallen trees. Deer sometimes will pass back and forth voluntarily between old and new yards after well-beaten trails are opened.

More areas exist where deer have adequate summer range than where they have adequate winter range, and the reason sometimes lies in the absence of warm night and resting cover. Evergreen blocks for cover may also establish a concentration area. Especially useful are evergreen blocks in burned-over areas growing up to hardwoods. The blocks should be small, perhaps not more than 5 to 10 acres.

Protection. Temporary or permanent refuges are needed where the population is less than the carrying capacity, where the sex ratio is unbalanced, or where it is desirable to maintain a concentration of deer for the general public to see. The number needed for the public to observe readily (and to keep resort owners happy) usually results in overpopulation. The size of the refuge is dependent upon experience and local conditions, but it is probable that a refuge for white-tailed deer should include not less than 5000 acres in one block; small or isolated refuges are difficult to administer and protect. It is necessary to mark the outer boundaries of refuges in such a way as to prevent innocent trespassing, and usually a single strand of No. 9 wire, 4 or 5 feet above the ground, suffices (though it appears to be at antler height). When desirable to surround a refuge with a fire lane, the lane should be placed a few feet inside the refuge boundary; fire lanes are easy walking, and hunters tend to patrol outside fire lanes during the hunting season. Deer usually stop and look before crossing openings, and so fire lanes on the outside of the boundaries may become nothing but death traps for deer.

Naturally, illegal hunting causes considerable loss, and in some places it may be as great as or even greater, at times, than the legal kill, especially in areas where "shackers" live. Illegal hunting usually makes no discrimination between bucks and does and thereby handicaps maintenance of a proper sex ratio. Laws that close the woods to "gun toting" during the closed seasons may prevent some poaching. Proper synchronization of hunting seasons is also beneficial in reducing poaching.

The present state of our knowledge of predation shows that predators have little influence upon deer except under extraordinary circumstances (Fig. 11.4). Wolves, coyotes, bobcats, lynx, and cougars prey upon deer or fawns occasionally, but there is no evidence that the losses from these predators are more than generally unimportant. Eagles have been reported occasionally to kill fawns, but this is likewise insignificant in management practice.

Isolated farms are universally problem areas in the white-tailed deer country. Deer often raid crops of these farms and cause some damage, but the experience of wardens shows that claims from isolated farms are nearly always out of proportion to the actual injury. On the other hand, wardens find that isolated farms are often places where systematic poaching or market hunting occurs. Proper rural zoning prevents increase in the number of isolated farms, but it also removes farms that break up the woods.

Regulation of the Take. The length of season and the number of deer to be taken should, of course, be based upon the population and hunting pressure. The population varies from area to area, and proper regulation calls for variation in the amount of the take and distribution of hunting pressure. Unfortunately, regulations still must be based more on expedience than experience, but it is likely that the situation will improve.

The ratio of bucks to does obviously is the one that assures a full fawn crop, but the maximum ratio is probably 1 buck to 5 does. The ratio must be higher in sparse populations where a ratio of 1 to 1 may not be unusual. The season on antlerless deer can either coincide with the season on antlered deer or it can be a separate season following the regular buck season. An antlerless deer season after the buck season allows the hunter who did not get his buck during the regular season, as well as other hunters, to get deer later, which may not be an advantage, but a season on any deer makes it possible to take the number in a shorter time.

Fig. 11.4. This deer was killed by a timber wolf, and the predation was of management value. The deer starved on the conifer browse, as shown by the condition of the deer and the trees in the background. It is likely that 20 per cent of the deer could have wintered well here had the remainder been removed.

If the hunting season precedes the rut, the bucks will be removed before their period of usefulness, though this is not a serious consideration if enough bucks are left. The bucks are fat before the rutting period and the meat at its best. On the other hand, deer are hard to track before snow, and venison is subject to spoilage during the warm weather of an early season. This factor may not be serious in settled regions, however, because of the presence of modern storage lockers. An advantage of an early season in the North is that hunters can travel more easily because of less snow, especially in the mountains; consequently the hunters concentrate less in areas of easy access.

A late hunting season (after the rutting period) finds the animals thinner, but the period of usefulness of bucks is over, which makes it possible to remove a larger number of bucks than in an early season because young bucks will be mature by the next breeding season. There is also less spoilage of venison in the woods during the colder weather of a late season, as well as a smaller amount of loss from cripples in the North because cripples can be tracked in the snow. As a general rule for deer regulations, early seasons seem best for mountain country, late seasons elsewhere.

Census and Marking Methods. There are several possible means of obtaining population figures and estimates of deer, and the method employed will depend upon the available manpower and the conditions of the census area. The most frequently used methods fall into the following classes:

>   Deer drives.
>   Sample counts on isolated areas.
>   Yard mapping and counting.
>   Frequency of occurrence.
>   Airplane counts.
>   Track and bed counts.
>   Flushing counts.
>   Checking stations.
>   Pellet-group counts.

White-tailed deer are caught and marked in the same way as blacktails.

Moose (*Alces americana*). The moose originally inhabited the northern part of North America from Alaska to Quebec and Nova Scotia, south to the northern fringe of the United States, and to Pennsylvania and Wyoming in the mountains. It has been extirpated from most of the southern edge of the original range. There are several thousand moose in the United States and several times as many in Canada and Alaska.

Habitat Requirements. The moose is a forest animal usually associated with deep forests, willow flats, lake margins, and stream bottoms. It is rarely found in the open far from cover. Moose seek shelter from the hot sun of summer in thick conifers, which also give them protection from wind in winter. They may go far out into lakes to escape insects. The moose is sedentary and tends to confine its daily wanderings to a small area, perhaps of less than half a square mile. Both winter and summer are spent in practically the same area. The moose is a solitary rather than a gregarious species.

A population of at least 1000 built up on Isle Royale (Michigan) in the early 1930's. The island contains 220 square miles, which indicates a population of about 5 to the square mile or one to 140 acres. The population increased to perhaps 3000, or 14 to a square mile, a density of one to 47 acres, but this increase was followed by a drop. The actual local density was no doubt higher than the figure indicates, for the animals were not evenly distributed over the island. The number was in excess of the range capacity because the moose seriously damaged the vegetation by overbrowsing; even a density of one to 140 acres is more than the island can carry. One to 14 square miles has been reported for Nova Scotia.

Food Habits. Although the moose is primarily a browse eater, it is not entirely dependent upon browse, for it also feeds upon grasses, algae, forbs, and especially sedges. When feeding upon high branches, the animals grasp the branches in their mouths and strip off the leaves and twigs. A branch that is too high for this operation is broken down by seizing its end in the mouth and pulling. Saplings up to 2½ inches in diameter are broken over by riding the stem with the muzzle. The moose ordinarily reach browse to a height of 8 or 9 feet from the ground, a height that may be increased when the animals stand upon packed snow. The moose will feed in water to a depth of about 6 feet, often eating all aquatic vegetation in a lake. The animals live around small lakes with vegetation rather than large or rocky ones without it.

The principal food species are aspen, willow, birch, hazel, dogwood, alder, mountain ash, cherry, maple, honeysuckle, and forbs (such as asters), sedge, pond weeds, and ground hemlock. Birch, willow, and aspen seem to be the preferred foods. The same browse species are eaten in winter as in summer, with the addition of cedar, balsam, and some spruce, but the last two are probably of low nutritional value. Moose on Isle Royale were reported to require about 25 pounds of mixed birch and balsam browse a day.

Improving Food and Cover. Because the moose is rather intolerant of human disturbance and environmental changes, disturbing human elements, such as isolated farms and roads, reduce the range desirability for them.

The value of moose—for the hunter, tourist, and nature lover—is materially lowered by the loss of "wildness" that comes with excessive number and consequent tameness. Adolph Murie has stated this in the following words:

For the greatest enjoyment of the moose, it is not particularly desirable to have them so plentiful that we involuntarily compare the gatherings of them to a prosperous barn-yard.

Where moose are given priority, various methods can be used to advantage; among these are the felling of large saplings and trees in browsed-out areas to bring the tops within reach of the animals, or cutting in order to induce sprout growth.

They inhabit well-watered country and are usually found in the vicinity of lakes and streams; no special provisions need be made for water. Moose require salt, perhaps more than other deer except possibly elk, but natural licks are somewhat scarce in moose country.

Census Methods. There are no adequate methods for censusing moose, which ordinarily live in low density. Familiarity with the area seems to be the best basis for judging populations. The known size of moose range is learned sometimes by following individuals that have distinctive markings, such as unusual antlers. The known size of individual territories can then be utilized to arrive at a population estimate for the region, but the resulting figure is but a rough approximation at best. Methods for marking moose for later recognition have not proved satisfactory as yet. Tracking in the snow may be of some value. Airplane counts have been made in open and brushy country when the leaves are gone in winter.

SUGGESTED READING

Bartlett, I. H., 1950, *Michigan Deer*, Mich. Dept. Cons., Lansing.

Cahalane, Victor H., 1947, *Mammals of North America*, The Macmillan Co., New York.

Dixon, Joseph S., 1934, "A Study of the Life History and Food Habits of the Mule Deer in California," *Calif. Fish and Game*, 20:181–282, 315–354.

Grange, Wallace B., 1949, *The Way to Game Abundance with an Explanation of Game Cycles*, Charles Scribner's Sons, New York.

Hamilton, W. J., Jr., 1939, *American Mammals*, McGraw-Hill Book Co., New York.

Kelker, George Hills, 1947, "Computing the Rate of Increase for Deer," *Jour. Wildlife Management*, 11:177–183.

Krefting, Laurits W., 1941, "Methods of Increasing Deer Browse," *Jour. Wildlife Management*, 5:95–102.

Leopold, Aldo, Lyle K. Sowls, and David L. Spencer, 1947, "A Survey of Overpopulated Deer Ranges in the United States," *Jour. Wildlife Management*, 11:162–177.

Murie, Adolph, 1934, "The Moose of Isle Royale," *Univ. Mich. Mus. Zool. Misc. Publ.* 25.

Nichol, A. A., 1938, "Experimental Feeding of Deer," *Univ. Arizona Tech. Bull.* 75.

Seton, Ernest Thompson, 1925–1929, "Lives of Game Animals," 4 vols., Doubleday, Doran and Co., Garden City, N. Y.

Trippensee, Reuben Edwin, 1948, *Wildlife Management*, McGraw-Hill Book Co., New York.

Young, Vernon A., 1938, "The Carrying Capacity of Big Game Range," *Jour. Wildlife Management*, 2:131–134.

Young, Vernon A., and W. Leslie Robinette, 1939, "A Study of the Range Habits of Elk on the Selway Game Preserve," *Univ. Idaho Bull.*, Vol. 34, No. 16.

12

Game Management in the Open Range

We have long designated much of the West as a land of the open range, though this is really a matter of tradition and custom rather than true cultural and biological fact. But the animals that live in the prairie, steppe, and desert can logically be treated together. The range country is the natural home of the buffalo, antelope, jack rabbit, and many others. The jack rabbit is the only one that still occupies essentially its ancestral area, the whole of the range country. The prairie chicken and buffalo lived in suitable areas as far east as New York and New England; the sharp-tailed grouse lives on the range and far north of the area here considered as the range country. It is not to be expected that animals of the open range or any similar unit will confine themselves to an area delimited by man.

The original area of range land in the United States embraced some 850 million acres, of which about 728 million remain. This is roughly 40 per cent of the land area of the nation. That of Canada has been more completely converted to farms, especially to wheat farming, owing to the greater rainfall effectiveness in the cooler northern prairies. The conversion still goes on, and the cultivated land of Canada rose in the prairie region, for example, from 32 million acres in 1920 to 43 million in 1947.

Of the existing range land, 52 per cent is in private ownership, 9 per cent in state and county hands, and 39 per cent still in federal ownership. The policies of both the Canadian Parliament and the United States Congress have encouraged the taking up of land under the various homestead laws, and an all-time high was reached with 53,252 homestead entries for some 10 million acres in 1913.

The student should take note of the different meanings of the term *open range*, even as the term *range* has several meanings. As used here, open range means open country originally covered by grass and other dry-land vegetation. In the legal sense and that of the Old West, open range means an area where fencing of stock is not required; hence the landowner must fence *against* the stock, rather than that the stockman must fence his stock against damage to others. Fence laws have cut down the amount of open range in this sense.

Some parallel can be noted in the use of the generalizations *open-range game* and *forest game*. We find forest game wherever conditions are suitable, whether the wooded area lies in a great forest or among farms. And so also do open-range species live wherever suitable open-range conditions occur, surrounded by farm land or in a great burn in the forest or perhaps even at higher altitudes.

The biological data of seven principal open-range game species is given briefly in Table 12.1, although only five will be discussed here.

The decline in abundance of the bison, more commonly known as buffalo (*Bison bison*), has long been cited as a saga of cruelty, greed, and wanton waste (Fig. 12.1). There can hardly be any doubt of the waste, greed, and cruelty involved in slaughter of the buffalo. The men who did it were not gentle parlor sportsmen; they were the usual rough element attracted to a frontier ahead of the pioneers, and they were not always representative of the best citizenry. The substitution of domestic stock and farming for the buffalo was only inevitable; in no other way could the great and prosperous prairie region have been developed. What now seems regrettable is that large sections of the virgin lands and relatively valueless public domain were not reserved for a buffalo park in order to preserve the buffalo and the prairie biota in the interests of future generations, even as the woods buffalo now has a reserve in northern Canada, or as big game lands of Africa are being set aside as reservations while still available.

Although most larger open-range animals have declined, the coyote (*Canis latrans*) has held its own, or even increased, because of its resistance to control and the fact that the abundance of rodents attendant upon overgrazing has expanded its food resources. Much of the West is severely overgrazed, and the rest is overgrazed in varying degrees. No doubt the elimination of the wolf (*Canis* sp.) that followed the bison has also favored the coyote.

Sage Grouse (*Centrocercus urophasianus*). The original range of the sage grouse embraced the northwestern quarter of the United

TABLE 12.1
BIOLOGY TABLE FOR OPEN-RANGE GAME

Species	Range	Weight	Mating*	Normal Limit of Sex Ratio	Breeding Season	Parturition or Hatching	Gestation or Incubation Period	Number of Eggs or Young	Food	Environment
Greater prairie chicken (*Tympanuchus cupido*)	Central and eastern states and provinces (formerly East)	600–1000 grams	Pol.	1:5 ?	April–June	May–July	21–24 days	5–17 (11)	Seeds, berries, herbage	Open fields, meadows, dry marshes
Lesser prairie chicken (*Tympanuchus pallidicinctus*)	Southern great plains	500–800 grams	Pol.	1:5 ?	April–June	May–July	21–24 days	?	Seeds, berries, herbage	Open plains, fields
Sharp-tailed grouse (*Pedioecetes phasianellus*)	Northern and western North America	550–950 grams	Pol.	1:5 ?	April–June	May–July	21–24 days	9–17 (11)	Buds, berries, herbage	Bunch grass, sagebrush
Sage hen (*Centrocercus urophasianus*)	Western North America	5–8 lb	Pol.	1:5 ?	March–June	April–June	22 days	6–10 (8)	Herbage	Sagebrush
Gambel quail (*Lophortyx gambeli*)	Southwestern United States, northwestern Mexico	155–180 grams	Mon.	1:1	March–May	March–June	21–23 days	7–8 (9)	Seeds, herbage	Desert
Jack rabbit (*Lepus* sp.)	Western North America	5–8 lb	Pol.	1:5 ?	September–October	May–June	35–38 days	1–2	Grass, herbage	Plains, sagebrush
Antelope (Pronghorn) (*Antilocapra americana*)	Western North America	80–120 lb	Pol.	1:3 ?	September–October	May–June	33–36 weeks	1–3	Browse, herbage	Plains, sagebrush

* *Mon.* means monogamous; *Pol.* means polygamous.

Sage Grouse

States and parts of southwestern Canada. It extended north to southern British Columbia, east to southern Saskatchewan, the Dakotas, and Nebraska, and south to northeastern California, Nevada, New Mexico, and Colorado.

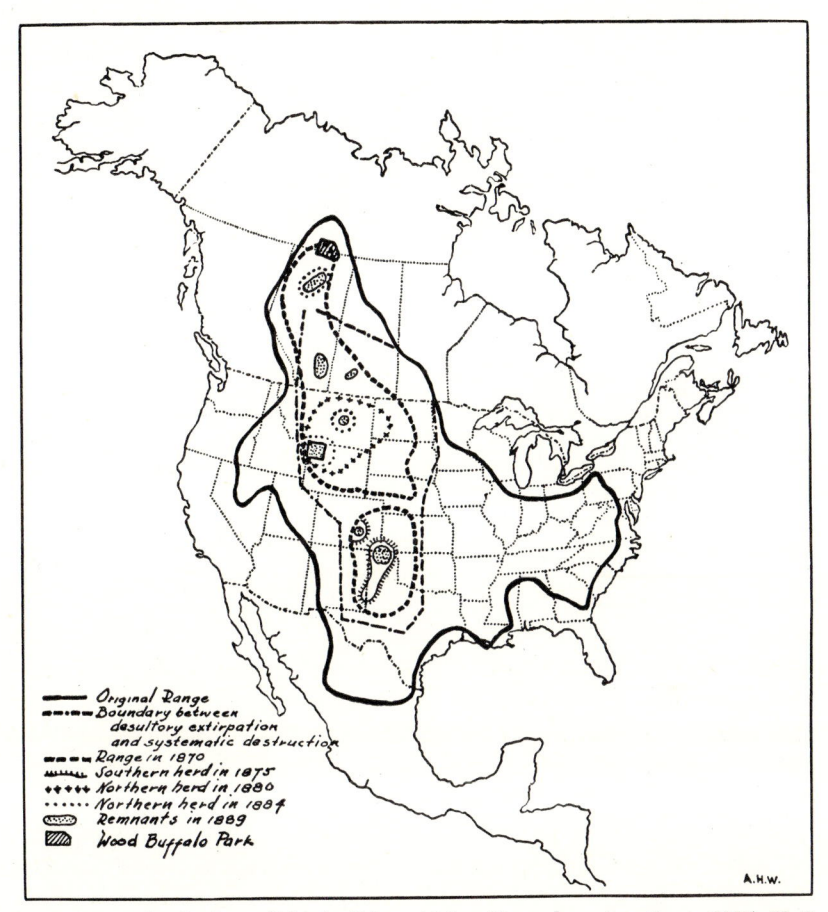

FIG. 12.1. The decline of the buffalo. (After Hornaday, *Am. Rept. 1887, U. S. Nat. Mus.*) The only wild buffalo today are in Wood Buffalo Park, as indicated on the map.

The numbers have been very greatly reduced by settlement, grazing, and hunting. Today the largest numbers are found in Wyoming, and Colorado, with only slightly less abundance in parts of Utah and Idaho. But nowhere do the numbers approach those of earlier days.

Habitat Requirement. As might be expected, sage grouse and sagebrush (*Artemisia*) go together. By long evolutionary adaptation, the sage grouse has become so dependent upon sagebrush that it is rarely found away from it, except temporarily. Its whole life is wrapped up in the dry, desert, sage country. But the bird seems to be somewhat dependent upon open water sources also, perhaps more than is realized; some observers report that it must go to water daily during the dry parts of the year, usually traveling in early morning but occasionally in evening. Development of additional water sources may be an important management technique.

The sage grouse of the northern or higher parts of the range withdraw in winter to lower or more sheltered areas. They gather into bands in winter, the largest perhaps of any of the Tetraonidae. Writings of early naturalists report flocks running into several thousand birds, but the largest ones known today total only several score or a few hundred at most.

In irrigated regions and sometimes in dry farming areas the sage grouse comes into farm fields and may even nest there.

The birds bathe in dust, which seems always available in the desert, except perhaps in hard-baked clay soils.

Food Habits. The year-round diet of the sage grouse is fully three-quarters, and more, sagebrush. The birds eat stems, twigs, leaves, flowers, and seed heads. Their flesh may develop a strong sage flavor. The young feed upon insects at first but shift to sage as they grow older. Adults may feed extensively upon grasshoppers when available. Whether some types of sage plants are more attractive than others is unknown.

Census Methods. Sage grouse may be counted on the communal courtship grounds to which they repair in spring, often year after year in the same spot. Courtship takes place from about early March, or sometimes late February, until June. As many as 400 birds may use the same dancing ground. Observation indicates that only a small portion of the males (as low as 3 per cent) accomplish most of the mating (as much as 90 per cent), so that presumable variations in physical and physiological make-up give the effect of unbalanced sex ratios. Probably the sage grouse breeding habits mark deferred maturity characteristic of many polygamous animals. Sage grouse may be counted on known dancing grounds by land visits or from airplanes. They may be photographed sometimes for later checks.

Nest and brood counts are useful and not difficult to make, though they may be time-consuming and physically laborious.

Prairie Chicken[1] (*Tympanuchus cupido, T. pallidicinctus*). The original range of the greater prairie chicken (*T. cupido*) covered most of the eastern and central parts of the continent from the Atlantic to Alberta, Colorado, and Texas. It extended from southern Canada and New England south to Virginia, Arkansas, Louisiana, and Texas, but the species is now extirpated from the eastern and southern parts. The Attwater prairie chicken originally occupied a detached strip of the coastal prairies of Texas, but its range and numbers have shrunk greatly. The lesser prairie chicken (*T. pallidicinctus*) inhabits the region west of that of the greater prairie chicken, living in Colorado, West Texas, and New Mexico.

The prairie chicken is associated with open range today; it inhabits prairies, dry marshes, and formerly pine barrens and brushy plains of the Atlantic coastal region. Being partially tolerant of man and environmental changes, it sometimes survives in cultivated farm land where the prairie chicken climate seems to have been optimum in presettlement times.

Habitat Requirements. In the northern part of the range prairie chickens partially migrate. Migration is differential in that the females seem to be the longer migrants; males may migrate little or not at all. The original summer home was mostly upland prairies, but a combination of upland and dry marshes makes good habitat. The prairie chicken now frequents dry marshes to a great extent, probably because marshes mean grass areas that are the nearest approach in the northern areas to prairie. The Attwater prairie chicken inhabits the coastal prairies, often used for pasture or rice fields by ranchers.

The *booming ground* becomes the focus of the flock movement as the males gather there in the spring for the courtship performance called *booming*. The size of the booming ground varies, but it is usually small and occupied by 3 to 18 males. Most often 8 or 9 males use a booming ground together. Booming grounds generally are "permanent" in that when undisturbed they may be occupied generation after generation, but casual booming occurs elsewhere than on the regular booming grounds, especially if the booming ground has been flooded. The return to the booming ground year after year has been cited as an example of the operation of *tradition* in nature.

---

[1] Throughout much of the West the sharp-tailed grouse, a different species, is known as prairie chicken, which makes the name rather confusing. The true prairie chicken is sometimes called pinnated grouse in the Midwest, and an extinct subspecies was known in the East as heath hen.

Prairie chickens, which select herbaceous cover in open situations for booming, tramp down the vegetation by their antics, so that by summer well-worn paths indicate roughly the stand of the individual males.

Desultory booming may occur on the booming ground or elsewhere in off seasons. The booming ground may be used also for resting in winter, especially on clear days.

The females nest within a mile of the booming ground, often seeking mixed cover of sedges, grasses, or forbs.

Standing water seems not to be a necessity for prairie chickens, though they may use it when available. Possibly on drier range water is necessary, but elsewhere snow, dew, insects, fruits, and succulent vegetation seem to provide the needed external source.

Food Habits. The prairie chicken "buds" a little in the North but less than other grouse. Its dependence upon seeds rather than upon buds probably makes it possible for the range to extend farther south but less far north than the range of other grouse. In winter prairie chickens feed upon seeds and berries of various trees, shrubs, forbs, and annuals. In spring the diet runs high to insects and herbage.

Improving Food and Cover. Prairie chickens seem to prefer shocked corn to standing corn, perhaps because of the ease of perching upon the shocks while feeding. They are reluctant to go under cover; consequently hoppers covered by a shelter may not attract them. Food can be scattered on the ground or placed in the open or on platforms 5 to 6 feet above the ground (Fig. 6.6). Corn is perhaps the best single winter food and can be fed as whole ears impaled upon spikes atop the platform feeder or impaled upon stakes in the snow. Ear corn is sometimes placed in wire baskets holding about 2 bushels or tied in strings and thrown over corn shocks. The amount of corn eaten by the prairie chickens varies with the weather as well as the amount of natural foods. One and a half pounds of corn (about two ears) is sufficient ration for a week for a bird.

Food patches have been used successfully, and grains such as millet, sorghum, soybeans, buckwheat, and corn are recommended. Probably $\frac{1}{4}$ to $\frac{1}{2}$ acre is the smallest food patch that should be provided; 4 or 5 acres are more attractive to the birds.

Scrubby woods indicate poor timber sites where attempts to grow timber are rarely successful but which sometimes can be converted into prairie chicken habitat. Controlled burning, not oftener than once in three years, may keep the habitat open in some areas. In wooded areas trees may squeeze out the open areas without controlled burning; it has already happened in parts of the lake states.

Brush piles may be used for idling and for escape cover, but they must be very large.

Census Methods. No reliable or easy census methods are available; prairie chickens form flocks, and by diligent effort it is possible to locate all the flocks on a large area and to count them. Counts can be made on booming grounds, which can be located by driving along roads in prairie chicken country and stopping to listen at half-mile intervals when booming is active and the weather calm. Counts can also be made at winter feeding stations from blinds. Track counts in the snow are satisfactory in counting the birds in a flock, and, as with bobwhites, the observer does not need to see his flock to get a count.

Trapping and Marking. Early market hunters favored a trap made of a crate or pit with a trap door in the top. Ears of corn baited the birds, which fell into the trap as soon as they stepped upon the trap door. Portable and non-portable traps, of the funnel and bobwire type, and the fyke trap are successful. Generally the traps are placed in the open at baited areas or at feeding stations.

Colored bands will last several years and are preferred for identification marks where birds will be observed from blinds, as at feeding stations and booming grounds. Colored feathers or dyes can be used to mark birds to be recognized in flight in the field.

Sharp-Tailed Grouse (*Pedioecetes phasianellus*). The sharp-tailed grouse inhabits the northern part of the continent from Alaska to Quebec, south to Michigan, Colorado, Utah, Oregon, and formerly to northern California. The major portion of the ancient range is still occupied, though in reduced abundance.

The sharp-tailed grouse is associated with open land, especially brush prairies, though it occupies open areas in the forested region. Although it inhabits an environment similar to that of the prairie chicken, it favors more brushy habitat. Actually the sharp-tailed grouse lives in the more boreal brush and prairie lands, whereas the prairie chicken occupies the more temperate prairies. An equivalent choice in habitat can be noted where the ranges overlap; the prairie chicken prefers the grass environment. The ecological requirements of the sharp-tailed grouse lie somewhat between those of the prairie chicken and the ruffed grouse.

Habitat Requirements. The sharp-tailed grouse has a noticeable migration in the more northern parts of its range. It is a plastic species, within somewhat elastic limits, and owes its wide range to its ability to utilize variable brush-prairie habitats. It occupies sparsely timbered areas and burnt-over lands, cleared areas, sand plains, and bunch grass, if the grass is near suitable deciduous brush and trees for winter buds.

Sharp-tailed grouse use *dancing grounds,* which are communal courtship grounds analogous to the prairie chicken booming grounds. On occasion an area may be used in common by the two species where their ranges overlap, as in the lake states. Dancing grounds are usually open knolls or open areas to which the birds resort generation after generation.

For night roosting the sharp-tailed grouse seeks ground cover of grasses, forbs, and brush close to the dancing ground.

Food Habits. The sharp-tailed grouse feeds more upon buds and herbage than the prairie chicken does. Authorities agree that birch and aspen buds and birch catkins are important winter foods and perhaps the main reliance during winter, over much of the range. Cottonwood and alder buds are important winter foods in the West, where sharp-tailed grouse feed upon them along water courses.

There seems to be an adequate supply of buds in winter. Grains are not eaten freely, perhaps because the sharp-tail is native to a grainless range and such seeds may not be associated with food in the instinct pattern. Sharp-tails may feed in grain fields before snow or cold weather but desert them in cold periods. Like many animals, they choose more natural foods in severe weather. Hard seeds from berries substitute for grit during snowy weather and on gritless range.

Improving Food and Cover. Food patches increase the carrying capacity during the prebudding season, as well as during the pinch of late winter and early spring. Suggested food patch plants are corn, millet, and buckwheat. Soft-stemmed plants may have to be cut and shocked.

Artificial feeding, about 2 pounds of food for each bird, may serve the grouse, but feeders need to be placed closer to brush for this bird than for the prairie chicken. Since the sharp-tails show less aversion to entering feeding shelters, the standard feeder is practical.

Possibly reflooding and maintenance of water levels will induce cottonwood, aspen, alder, and birch growth along marsh borders and water courses. Such trees, if planted, may grow in dry regions, even though they may not reproduce there. They can supply fire wood and fence posts to farmers and ranchers.

Controlled burning may be of use in regulating ecological succession on grouse range. Overgrazing sometimes hurts the range for sharp-tails, but plowing is far more destructive. Fencing of small areas for nesting cover may help them.

Whether the clearing of areas or throwing up of knolls would be a management technique for improvement of dancing grounds is not known.

It is probable that insects, succulent vegetation, dew, and berries supply the normal water needs of the species, but birds are generally found within a mile or two of water in arid and semiarid parts of the range. Water improvement may be a useful technique on dry range.

Census Methods, Trapping, and Marking. The census, trapping, and marking methods applicable to prairie chickens are also suitable for sharp-tails.

Pronghorn Antelope (*Antilocapra americana*). The antelope is a native of western North America and belongs to a family all its own. Its range extends from Saskatchewan, on the north, to northern Mexico, on the south. Originally it ranged east to Manitoba, the Dakotas, and central Texas. Now, however, the antelope is extirpated over much of this original range, particularly the eastern portion.

Habitat Requirements. Antelopes inhabit dry plains, both arid and semiarid, where they are associated with sagebrush, desert shrubs, and bunch grass. They require relatively large areas, more or less free from human disturbance, and such area must be open country, for they rarely use cover of any density. The antelope has, however, adapted itself to areas of thin timber at the desert's altitudinal limit in parts of the Southwest.

The antelope is sedentary in the more temperate parts of the range but migrates in the North, where the climate is severe. These migrations, though usually but a few miles in length, are thought to have reached 100 to 150 miles in earlier times. During the winters in the northern part of the range also, the antelope seeks sheltered valleys, draws, and sometimes areas of sparse timber or heavier sagebrush.

The antelope does not establish an individual territory but occupies a range common to small bands. The size of range belonging to a single band varies; ranges have been reported to be as small as 2 miles in diameter and to have held a band of 20. This would indicate a density of one antelope to 100 acres.

Antelopes use water holes, and on some dry range they travel twice daily to water. It appears, however, that they can exist on waterless range when succulent plants and other moisture producers are present.

204   Game Management in the Open Range

The antelope feeds upon most of the plants about it on the range, although its main reliance seems to be upon sagebrush and perhaps bunch grass; in the more arid parts it feeds extensively upon desert shrubs and cactus.

Protection and Management. Because of its color pattern and great speed, the antelope is said to be the most deceptive big game for the hunter in North America. Overhunting and poaching, however, espe-

Fig. 12.2. Antelope are driven into catching corrals from the trap funnel into which they are herded by planes and riders. (Photograph by Montana Game Department.)

cially in areas of small holdings, are serious handicaps to an increase in antelope numbers.

Antelope crossings of main roads are frequently places where collisions with automobiles occur. Sometimes the curiosity of the herd causes it to race across in front of a car. Signs that warn motorists of antelope crossings are placed in many areas to reduce accidents.

Antelopes are reintroduced on former range by liberating animals that have been caught wild or reared artificially after early capture. Care must be taken to avoid taming such captive fawns so that they will not become easy prey to poachers. Antelope are trapped in baited corrals or in wide-mouth traps into which they are driven by riders or airplanes (Figs. 12.2 and 12.3). They can be roped easily or caught in narrow chutes by hand. An antelope or deer doe or fawn can be captured and carried easily if grasped under the chin with the left hand and over the back and in the flank with the right hand. The right hand immobilizes the flank muscles and turns the hoofs outward at the same time.

Though hunting has been a prime factor in antelope decline, it has not been the only factor. Settlement and domestic stock have been equally important, or even more so, because they increase the pressure

Fig. 12.3. Attaching ear tag to antelope before transporting to a new range for restocking. (Photograph by Montana Game Department.)

upon the animals and upset the ecology of their land. Because stockmen are strongly influential, large areas of public domain are set aside for antelope with the greatest difficulty, but some antelope range can be purchased with private or game-department funds. Sometimes water holes also can be bought to control large range areas. Management activities on the antelope range include protection and fencing, increasing the available forage, and protecting the water. Antelope will crawl under fences that will turn cattle and sheep, sometimes diving under at high speed. It may be possible to freshen water holes by washing-out with spring runoff. Tanks made with bulldozers sometimes will impound water.

Salt can be provided at salting stations, or it can be dropped from airplanes.

Predation today seems unimportant in the life of the antelope.

SUGGESTED READING

Anonymous, 1936, "The Western Range," *Senate Document Seventy-fourth Congress, Second Session.*

Bent, Arthur Cleveland, 1932, "Life Histories of North American Gallinaceous Birds," *U. S. Nat. Mus. Bull.* 162.

Barnes, Will C., 1914, "Stock Watering Places on Western Grazing Land," *U.S.D.A. Farmer's Bull.* 592.

Bond, Richard M., 1945, "Rodents and Plant Succession," *Trans. Tenth N. A. Wildlife Conf.*: 229–234.

Cahalane, Victor H., 1947, *Mammals of North America*, The Macmillan Co., New York.

Einersen, Arthur S., 1948, *The Pronghorn Antelope, and Its Management*, Wildlife Management Institute, Washington, D. C.

Girard, George L., 1937, "Life History, Habits, and Food of the Sage Grouse," *Univ. Wyo. Publ. Sci.* 3.

Glading, Ben, 1947, "Game Watering Devices for the Arid Southwest," *Trans. Twelfth N. A. Wildlife Conf.*: 286–292.

Grange, Wallace B., 1949a, *The Way to Game Abundance with an Explanation of Game Cycles*, Charles Scribner's Sons, New York.

Grange, Wallace B., 1949b, *Wisconsin Grouse Problems*, Wisc. Cons. Dept., Madison.

Honess, Ralph F., and Edward M. Frost, 1942, "A Wyoming Sheep Study," *Wyo. Game and Fish Dept. Bull.* 11.

Lehman, Valgene W., 1941, "Attwater's Prairie Chicken; Its Life History and Management," *N. A. Fauna* 57.

Seton, Ernest Thompson, 1925–1929, *Lives of Game Animals*, 4 vols., Doubleday, Doran and Co., Garden City, N. Y.

Shantz, H. L., 1947, *The Use of Fire as a Tool in the Management of the Brush Ranges of California*, Calif. Board of Forestry.

Stoddart, Laurence A., and Arthur D. Smith, 1943, *Range Management*, McGraw-Hill Book Co., New York.

Stoddart, Laurence A., and D. I. Rasmussen, 1945, "Deer Management and Livestock Production," *Utah Agric. Exp. Stat. Circ.* 121.

Taylor, Walter P., 1930, "Methods of Determining Rodent Pressure on the Range," *Ecology*, 11:523–542.

Vorhies, Charles T., and Walter P. Taylor, 1933, "The Life Histories and Ecology of the Jack Rabbits, *Lepus alleni* and *Lepus californicus* ssp., in Relation to Grazing in Arizona," *Univ. Ariz. Agric. Exp. Stat. Tech. Bull.* 49, pp. 471–587.

Vorhies, Charles T., 1945, "Water Requirements of Desert Animals in the Southwest," *Univ. Ariz. Agric. Exp. Stat. Tech. Bull.* 107.

Young, Vernon, 1938, "The Carrying Capacity of Big Game Range," *Jour. Wildlife Management*, 2:131–134.

13

Southern Wildlife Species

Many species of animals range over large portions of the continent rather than being sectionally distributed. They are very appropriately considered as *farm game, fur bearers,* or *forest game,* as the case may be, and discussion of them will be found in other chapters. Yet a number of species reach northward only as far as the more southern states, and it seems useful to grant them the special attention that their status thus thrusts upon them, even though they cannot all be considered of equal importance or be reported upon equally (Table 13.1).

The southern region, as the term is used here, extends from the Atlantic to the Pacific as a relatively narrow band. Few species are confined to the Southeast alone, compared to the numbers that range northward from Old Mexico into parts of California, Arizona, New Mexico, and especially Texas. The presence of the land area of adjoining Old Mexico, rather than the Gulf, provides the bridge for this northward spread of many neotropical animals.

The western portion of this strip is a desert, the eastern part humid forest; in between lie gradations of grassland, brushland, and timber. The moss-festooned forest that reaches from the Carolinas to the Gulf Coast of Texas contrasts strongly with the xerophytic type extending from the post-oak country of Texas to the deserts and dry brush of Arizona and California. Perhaps when the store of knowledge has increased, we can separate the wildlife management treatment of the Southeast and Southwest.

Some special problems arise in biological work in a southern latitude, most of them ecological. Water often is scarce even in the humid parts because of rapid runoff and quick drying of the soil. Floods and the sudden rise and fall of streams with rains occur commonly. Heat and humidity become serious problems in some parts of the area, and heat and drought are problems in others. Humidity

Table 13.1
BIOLOGY TABLE FOR SOME SOUTHERN SPECIES

Species	Range	Weight (pounds)	Mating*	Normal Limit of Sex Ratio	Breeding Season	Parturition or Hatching Season	Gestation or Incubation Period	Number of Eggs or Young	Food	Environment
Opossum (*Didelphis virginiana*)	Southern North America	6–10	Pro. ?	?	January–September	January–September	13 days	5–14	Animal matter, vegetable matter	Brush, wooded areas
Ringtail (*Bassariscus astutus*)	Southwestern and western U.S. and south	2–3	Pro. ?	?	March–April	May–June	9 weeks	1–5	Animal matter	Brush areas
Jaguar (*Felis onca*)	Southwestern U.S. and south	100–200	Mon.	1:1	January	April–May	100 days	2–4	Animal matter	Woods, heavy brush
Ocelot (*Felis pardalis*)	South Texas southward	20–35	Mon. ?	1:1 ?	June	September–October	?	2	Small animals	Thickets
Eyra (*Felis cacomitli*)	South Texas southward	10–20	Mon. ?	1:1 ?	?	?	?	?	Small animals	Chaparral

Cougar (*Felis concolor*)	Southern Canada to Cape Horn	100–150	?	?	Year round	Year round	96 days	1–6	Larger animals	Wooded areas
Swamp rabbit (*Silvilagus aquaticus*)	Southern states	3–6	Pol.	?	January–September	February–September	30 days	3–6	Herbage	Bottom lands
Marsh rabbit (*Silvilagus palustrus*)	Southeastern states	2–3	Pol.	?	Spring	Spring	30 days	5–7	Herbage	Wet bottom lands
Javelina (*Pecari ungulatus*)	Southwest southward	45–65	Pol.	?	Year round	Year round	16 weeks	1–5 (2)	Vegetable matter, some animal	Brush areas
Armadillo (*Dasypus novemcinctus*)	Texas southward	10–15	?	?	July	March–April	120 days	4	Insects	Brush areas
Alligator (*Alligator mississippiensis*)	Gulf states	?	?	?	Spring	Late summer	9 weeks	30–70	Animal matter	Water areas
Chachalaca (*Ortalis vetula*)	Rio Grande southward	?	Pol.	?	April–June	May–June	22 days	3	Fruits, seeds, insects	Chaparral

* *Mon.* means monogamous; *Pol.* means polygamous; *Pro.* means promiscuous.

and drought each bring on a complex set of factors with which ecological management must deal.

Ecological succession usually moves faster, just as trees mature sooner, in warm regions; for the same reason, a long growing season brings on a telescoping of succession stages in comparison with cool regions. Soils are likely to be impoverished in the humid parts, though they may be rich with minerals in the arid and semiarid areas. Streams rarely run clear except in mountains.

It must be remembered that the southern latitudes form the natural winter homes for large numbers of northern and midlatitude migratory birds, and the amount of food needed for them is very great. Fortunately, however, the rapid growth of plants, moderate temperatures, and the long fall free of snow combine to provide or maintain the food supply. Fruit and mast trees and shrubs reach their peak in the southeastern states and supply quantities of food to resident and winter birds alike, as well as to mammals like the opossum and squirrels. Dogwood (*Cornus florida*), sumac (*Rhus copalina*), and *Crataegus* rank high as food producers for birds in some sections. Among the herbaceous plants are beggarweed, croton, ragweed, and lespedeza. But these have short stay in the ecological succession and may be evicted by many species producing less wildlife food.

Lespedeza bicolor, for example, is now used freely as a food producer for quail, though it seems to be little sought after by other birds. It is planted as borders, patches, and strips in fields and woods. A strip 1 by 20 rods will probably suffice for a quail covey. Multiflora rose and several similar roses are highly recommended, for even though they may become pests in some places, they make good hedge rows or other needed cover.

The need for water is indeed great, and water development forms an important technique in the Southwest. Farm tanks supply water, and they can be constructed quickly and inexpensively with bulldozers. More water facilities are usually essential for increased animal numbers. Farm fish ponds in the Southeast attract many land animals, especially when cover around the pond is suitable.

Diseases become more prevalent and invertebrate enemies more abundant with increase in temperature and humidity. The reduction effect of sunlight and heat, as in the desert, or of cold, as in the Arctic, is markedly less in the Southeast. Fungus diseases are also likely to be more abundant where humidity is high, but the spectacular epizootics, such as botulism, "distemper," or scabies, are missing.

Southern farming operations often require special techniques or precautions not used elsewhere. The ground often freezes little or not at all in winter. Some insects stay through the winter unharmed by cold so that cutting of weeds and cleaning of fields must be done each fall for some crops. In some soils of the Southwest plowing and ridging must be done before winter in order to decompose organic matter and put it largely out of the way of the next crop or field work. Cotton lands particularly may have to be cleaned of masses of vegetable debris.

Opossum (*Didephis virginiana*). The opossum represents in North America the marsupials, an ancient group of animals that was formerly widespread but has long been gone from most of the world. They still persist, however, in Australia, where they form the native mammal life. The opossums and their allies of the New World are most abundant in South and Central America, where there are several additional species.

The animal itself grows to about the size of a house cat, though it has a different shape and a naked tail of some prehensile capacity. It is at home in trees and bushes but may wander for considerable distances on the ground in search of food. The general appearance and action are those of an animal with low mental powers and slow reactions.

The opossum inhabits the general region of eastern North America, south through Mexico and Central America but including also most of South America. It ranges now from New York to the Great Lakes and south to the Gulf, Texas, and beyond. The spread into the northern sections has taken place in recent years, and the animal has reached southern Ontario. It was introduced into California in the early days of the century, or perhaps earlier, and has spread northward into British Columbia.

The opossum lives in a varied habitat, from bottom lands to wooded or brush hills. Probably the average type of farming has benefited the opossum by furnishing fence rows and brushy areas, but the preferred habitat seems to be bottom lands that have a mixture of fruit and mast trees and shrubs, for food, and hollow trees, for dens. The average nightly wandering (the animal is largely nocturnal) probably remains within a half-mile radius of the den. The seasonal movement likewise is low.

The opossum feeds upon almost any animal, fruit, or seed material in its path, especially insects and small rodents. The attraction of persimmons to the opossum is well known. The animal is harmless to farming except for an occasional raid upon chicken pens and fruits. Its pilfering of bird nests seems to be minor as far as bird populations go, and its destruction of some rodents and reptiles probably represents a gain for bird life.

Opossum pelts have some economic value because of their abundance, though the fur is of very low quality. Clothiers use it to trim coats, but it is seldom good enough for fabricating into "inexpensive" coats. Some better-grade opossum pelts, however, have been used to simulate fur of other species, especially skunk. In the South opossums have some economic value also as a "gamey" food.

There seems to be no immediate need for management activity for the opossum, principally because of the low pressure upon its numbers from hunters and trappers. During times of high fur demand, however, reduction of the trapping pressure may be in order. In any event control of the open season to prevent destruction of young and catching of unprime fur seems necessary. In the southern states the trapping season should end during February.

Ringtail (Cacomistle) (*Bassariscus astutus*). The ringtail is related to the raccoon and bears, even though it is now placed in a family of its own. The handsome, nocturnal little animal lives in the Southwest, south through Mexico to Panama, and also north along the coast to Oregon. It is not distributed uniformly over this range but rather scattered.

The ringtail, which prefers scrubby brushlands, is replaced in timber by the raccoon. It inhabits rocky areas, such as bluffs or cliffs, and may even live in stone walls and buildings. The den is a hole in the rocks and trees, or even a nest in sheds, cabins, and barns. The ringtail is at home on the ground and in the trees. Its fur has some market value in times of high prices, but on the whole is of little economic importance. The chief use of the fur is in trimming cloth coats.

The cacomistle feeds upon almost any animal food of its range, especially rodents, but also small reptiles, birds, and insects. It also feeds some upon fruits and nuts in season. Within the United States, at least, it has no particular conflict with man because of its mild habits; it lives chiefly in a ranch country, and ranchers are notably tolerant towards mild creatures.

The Cat Family (*Felis* sp.). Along the Mexican border and adjacent countryside live three members of the cat family whose main range is farther south. These are the jaguar (*Felis onca*), ocelot (*Felis pardalis*), and eyra (*Felis cacomitli*). All three have spotted or blotched coats rather than streaked ones, and the coats are highly prized because of their unusual appearance. The jaguar originally ranged northward as far as north Texas and possibly across the Red River into Oklahoma, but today there are few, if any, north of the Rio Grande. Its range extends southward into Argentina. The ocelot, which resembles a double-size house cat, has a coat that is perhaps the most ornamental of all mammals. Originally it reached northward as far as Arkansas, but none now live north of south Texas. In South America it reaches Paraguay. The eyra barely crosses into the lower part of the Rio Grande Valley; it lives as far south as Paraguay.

The jaguar feeds upon birds and mammals as well as lower forms of animal life. Javelinas provide an important part of the diet, especially strays and aged animals no longer with the bands. The jaguar is at home in the water, a most uncatlike habit. The ocelot lives in thickets, which are common in south Texas and southward in Old Mexico. The eyra occupies the heavy thicket also, but what constitutes the division of life forms between the eyra and ocelot is not known, although the eyra may be able to occupy thicker growth than the ocelot. The jaguar may, on occasion, cause some loss of stock, but there seems to be no damage chargeable to the smaller cats, unless it be a raid upon poultry roosts. Competition with hunters for small game seems low.

Swamp Rabbit (*Silvilagus aquaticus*). The rabbit family as a group is most numerous in more northerly habitats. The swamp rabbit is a southern representative of the cottontail group, and most of the general considerations for the cottontail also apply to the swamp rabbit, which, though southerly in range, is one of the largest of the rabbits. It is found from southern Illinois to Texas and Alabama.

It inhabits poorly drained bottom land and coastal marshes, though along the western border of its range it may be found in somewhat dry habitat. In poorly drained bottom land of Brazos County, Texas, a population count gave one rabbit to 7 acres, which indicates a lower support rate than in comparable cottontail habitat. Some overlap between the cottontail and this species occurs, and the differences in habitat preference are not known, except that the swamp rabbit prefers the moister habitat. If food habits differ, the difference has not been discovered. The chief "enemy" of the swamp rabbit is flood in the bottom lands and perhaps also in the flat uplands; alligators prey upon them, in addition to the other predators usual to rabbits.

The important parasites reported for the species are *Obeliscoides cumiciculi* (stomach worm), *Trichostrougyhus calcaratus* (fluke), *Pas-*

salunis ambiginis (intestinal worm), and *Cistotaemia ctenoides* (tapeworm).

No management recommendations differing from those for cottontails are available for this species.

Marsh Rabbit (*Sylvilagus palustris*). The marsh rabbit, whose range lies in the southeastern United States from the Carolinas to Alabama, shows a definite preference for wet bottom lands, sometimes occupying land as wet as that occupied by a muskrat. Even less is known about the marsh rabbit than about the swamp rabbit.

Javelina (*Pecari ungulatus*). The javelina or peccary resembles some of our semiferal domestic hogs in superficial characters. A tough, hairy coat of bristles, grizzled or grayish-brown in color, covers the body. The canines point downward rather than being curved. The javelina has a distinctive dorsal musk gland on the rump capable of emitting a strong musky odor, which accounts for one of its names, musk hog.

Within the United States the javelina lives along the border in Texas, New Mexico, and Arizona; formerly it reached Oklahoma. It extends southward into South America. The habitat north of the border consists primarily of brush, chaparral, and cactus country; earlier the animal may have occupied bottom lands also.

The javelina is a gregarious species; though herds of 30 are known, the animals usually move about in smaller bands. The food of the peccary includes fruits, mast, bulbs, roots, insects, and small mammals.

The javelina rarely is eaten by man on account of the musky odor, which cannot be removed or masked successfully, as yet, in cooking, although quick removal of the gland from young animals after death seems to prevent some off-flavoring of the meat. The hide has some commercial use for leather and the bristles for brushes. One of the javelina's most important values is control of *Lechuguilla*, a pest to ranchers. There is some possibility that the javelina can be developed into a warm-region domestic hog, either by itself or by breeding its climatic adaptability into the domestic hogs.

Armadillo (*Dasypus novemcinctus*). The armadillo is related to the sloth, spiny anteater, and others of the neotropical region. The armorlike plates covering the body are modified skin, and they protect the animal somewhat as a turtle shell protects its wearer. Incisors and canines are missing.

Originally the armadillo reached only south Texas but has spread northward and eastward in recent years; it has been reported from Oklahoma, Arkansas, and Louisiana. That it will spread much farther

Alligator

northward, however, seems unlikely, as it appears unable to withstand cold and drought. Southward the armadillo reaches over most of South America as far as Argentina.

The armadillo has long been famed for its characteristic of giving birth to four young, all alike and derived from a single egg. Another peculiarity is a delayed implantation of the ovum of about 14 weeks, which accounts for parturition in April and March, with a 120-day gestation period and July breeding season.

The armadillo makes its own burrows in abundance; many other animals utilize these burrows and may even be dependent upon the armadillo for dens. It digs small holes during its feeding activities, which are largely confined to insects, though it may feed upon almost any animal food.

There seems to be little economic conflict of the armadillo with man's interests, although it occasionally digs up lawns in searching for insects. The shells are sometimes dried and varnished to make flower pots and hanging baskets. Armadillo meat is considered by some to be a delicacy, especially as a barbecue.

Alligator (*Alligator mississippiensis*). The alligator, one of the largest living reptiles, occupies a unique position in the fauna. The nearest relative of the American alligator is *Alligator sinensis* of China, which fact alone gives our animal a special status as the representative of an ancient group now widely separated. The alligator also has the honor of representing the living reptile most closely related to the birds. *Alligator* is a corruption of the Spanish words *el lagarto*, meaning "lizard."

Alligators live in warm marshes, swamps, rivers, and ponds from North Carolina around the Gulf about to the Rio Grande. They may appear elsewhere as the aftermath of tourist visits to their range.

Alligators feed upon almost any living thing that comes within reach and that they can kill. Most animals are seized with the jaws, but large ones may be stunned by a blow from the tail.

Sexual maturity comes at approximately 6 years of age, when the animals are about 6 feet long, but growth will continue at about a foot a year for the next 3 years or so, lessening considerably thereafter. A 15-foot individual is about 40 years old. The longest alligator authentically reported is 19 feet and 2 inches, but few animals longer than 13 feet have been found since 1900.

It is reported that, in the glare of a strong light at night, the eyes of old males shine red, whereas those of females or young animals reflect green or amber. The bulls also bellow, a noise made by passage of exhaled air over specially developed folds in the laryngeal cavity, as vocal cords are wanting.

In constructing their nests alligators remove marsh vegetation from near their holes, which gives open water of some importance to aquatic animal life such as water birds, fish, and perhaps muskrats. Ridges or other dry land seem necessary for nesting and perhaps also for resting on shore. Whether "islands," like those developed for waterfowl, would be useful is not clear. The only management techniques, if they may be so called, are protection and manipulation of the seasons and bag limits.

The alligator has some importance for commercial products, principally hides for leather. There is some sale of teeth for trinkets and of the young as curiosities for tourists. The principal alligator states are now Florida and Louisiana; in Florida the alligator has regularly produced more than a million dollars' worth of hides alone in some years.

Chachalaca (*Ortalis vetula*). The chachalaca represents a different type of gallinaceous bird from others in the United States and Canada. It is a tree bird, even nesting in trees and bushes. The family Cracidae, to which the bird belongs, is a neotropical family of wide distribution south of the Rio Grande. In a sense the Cracidae represent the warm-region counterpart of the Tetraonidae.

The chachalaca is rather strongly territorial in the breeding season, though later the birds may roost together in numbers up to a hundred.

Water seems an essential part of the range in the Rio Grande Valley, as do moisture-producing insects and berries. Subtropical brush such as that formed by chaparral is necessary. These two essentials can be provided in limited quantities as a management technique.

The chachalaca long has been tamed by peoples of Mexico and Central America, who have an aptitude for taming birds, and perhaps it offers a potential addition to our domestic poultry.

SUGGESTED READING

Anonymous, 1945, *Principal Game Bird and Mammals of Texas; Their Distribution and Management,* Texas Game, Fish, and Oyster Comm., Austin.

Allan, Philip F., and Cecil N. Davis, 1941, "Ponds for Wildlife," *U.S.D.A. Farmer's Bull.* 1879.

Bent, Arthur Cleveland, 1932, "Life Histories of North American Gallinaceous Birds," *U. S. Nat. Mus. Bull.* 162.

Cahalane, Victor H., 1947, *Mammals of North America,* The Macmillan Co., New York.

Suggested Reading

Davison, Verne E., 1941, "Wildlife Borders, an Innovation in Farm Management," *Jour. Wildlife Management,* 5:390–394.

Davison, Verne E., 1948, "Bicolor Lespedeza for Quail and Soil Conservation in the Southeast," *U.S.D.A. Leaflet* 248.

Giles, LeRoy W., and Vandiver L. Childs, 1949, "Alligator Management of the Sabine National Wildlife Refuge," *Jour. Wildlife Management,* 13:16–28.

Glading, Ben, 1947, "Game Watering Devices for the Arid Southwest," *Trans. Twelfth N. A. Wildlife Conf.:* 286–292.

Hamilton, W. J., Jr., *American Mammals,* McGraw-Hill Book Co., New York.

Kalmbach, E. R., 1943, *The Armadillo; Its Relation to Agriculture and Game,* Texas Game, Fish, and Oyster Comm.

Ligon, J. Stokley, 1946, *History and Management of Merriam's Wild Turkey,* New Mexico Game Comm.

Lincoln, Frederick C., 1945, "The Mourning Dove as a Game Bird," *Fish and Wildlife Circ.* 10.

Pearson, Allen M., and D. G. Sturkie, 1944, "Food Crops for Game Birds on Farm Lands," *Alabama Agric. Exp. Stat. Circ.* 90.

Reese, Albert M., 1915, *The Alligator and Its Allies,* G. P. Putnam's Sons, New York.

Stevens, Ross O., 1944, *Talk about Wildlife, for Hunters, Fishermen and Nature Lovers,* Bynum Printing Co., Raleigh, N. C.

Seton, Ernest Thompson, 1925–1929, *Lives of Game Animals,* 4 vols., Doubleday, Doran and Co., Garden City, N. Y.

Stoddard, Herbert L., 1931, *The Bob-White Quail,* Charles Scribner's Sons, New York.

Stoddard, Herbert L., 1939, *The Use of Controlled Fire in Southeastern Game Management,* Coop. Quail Study Ass'n.

Vorhies, Charles T., 1945, "Water Requirements of Desert Animals in the Southwest," *Univ. Ariz. Agric. Exp. Stat. Tech. Bull.* 107.

14

Northland Wildlife

Although the variety of wild animal species in the Northland runs into large numbers, just as it does anywhere else, a few species whose interest or relationship to man is greater than usual will be given brief treatment here. The discussion will aid the student in understanding some of the problems peculiar to the Arctic and Subarctic, here considered as the *Northland*.

Important biological and ecological factors need early examination in studying Northland problems, for most people have first-hand knowledge of midlatitude areas rather than of the Northland. One item of very great importance is the long, cold winter with long hours that are sunless though not pitch dark. The cold of winter dominates the lives of all sedentary species and influences even the lives of seasonal visitors, like the migratory birds. A bird or mammal must eat to live and, in the Arctic, to provide the heat to resist cold, and it must find its food in the few hours of relative light in winter and carry on through the longer ones of darkness. Beyond the Arctic Circle (66° 30′ North) the day is a twilight, at best, in winter. Summer days are the opposite, with long hours of daylight—24 beyond the circle in midsummer—and a low sun in the sky. Radiant energy, even ultra-violet, has relationships to the environment differing from those in midlatitudes or low ones.

The long hours of daylight give considerably more time for life activities, though the body still must have its quota of rest. We do not yet know how resident birds are able to find enough time to feed in the low light of winter to keep the body warm and life activities high. Small-eyed birds that feed upon small objects, such as seeds and insects, are largely absent in winter. The eye of diurnal adaptation resolves small objects with difficulty in low light. The Tetraonidae, for example, feed upon needles, buds, and twigs that require little searching and identifying in the dull light and low sun of winter.

Northland Wildlife

The sight of most Northland animals is very keen, particularly those that live beyond the limit of trees, as one would expect of animals living in a land of long distances. The polar bear, for example, has eyesight keener than that of any other bear. The moose of the forest has a markedly keen hearing, but its sight is not so acute.

Northern birds have developed heavy coats of feathers, though not necessarily as heavy as those of sea birds, and mammals have heavier guard hairs and a heavier undercoat than mammals farther south.

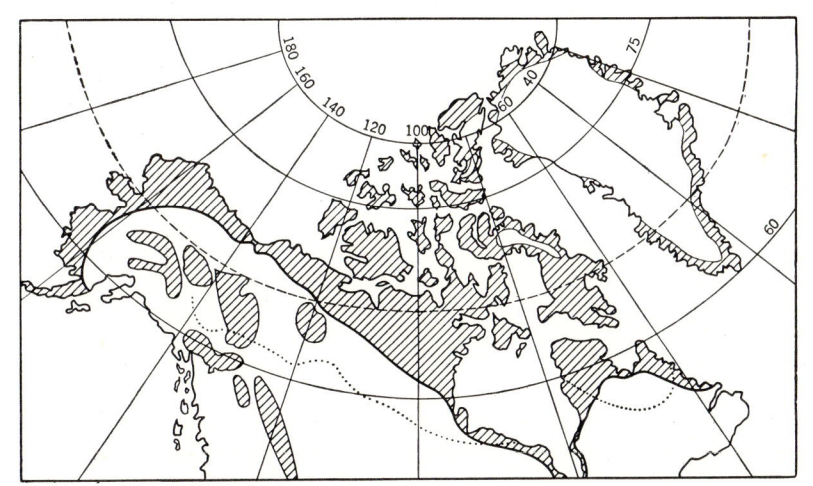

Fig. 14.1. The general distribution of tundra is shown by the shaded areas. The heavy line gives the limit of trees. The limit of permafrost is shown by the dotted line.

The musk ox shows this protection with its heavy wool-like coat under a thick covering of outer hairs that serves as a windbreaker. A layer of subcutaneous fat also helps to insulate the body of the mammal, though land birds may not develop a large fat layer. Ecological succession and vegetation decay are both slow in the high latitudes, as one naturally expects where plants grow slowly. At 65° North about 50 years are required for the same relative ecological progress in the succession as occurs in 5 years at 35° North. But it must be remembered that the continental interior shows northern conditions reaching far southward. The fact that permanent frozen ground underlies large areas seems to affect wildlife little, except through depression of plant growth (Fig. 14.1).

Except on a local scale, animal populations do not reach the numbers that are characteristic of regions farther south. The cold of land

and water make for few organisms in abundance, but one must not forget the spectacular exceptions, the unbelievably great hordes of mosquitoes and sometimes black flies and no-see-ums. Many shallow and therefore warm pools may produce large quantities of aquatic organisms for a short period in summer. Extremes frequently characterize the Northland. Even plants may show great production, as in the thousands of square miles of blueberries ripening together just as thousands of square miles of mosquitoes arise almost simultaneously

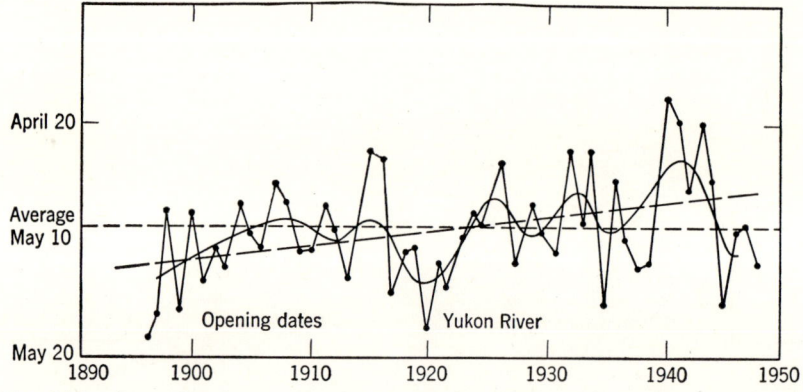

FIG. 14.2. Spring break-up varies from year to year in a cyclic swing. The broken line shows the trend for earlier opening in the past decades.

from thaw-water pools, only to decline as the pools disappear in midsummer. The lack of food sources during most of the other months makes many of these abundant transitory crops usable only seasonally by seasonal animals like migratory birds. Sometimes shore birds turn to the berry crop, and other animals do likewise when the abundant foods of this sort make mass-production feeding profitable. The limiting effect of weather upon animal populations seems more important even than food or any other need or hazard of life. Although diseases are present in northern animals, they play a less important role than in the warmer regions, except for the diseases attendant upon low temperatures.

Considerable year-to-year variation occurs in the onset of winter and coming of spring, which is shown phenologically by the ice break-up in spring and freezing-over of waters in the fall (Figs. 14.2 and 14.3). A northward march of climate has been in progress since the Pleistocene epoch, and we are obviously still in the receding phase of the last glacial stage, even if not in an interglacial stage. A northward

Northland Wildlife

march of perhaps 75 miles a century appears to be taking place now, though we cannot determine as yet how much of this is a progression and how much is part of the ebb and flow phenomena of the Northland.

Mild and hard winters have an important role in survival, which, combined with below-average reproductive seasons, brings about low populations or high ones, alone or in combination with other influences. We have no measure yet of mild and hard winters for the Arctic, but

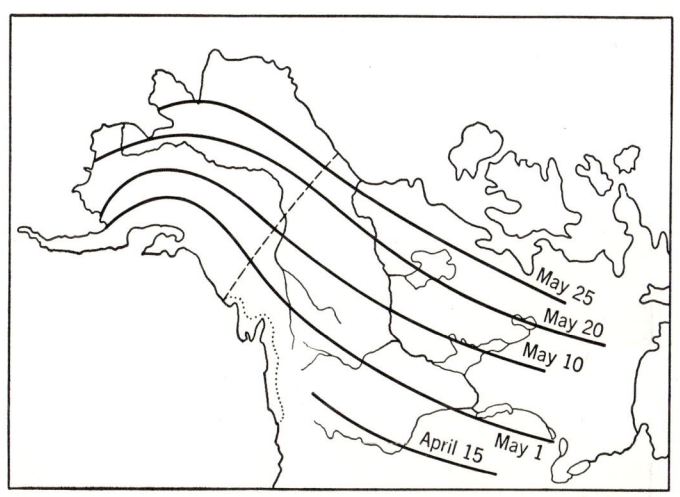

FIG. 14.3. The northward advance of spring as measured by the break-up of rivers.

the length of the closed period of rivers and lakes gives some measure of the length of winter and summer (Fig. 14.4). Because hibernating mammals must depend entirely upon stored fat for the nourishment that carries them through the winter, the length of winter is important to them, presumably more important than the severity of cold, which is likely to influence them little in their dens. Northland mammals that do not hibernate lay on an abundance of fat also. The caribou will accumulate a layer of dorsal fat, some 3 inches thick, that reaches from the shoulders to the rump. To such an animal both the length and severity of winter are important in the success of the fat reserve as a supplement to winter forage. Because the fat also serves to insulate the body, its reduction may intensify the energy demands of the animal.

Many of the birds and mammals of the American Arctic are circumpolar in distribution, and we must keep this in mind. The ptarmigan,

Arctic fox, and polar bear, for example, range over the Old and New World Arctic. Even the reindeer of the Old World is but a caribou, perhaps of the same species as our own.

Most of the land area in the Arctic is publicly owned Crown or unorganized domain and no doubt destined to remain largely as such. Private-property conflicts, as with predators, and game-damage com-

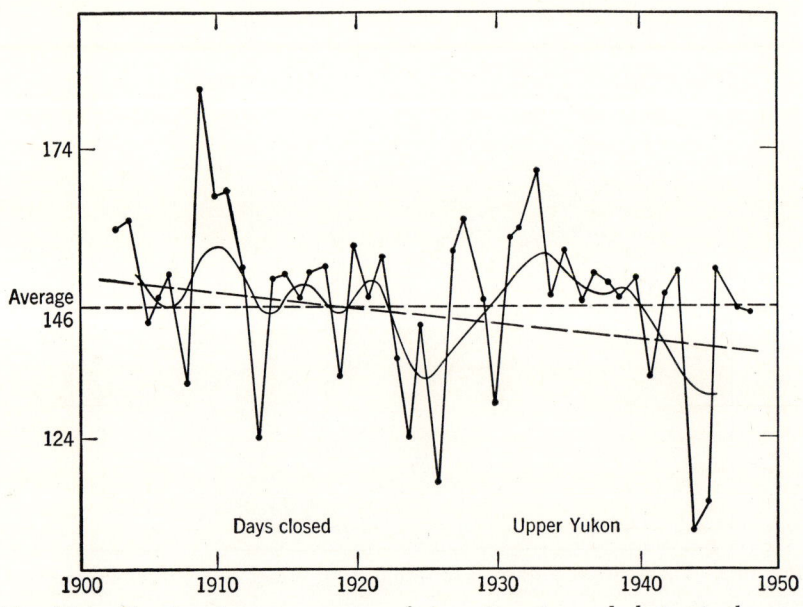

Fig. 14.4. The days between opening of rivers in spring and closing in the preceding fall give a measure of winter length. The days closed at Whitehorse on the Upper Yukon varied from 188 in the winter of 1908–1909 to 104 in the winter of 1943–1944. The broken line shows the trend for shorter closed periods in recent decades.

plaints are generally absent, other than for the perennial hunter complaints against all flesh-eating animals. The presence of bands of reindeer in the western Arctic calls forth some complaints about the larger predators, but since reindeer herders seem able to live without organized official help in the Old World Arctic, ours should be able to also. The lack of private land holdings especially simplifies the public relations aspects of administration. Alaska, for example, has but 1 per cent private land, with the rest in public title, mostly the federal government. The Yukon, Northwest Territories, and other parts of the Canadian Arctic are almost wholly Crown land.

Brown Bear

The tundra of Alaska covers some 150,000 square miles (Fig. 14.1); forest, 345,000 square miles; and grassland but 55,000. Apart from small areas in the mainland and the Alaska panhandle, little merchantable timber exists or is likely to be produced except for local use. The Canadian Northland also produces or is likely to produce little timber. Throughout the Northland, forestry will have to remain subordinate to fish, fur, and game in the foreseeable future.

The economy of the Northland has been since the beginning of white settlement largely extraction and exploitation of the mineral and fur resources. The fur industry is the most permanent feature of the general economy and can be carried on indefinitely and can even be increased under a general program; the initial steps have been taken already, but the stage of organization and the fund of biological knowledge needed for management administration are lagging behind settled areas farther south. The remote control of the political and administrative life of the region, in Ottawa and Washington bureaus, handicaps the development of local consciousness of management application so essential to success in the wildlife field; it also handicaps continuity of effort. For the moment a strong territorial conservation agency is the greatest need of wildlife management.

Some measure of the productivity of the land can be obtained from the amount of land evidently needed to support the native peoples, still largely dependent upon a fur, fish, and game economy. Even with trade to the outside for many articles of subsistence, the present native population in the Northwest Territories averages about one to 120 square miles and about the same in the Yukon. The aboriginal ratio in the states area was probably around one to 12 square miles.

Table 14.1 gives a brief biology table for northern game species.

Brown Bear (*Ursus gyas*, sp.). The Alaska brown bear enjoys many claims to fame, one of them that it is the largest carnivorous animal in the world and certainly the King of Beasts. One specimen weighed 1600 pounds, and probably larger ones have lived unweighed. The brown bear is more closely related to the smaller grizzlies than to the black or polar bears; it may actually be a coastal derivation of the grizzly.

The brown bear occupies a rather narrow coastal strip running from the Alaska panhandle to the Aleutians. Its life habits include a "salmon culture" that probably helps to restrict it to coastal areas with streams that salmon ascend for spawning. Overfishing of salmon by commercial fishermen has so reduced the run in some streams that the take by the bears competes with that of the fishermen. A drastic

Table 14.1

BIOLOGY TABLE FOR NORTHLAND GAME

Species	Range	Weight (pounds)	Mating *	Normal Limit of Sex Ratio	Breeding Season	Parturition or Hatching Season	Gestation or Incubation Period	Number of Eggs or Young	Food	Environment
Brown bear (*Ursus gyas*)	Alaska	1300–1500	Mon.	?	June–July	January	7 months	2–3	Animal matter, fruits, herbage	Coast and adjacent islands
Polar bear (*Thalarctos maritimus*)	Arctic	700–1000	Mon. ?	?	June–July	January	7 months	2	Animal matter, herbage	Arctic coast
Arctic fox (*Alopex lagopus*)	Arctic	6–15	?	?	March	May–June	8–9 weeks	4–7	Animal matter	Tundra

Biology Table for Northland Game

									Vegetation	
Arctic hare (*Lepus arcticus*)	Arctic	6–12	Pol.	?	May	June	30 days	2–6	Mosses, lichens, herbage	Tundra
Caribou (*Rangifer arcticus* R. *caribou*)	U. S. northward	200–300	? Pol. ?	?	October	May–June	8 months	1–2	Tundra, bogforest	Tundra, bogforest
Musk ox (*Ovibos moschatus*)	Arctic	500–900	Pol. ?	?	July–August	April–June	9 months	1	Sedges, grasses, herbage	Tundra
White mountain sheep (*Ovis dalli*)	British Columbia to Alaska	150–225	Pol. ?	?	November–December	May–June	6 months	1–2	Mosses, lichens, sedges, herbage	Timberline
Willow and rock ptarmigan (*Lagopus mutus* and *L. rupestris*)	Arctic	400–600 grams	?	?	May–June	June–July	21 days	6–10	Sedges, buds, berries, insects	Tundra, bare ridges, slopes
White-tailed ptarmigan (*Lagopus leucurus*)	Northwestern North America	300–450 grams	?	?	May–July	May–July	21 days	6–9	Insects, buds, berries, sedges	Above timberline

* *Mon.* means monogamous; *Pol.* means polygamous.

curtailment of fishing until the run has built up to the capacity of the streams would doubtless give more salmon for salmon canneries and eliminate complaints of bear feeding, temporarily at least, and probably be sounder biologically than other means.

During the salmon run, which may last from summer well into the fall, brown bears feed freely upon salmon. The bear usually seizes the fish with the jaws alone, or with the jaws and fore paws, but it sometimes flings them ashore with a swift scoop of the paw. Rodents are eagerly sought too, and tremendous amounts of energy may be spent in digging them. Winter kills of carrion may be eaten, as well as large quantities of vegetable foods, such as kelp of the coast, bulbs, and even grass.

In most areas of its range the brown bear has been seriously reduced in numbers by hunters who are looking chiefly for trophies. The bear's slow reproductive rate makes it unable to stand much hunting pressure, for the bear requires 6 or 7 years to reach maturity, and females breed but once in 2 or 3 years. Because it is so large, a single animal needs many square miles in which to find food, unless it lives near concentrations of meat or vegetable foods.

Polar Bear (*Thalarctos maritimus*). The polar bear lives along the Arctic coast, never far from water, though on occasion it may wander many miles inland. It is essentially a marine mammal attached to land and no doubt is evolutionarily radiating seaward. Its use of the forefeet in swimming reflects this seaward trend in life habit, but most of the bears reported distant from land probably floated out on ice floes. Like marine mammals and birds in general, the polar bear wears a heavy layer of fat under the skin, along with a water-repellent, oily pelage. The exceptional weights reported for this animal (up to 1600 pounds or more) can be attributed to fat accumulation. Pregnant females hibernate, but others do not.

Polar bears feed primarily upon sea foods, especially upon seals. Before whalers reduced the whale population, polar bears had more dead whales to feed upon than they have now. Arctic explorers attest to the omnivorous habits of the bear; if need be, it will eat herbivorous forage like other bears.

The polar bear has been reduced in numbers by white men and rifle-equipped Eskimos, and it is now rare over much of its range where it was once abundant, for a bear population.

Arctic Fox (*Alopex lagopus*). The Arctic fox occupies the whole general Arctic beyond the limit of trees, including the Arctic islands, from the Aleutians to Labrador and the Old World Arctic also. It eschews the water and ventures away from land only on the ice.

The Arctic fox wears brown in summer, as do several other Arctic animals, and white in winter. There are two color phases, the normal white and a gray color commonly called "blue fox." Blue foxes have been raised commercially on several of the Alaskan islands with some success but with little elsewhere.

The Arctic fox avoids the timber and inhabits open plains and beaches, especially where rock-strewn. A marked southward movement is noted at intervals, presumably by young animals. These movements perhaps relate to population highs, which in turn relate to the rise and fall of bird and mammal prey, particularly of lemmings, the forage animal of Arctic meat-eaters. The rise and fall of the lemming cycle at 4- to 5-year intervals markedly influences the life of the Arctic fox, as it does other meat-eaters in the Northland. The Arctic fox feeds also upon many other small mammals available, as well as birds, their nests, and their young.

There can be little doubt that the Arctic fox has an important role in the biota and economy of the Northland. The number of pelts taken each year is high, and the value of the fur, which has exceeded a million dollars annually, brings a substantial income to the region, even though much of the value accrues elsewhere.

Arctic Hare (*Lepus arcticus*). Like the snowshoe rabbit of the coniferous forests, the Arctic hare and its close relative the larger Greenland hare (*Lepus groenlandicus*) turn pure white in winter. Both are inhabitants of open, treeless country and largely avoid even the scrub willows, a life habit in marked contrast to that of the snowshoe rabbit. They have developed heavy fur coats that protect them against the Arctic wind and cold; the coat of the Greenland hare is a thick wool perhaps rivaling that of mohair goats.

The Arctic and Greenland hares show the famed population cycles, just as the snowshoe rabbit does. They live in a rigorous region, and but slight shifts in favorable or unfavorable conditions reverberate through the populations. Carnivores depending upon them for food fluctuate in turn. The food seems to include most plants in their homeland. The Greenland hare has larger upper incisors than the mainland mammal, and it employs them in breaking through the snow to obtain food.

Whether the hares have any economic importance except to Eskimos seems doubtful, though possible use of the superior wool has been suggested.

Woodland Caribou (*Rangifer caribou*) **and Barren-Ground Caribou** (*Rangifer arcticus*). The caribou has many claims to attention, one of them that it is related to the reindeer of the Old World and of Christmas stories. The females of the entire genus *Rangifer* bear antlers similar to, though smaller than, those of the males. It is the only female of the Cervidae so adorned. The antlers are characteristically palmate, large, and sweeping; like other deer antlers, however, they are shed annually.

Though caribou break up into a dozen taxonomic races, they seem to fall into two main groups, the woodland caribou, ranging from northern United States to southern Labrador and southern Alaska, and the barren-grounds group, occupying the country to the north. The western part of the forest zone is sometimes assigned to a third group, the mountain caribou. The barren-grounds animal is smaller than the woodland caribou and has smaller antlers. It is both more gregarious and more numerous.

The barren-grounds caribou move over the great tundra in large herds, sometimes herds that run into millions of animals wandering about in a vagrant way. The herds are partly controlled by winds (an upwind movement in fly and mosquito seasons), and this control is effective in preventing overgrazing of the Arctic vegetation so slow to regenerate. Years may pass before a great herd will pass over the same area again, which gives the tundra time to recover from the previous overrunning. Some routes along mountain ridges or river valleys are traveled regularly as the caribou pass from one area to another, however, and these routes are often well known.

The enemies of the caribou are chiefly insect pests (particularly warbles, flies, and mosquitoes) and the severe climate, though the caribou is well adapted for resisting its strenuous environment. Although wolves prey upon caribou, they are successful consistently only in pulling down calves, immature animals, wounded ones, and the aged, and need not be considered a serious enemy of prime animals.

Caribou eat almost any vegetable material in their habitat. They gnaw shed antlers perhaps more than other deer do, which may reflect a mineral shortage in the food supply.

The principal drain upon caribou by man is the hunting and trapping by Indians and Eskimos in the more remote parts and by white hunters in the accessible areas. Caribou have declined sharply in those areas accessible to white man and those near Eskimo or Indian settlements in the years since rifles have been available. The introduction of reindeer into the caribou range probably spells a decline for the caribou from competition and disease. Pressure to destroy the caribou in order to protect the introduced reindeer in its use of the forage can be expected also.

It has become customary to place curbs upon white hunters in the Northland in order to protect caribou and to favor the native Indians and Eskimos. The restrictions are in the form of closed seasons for the white man and prohibition of caribou hunting in some areas, as in a 5-mile strip along either side of the Steese Highway in Alaska. The woodland caribou, too, has declined in the easily reached areas where closed seasons and closed areas are invoked. Special efforts are being made to protect and restore the remnants of caribou in the few northern states that have them.

Musk Ox (*Ovibos moschatus*). Just as the caribou evolved as the intrusion of the Cervidae into the Arctic prairies, the musk ox evolved as the Bovidae invader. What ecological preferences separate the respective caribou and musk ox niches is not clear, but the caribou apparently utilizes lichens more than the musk ox, which in turn seems to prefer grasses, sedges, flowers, and the like. The musk ox also has a greater ability to withstand exposure and seeks shelter less and migrates less. A long outer coat of coarse hair overlying an inner coat of fine wool, somewhat like a windbreaker over a woolen jacket, provides the musk ox with superior resistance to storm. The nearest living relative of this Arctic invader seems to be the American bison farther south.

The original range of the musk ox covered the region from the Arctic coast of Alaska across to Greenland south to about the limit of trees. But this range shrank on the Alaska end in the recent geological past and elsewhere in historical times, especially where natives received high-powered rifles and in areas of easy access to white man. Unlike the primitive weapons of low killing power, the rifles permitted the natives to kill the animal in excess of its reproductive capacity. The habit of the musk ox to form a circle for defense worked well with wolves but not with man and dogs, who thus were enabled to slaughter the apparently "stupid" animals responding to enemies as they know them in the instinctive manner.

The weight of the bull perhaps may approach 1000 pounds in large specimens, but probably it averages nearer 600. Cows reach about two-thirds the weight of bulls.

Little is known of the life history and ecology of the species. Efforts have been made to restore it to the Alaskan tundra, with some success attending these efforts. The Canadian authorities have shown especial interest in giving the musk ox protection from white and native hunters alike so that its numbers may increase. A special refuge, the Thelon Game Sanctuary, has been established north of Great Slave Lake for the musk ox. In the more inaccessible areas of Greenland, the animal is reported to live in about the same numbers as ever. Seton estimated the original number to have totaled about a million, and modern estimates have placed the number at about 25,000 for the entire Arctic, which indicates an important decline in the available energy resources of the Northland.

White Mountain Sheep (*Ovis dalli*). Taxonomists sometimes consider the white or Dall sheep of the Canadian Rockies and adjacent Alaska as but a white race of the bighorn, despite the white sheep's smaller size and other characters. The general life habits, however, are about the same as those of the bighorn as far as currently known. No doubt intensive studies will reveal many important differences.

The Dall mountain sheep occupies the mountain slopes and uplands from northern British Columbia and adjacent Yukon to northern Alaska; it avoids timbered areas within this general range.

The white sheep have declined in regions readily accessible to white hunters, though they have held their own in less accessible areas. Studies in the Mount McKinley National Park indicate rises and declines of population levels over the years, which untrained observers have charged to wolves though competent study shows otherwise. The horns of the mountain sheep show year-marks that enable determination of exact age and year class, a determination not possible in other land vertebrates. The sheep reach their full vigor at 3 years of age (some perhaps as early as 2), and the decline of age sets in after the eighth year of life. Fourteen years seems to be about the greatest age ordinarily to be expected in the wild. Wolf predation selects the weak animals, those not yet in the full vigor of life, those past their prime, or those weak from sickness, if in the prime years of 3 to 8. This selection is a clear example of the biological importance and benefits of predation.

The chief action so far to aid the sheep has been control of hunting along with closed seasons and closed areas. Enforcement of restrictions has not been very successful, largely because of the remoteness of much sheep country and the inadequate authority for local conservation control in Alaska.

The practice of requiring guides for non-resident hunters provides some opportunity for local people to benefit commercially from the game of the region, but it has also made it profitable for the same local people to exploit these game resources. The increase in efficiency of the guide-directed hunting over scattered hunting has played a part in the consequent decline of sheep and other big game animals of the region. It must be remembered that the productivity of high-latitude or high-altitude land is low, and few animals can be taken by hunters without draining the breeding stock. Because big game animals like sheep are tied to their home range, it takes a large population to build up the pressure needed for rapid spreading back into shot-out range. Low populations can hardly be expected to repopulate depleted ranges very rapidly.

There seem to be no figures on the density of sheep other than that several square miles are needed for a band. The sheep run in bands and seem unable to survive well without sufficient numbers to form these bands.

Willow Ptarmigan (*Lagopus lagopus*) **and Rock Ptarmigan** (*Lagopus mutus*). The two species of ptarmigan found in the Northland have spread into the Old World, so that they are both circumpolar species. The famed red grouse of the British Isles is really but a willow ptarmigan whose habit of changing to a white plumage in winter has dropped from the chromosomal make-up. The white-tailed ptarmigan overlaps the others at the southwestern edge of the Northland. All ptarmigan are unique in donning a white plumage at the post-nuptial and post-juvenile molts of fall and return to browns again at the pre-nuptial molt of spring.

The two species inhabit the tundra country from Alaska to Greenland in the New World and follow southward where suitable tundra-like conditions occur atop mountains. The rock ptarmigan lives farther north, and in the region of overlapping range occupies the ridges and higher elevations, especially when they are rocky. Except for these distinctions, few differences in ecological choice have yet been determined.

Both species migrate southward in winter, but the rock ptarmigan, the stronger flyer, is likely to migrate farther. Both abandon the northern parts of their ranges and leave but few stragglers behind at most. The rock ptarmigan may fly long distances over water in migration, and there is every reason to believe that it has the greatest powers of sustained flight of all gallinaceous birds. Some of the more pronounced migrations take on aspects of invasions of more southerly regions and may be associated with population cycles, which are pronounced in these species.

The food of the ptarmigans consists of insects, berries, leaves, and other vegetation in summer; buds and twigs suffice in winter. Some birds have been reported eating spruce needles, which may indicate a near-starvation diet.

The ptarmigan plays an important part in supplying the natives in the Arctic when the caribou herds fail to appear. They serve also as a forage food for predators, many of them important fur bearers. In the Scandinavian countries skins in the white plumage are sometimes sold commercially for decorating women's apparel, a practice not followed in the United States and Canada.

Some heavy mortality of ptarmigans is reported where telegraph wires have been strung across the tundra; ptarmigan do not seem to recognize obstructions of this kind, presumably because the brushless habitat gives them little instinctive or habit familiarity with obstructions to flight.

White-Tailed Ptarmigan (*Lagopus leucurus*). The white-tailed ptarmigan differs little in general behavior from the ptarmigan of the tundra. Distinction seems largely attributable to habitat differences, for the bird ranges along the mountain tops above timberline from central Alaska to northern New Mexico and Washington. Although alpine conditions above timberline resemble the tundra, they are not true tundra and are best termed *mountain tundra*.

The white-tailed ptarmigan prefers rather steep slopes, often those with broken rocks. In the summer the birds feed upon flower heads (*Carex*, for example), berries, and insects. The ptarmigan descend to the edge of timber in winter to feed upon buds and twigs of willow and other deciduous species.

Because the home of the ptarmigan is above timberline, it is exposed to hunting only occasionally in the fall. The chief influences unfavorably affecting the survival of remnants in much of the western states' ptarmigan range seem associated with forest-fire lookouts, roads crossing high ridges, "truck trails," and stockmen. Evidently relying upon its coloration and immobility for protection, the ptarmigan has an unsuspicious nature, which exposes it to easy destruction by man. Education seems the best approach to the problem of controlling poaching of this bird.

SUGGESTED READING

Bent, Arthur Cleveland, 1932, "Life Histories of North American Gallinaceous Birds," *U. S. Nat. Mus. Bull.* 162.

Suggested Reading

Cahalane, Victor H., 1947, *Mammals of North America*, The Macmillan Co., New York.
Dufresne, Frank, 1946, *Alaska's Animals and Fishes*, A. S. Barnes and Co., New York.
Hadwen, Seymour, and L. J. Palmer, 1922, "Reindeer in Alaska," *U.S.D.A. Bull.* 1089.
Hamilton, W. J., Jr., 1939, *American Mammals*, McGraw-Hill Book Co., New York.
Hewitt, C. Gordon, 1921, *The Conservation of the Wildlife of Canada*, Charles Scribner's Sons, New York.
Jackson, Hartley H. T., and others, 1949, "Literature on the Natural History of the Arctic Region with Special Reference to Alaska and Canada," *Fish and Wildlife Serv. Leaflet* 317.
Murie, Adolph, 1944, "The Wolves of Mount McKinley," *Nat. Park Serv., Fauna Ser.* 5.
Murie, Olaus J., 1935, "Alaska-Yukon Caribou," *N. A. Fauna* 54.
Palmer, Lawrence J., and Charles H. Rouse, 1945, "Study of the Alaska Tundra with Reference to Its Reactions to Reindeer and Other Grazing," *Fish and Wildlife Serv. Res. Rept.* 10.
Rand, A. L., 1945, "Mammals of Yukon, Canada," *Can. Nat. Mus. Bull.* 100.
Seton, Ernest Thompson, 1925–1929, *Lives of Game Animals*, 4 vols., Doubleday, Doran and Co., Garden City, N. Y.
Soper, J. Dewey, 1941, "History, Range, and Home Life of the Northern Bison," *Ecol. Monographs*, 11:347–412.
Stefansson, Vilhjalmur, 1944, *Arctic Manual*, The Macmillan Co., New York.

15

Fur-Bearer Management

The protection of fur bearers is a complicated undertaking that involves not only an exploitation industry measured in millions of dollars but also many people, especially those in lower-income brackets, who receive income from the trapping of fur bearers. Management operations as well as straight protection are needed in varying degrees to protect the public interest and the livelihood of people dependent upon peltries. We should distinguish clearly between fur farming, which will not be considered here, and the management of wild fur bearers.

Decline in Numbers. Like many game species, most fur-bearing species have progressively declined in abundance since the beginning of settlement. For more than three centuries, pelts of the beaver and other furs were the chief products exported from North America, even as they are still in many parts of the Northland. Fur bearers have been extirpated in many regions, and the shift in emphasis from the beaver and the other producers of high-quality furs to the muskrat, which produces a pelt of less value, testifies best to the decline of fur-bearer populations. Domestic furs brought to market from fur farms have not influenced trapping, as might normally be expected; it has not arrested the pressure upon wild fur bearers. The major causes of reduction in the numbers of fur-bearing animals are the usual overtrapping, habitat destruction, and depletion of food supply, along with the additional destructiveness of predator- and rodent-control campaigns, all associated intimately with land settlement.

The early explorations in this country were made principally for fur trading; the trader and trapper preceded the settler by many years; indeed they often preceded the explorer. We look upon the explorers as the first adventurers to penetrate the wilderness of North America, but they were only those whose journeys became known by written accounts of their travels. They regularly depended upon traders and trappers, not only for information about the country through which they passed but even for guidance, subsistence, and information about the country and people ahead. The beaver has been justly called an "empire builder" and "the most important single fact in American history." The beavers and the millions of other fur bearers, especially those having pelts of great value, must be credited with much of the stimulus for penetration of the frontier and for much of the impetus that led to settlement of central, western, and northern North America. For that reason, if for no other, we may rightly protect them as living exhibits of a glorious past.

As has been noted already, a factor that bears upon management is the shift in the relative importance of species owing to the decline in abundance of the more valuable fur bearers. The beaver, marten, fisher, and otter have declined, and the muskrat, skunk, and opossum have grown in importance. The opossum, of course, has been trapped on this continent since earliest times, but its importance was overshadowed by fur bearers of higher value. One has only to visit a fur house to note dependence upon low-value pelts.

Habitat Requirements. The habitat needs of most fur bearers are little known, except in a general way, and research studies have not yet resulted in sufficient knowledge of the ecology of fur animals for much management technique. Table 15.1 attempts to summarize the principal habitat requirements of the leading fur animals of North America. Most are carnivorous and live wherever their forage animals exist, provided, as would be expected, that they are tolerant of disturbances. The possession of such tolerance is as variable among fur bearers as among game or other species. The opossum, muskrat, and skunk show the most tolerance and the lynx, wolverine, fisher, and marten perhaps the least.

The home site selected, though variable (Table 15.2), is frequently a den excavated in the ground, taken over from others, or used after abandonment by the original owners. Hollow trees, butts, or logs may be left wherever possible, without unduly endangering the general productiveness of the producing forest, because all these hollows are useful in fur management. Although no great number of tries have been made, it seems worthwhile to develop means, if necessary, for supplying hollow logs or other den structures.

Beavers and muskrats are the fur bearers that habitually build elaborate structures for their homes, erecting houses in water-covered areas where such quarters are naturally absent. Without the ability to construct lodges of their own, beavers and muskrats would be restricted to the shore around marshes; their travel radius is too low to permit them to travel far from a burrow. A few fur bearers are able to excavate burrows for themselves, but many must use hollows already available, thickets, or the homes of their prey.

TABLE 15.1

PRINCIPAL FUR BEARERS AND CHIEF HABITATS

Species	Farm Land	Second-Growth Hardwood	Open Range	Streams, Lakes, or Marshes	Conifer Forest
Opossum	x	x	..	..	..
Raccoon	x	x	..	x	..
Marten	..	..	..	..	x
Fisher	..	..	..	..	x
Weasel	x	x	..	..	x
Mink	x	.	..	x	..
Wolverine	..	..	..	..	x
Otter	..	..	..	x	..
Sea Otter	..	..	..	..	..
Skunk	x	x	x	..	..
Badger	x	..	x	..	..
Red fox	x	x	x	..	x
Gray fox	x	x	..	..	..
Arctic fox	..	..	x	..	..
Coyote	..	..	x	..	..
Timber wolf	..	..	x	..	x
Lynx	..	..	..	..	x
Wildcat	..	x	..	..	x
Fur seal	..	..	..	..	..
Beaver	..	..	..	x	..
Muskrat	..	..	..	x	..

Gathering Data on Fur Bearers. To be efficient, programs for fur bearers, like those for any other wild species, must have data on the existing populations and upon the drain from trapping and other causes. Most states require trappers to report the catch, but though such reports may be indicative, they generally are of only partial accuracy at best. Reports of fur buyers suffer from inaccuracies; in addition, it is often difficult to determine the origin of furs reported or to avoid duplication with other reports. Questionnaires sent to trappers may give some information, if followed by personal interviews, but the questionnaire and other forms of "mail-order research" have little to recommend them as substitutes for field work in biological investigations.

The personal interview, though time-consuming, is the best means of gathering reliable information from trappers and fur buyers, but

Gathering Data on Fur Bearers

it requires the interviewer to be especially apt at soliciting information. The economic status of the trapper and the industry can be determined best by the interview method. Examination of the incoming pelts in fur houses can give extensive information of sex ratios, primeness, size, and abundance of the fur animals. The locality of the catch, however, may be known only in a most general way. Collecting carcasses from trappers will also extend the biologist's working circle.

TABLE 15.2

CHIEF LOCATION OF FUR-BEARER DENS

Species	Hollow Trees	Hollow Stumps or Butts	Hollow Logs	Burrows	Caves and Crevices	Other
Opossum	x	x	x	..	..	..
Raccoon	x	x	x	..	x	..
Marten	x	..	..	..	..	..
Fisher	x	x	x	..	x	..
Weasel	..	..	x	x	x	..
Mink	..	x	x	x	x	..
Wolverine	..	x	x	x	x	..
Skunk	..	x	x	x	x	..
Badger	..	..	..	x	..	..
Fox	..	x	x	x	x	..
Coyote	..	..	..	x	x	..
Wolf	..	x	x	x	x	..
Lynx	x	x	x	..	x	..
Wildcat	x	x	x	..	x	..
Beaver	..	..	..	x	..	x
Muskrat	..	..	..	x	..	x

Fur surveys usually cover small areas, such as counties or watersheds. Because the chief fur bearers generally concentrate along streams, streamside fur surveys can be made by repeated cruising, usually throughout the year but often only in summer. Men skilled in reading and finding sign conduct a streamside survey by walking the banks, frequently in pairs, with one man taking the notes. A reliable map of the stream reduces the number of notes that must be entered in the notebook and presents data in a briefer and more graphic style because the data can be recorded on the maps by symbols (Fig. 15.1). Fur sign consists of tracks, trails, droppings, feeding grounds, food remnants, cuttings, dens, and a multitude of other indications. Old sign often is not entered on the map or in the notes, except for permanent structures such as dams or dens.

Fur-Bearer Management

Census techniques for fur bearers are poorly developed, chiefly because fur animals are wary or mostly nocturnal. The indirect evidence, as referred to previously, must generally be relied upon. *Marking* fur bearers is done in a number of ways (Fig. 5.6), depending upon the species and the materials available. Species with large ears like the coyote are marked with ear tags. Adult and young muskrats and perhaps some other species can be marked with tags inserted into a fold

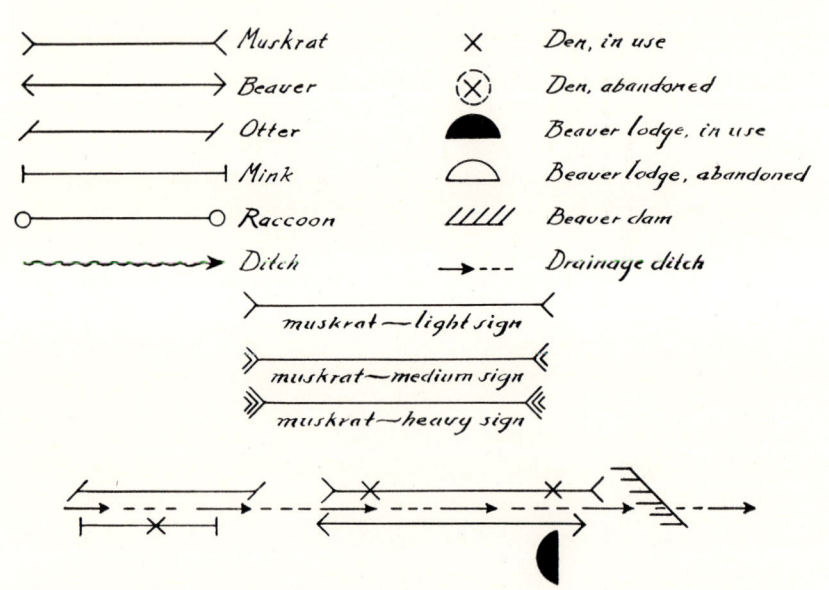

Fig. 15.1. Symbols used in a fur survey. The lower portion shows the method of indicating fur sign along a drainage ditch. (After Hamerstrom and Blake, 1939.)

of skin in the back. Even a tag around the tendon of Achilles has proved successful. Toe clipping, toe and ear punching, branding, and tattooing have served for marking some species.

Relation of Fur Bearers to Other Animals. Most fur bearers are predators also, a fact that has caused considerable controversy over the merits and demerits of various species as viewed from the standpoint of personal interests. Flat condemnation of fur-bearing predators ignores their economic value, which may often outweigh any real or assumed destructiveness.

Between 1915 and 1935, for example, Pennsylvania paid $2,060,290 in bounties for five species of fur-bearing predators, plus the costs of administering such a bounty program. It is doubtful that bountying

Protection 239

has any really great value in increasing the game species; on the contrary, any value to game increase is generally less than the economic loss through destruction of valuable fur animals. The bounty system has been abandoned by progressive states and provinces because it has failed to increase game species and has destroyed much valuable fur. It also results in many frauds and administrative difficulties. The usual practice of turning animals in to county clerks or other untrained personnel results in poor identification of animals presented for bounty. In any event the state or body that offers the highest bounty is usually the one that gets the bounty business.

The interrelations of fur-bearing predators and game prey are complex to say the least. Since rodents constitute the basic forage food of many fur bearers, organized poison campaigns for the eradication of rodents may deplete the forage foods for these valuable fur bearers. Often poison campaigns against rodents follow upon the heels of campaigns against predators which themselves are the natural enemies of rodents. Where some predators, like the skunk, are numerous, they may prey upon ground-nesting birds, but the principal food of the skunk is rodents and insects, and destruction of rodents may benefit many birds.

Protection. The protection of fur bearers has lagged behind that for other wildlife, owing in part to the public misconception of the role of predators. Trapping seasons are generally longer than the status of the fur-bearer population warrants; the number of trappers is likewise generally in excess of the trapping possibilities. The most important measure for the increase of fur bearers, we are bound to conclude, is still protection.

Poaching is reduced materially by increased activity of enforcement officers. Trapping licenses also can help to reduce excess trapping, and the introduction of name tags and seals for traps helps greatly to control poaching and to reduce trapping pressure by identifying the traps and trapper, which thus makes it possible to control the number of trappers and the amount of trapping.

The practice of fur buyers and fur houses of issuing price lists early in the season tends to stimulate trapping and thus to cause a rush of trapping early, before the fur is prime. Fictitious quotations for highest-quality pelts lead trappers to expect extraordinary prices for their catch. Few pelts (if any) ever qualify for these high quotations, and so the practice only encourages continued overtrapping and catching of unprime fur; therefore early and unrealistic quotations are to be condemned. Several fur houses offer daily and seasonal prizes for *best-prepared* pelts, irrespective of kind, which encourages better care and less waste of pelts. (But in actual practice fur houses keep records of winners, and subsequent prizes are usually passed around to those who have not previously won.)

Laws that require the landowner's written permission before a trap may be set on his land are beneficial because they reduce the trapping pressure and place trapping more closely under control of the landowner. Probably a royalty to the landowner would encourage him to be more solicitous of the fur bearers on his land.

Raccoon (*Procyon lotor*). The raccoon, commonly known as "'coon," ranges over North America from the Atlantic to the Pacific and from Canada to Panama, although now extirpated in many regions. Extirpation occurs most often in the more arid and more open parts of the West.

The raccoon prefers hardwood forest and bottom lands, and it is associated with wooded streams; indeed it seldom goes far from water in its wanderings. The den is placed in a hollow tree or occasionally in hollow logs or similar situations. The 'coon is omnivorous and feeds upon mast, fruits, berries, frogs, crayfish, clams, and small mammals. There are no organized management procedures for the raccoon, but it can be aided materially, along with other hollow-tree dwellers, by the preservation and increase of hollow trees and logs.

Weasel Family (*Mustelidae*). The members of the weasel family are widely distributed over North America, especially in the forested parts of the northern two-thirds of the continent. Although they are primarily carnivorous, nevertheless they will eat many different foods when necessity demands it and at times become somewhat omnivorous. The skunk is the most insectivorous and the otter the most piscivorous; it is hardly correct to speak of any weasel representative as the most herbivorous.

The badger has evolved as a fossorial predator of rodents and consequently lives in the prairies and dry lands. It has invaded the bordering forest regions but little and then only in open forests or in the wake of settlement. Its range extends from California to the Great Lakes and from the prairie provinces to Texas and Old Mexico. The coarse, hairy fur of the badger is of little worth, though many pelts are marketed, but the destruction of rodents makes them valuable animals and worth protecting and encouraging. The holes that they dig for rodents were formerly more annoying to ranchers than they are now; ranchers ride in cars when feasible and rarely pursue cattle at full speed on a horse, for running modern cattle runs money off the meat scales.

There are no management practices available for the marten, fisher, wolverine, and otter. Generally speaking, they have been reduced in numbers throughout the ranges and extirpated in many places. Extirpation is especially true of the otter, which is now absent from most of the original range within the settled regions. Many claims have been made, erroneously, that the otter is a serious competitor of the fisherman. The several species mentioned require protection if they are to be returned to a semblance of their former abundance. Though it is the general impression, and perhaps correctly so in many cases, that all are intolerant of human disturbance, in England otters frequent rivers and streams in the heavily settled parts of the country. Martens live in some city parks in Europe, and it may be that martens, or at least the European ones, have more tolerance for human disturbance than we think. It seems logical that if we give some of our fur animals traditional protection, as we do our songbirds, many will maintain permanent stands near centers of population; the otter should be able to live in most of the unpolluted streams of northern and middle North America. Otters living there would be sources of great civic pride to the community.

Minks are associated with streams and lowlands and are more closely tied to water than weasels, which may wander or live far from streams and swamps. Both are partial to log jams, windfalls, fallen trees, stone fences, and heavy brush piles. Weasels may destroy eggs of ground-nesting birds upon occasion; this destruction can be identified as the work of the weasels because they remove the eggs some distance from the nest before consuming them. They eat eggs by biting out a hole and licking out the contents in a manner similar to that of the skunk.

There are no definite management suggestions for the skunk, which on the whole has profited from farming. Skunks, when not overtrapped, can take quick advantage of the changes brought about by farming. Because their burrows frequently are those of woodchucks and others, the skunk benefits from an abundance of hole diggers. The work of skunks in destruction of ground nests can sometimes be recognized by the manner in which they have bitten off the tops of the eggs, licked out the contents, and left the shells in a group. But it takes practice to recognize the work of the skunk or weasel.

Red Fox (*Vulpes fulva*) **and Gray Fox** (*Urocyon cinereoargenteus*). The red fox occupies most of North America, but the gray fox ranges northward only to southern Canada. Although both are carnivorous, they will eat any food when necessary. Rodents and rabbits are the forage animals, but foxes will also feed upon carrion, especially winter-killed animals.

Both species are rather tolerant of human disturbance and increase in settled areas having the right habitats and the right protection from man. The foxes usually are not present in great numbers; probably one or two to the square mile should be considered a high density. The depredations of foxes upon game have been shown to be largely confined to game animals living under conditions of insecurity or in marginal habitat, circumstances where losses are bound to occur, not only from foxes but also from other predators (and the elements, if not the predators).

The value of the fox as a game species outweighs its value as a fur producer in those regions where fox hunting is practiced, and it has been found worthwhile to reduce or even to prohibit trapping in such regions in order that the fox may serve a higher form of "use" to fox hunters than to fur trappers.

Lynx (*Lynx canadensis*) **and Bobcat** (*Lynx rufus*). Two different short-tailed cats live over most of North America from central Mexico to the limit of trees. The lynx occupies the northern part and the bobcat or wildcat the southern and warmer part. Their habits are similar. Both feed primarily upon rodents and rabbits, though other animals may be taken when easier to get. The numbers of the lynx rise and fall with the fortunes of the snowshoe hare, upon which it depends for food. The lynx is a valuable fur animal and should be protected wholly for its fur qualities. Bobcat fur is much less valuable, but large numbers of pelts are sold in the market. The bobcat's rodent destruction justifies protection over most of its range. The role it plays in game bird abundance, though not clearly known, is presumed to be slight.

Beaver (*Castor canadensis*). The beaver originally occupied most of the continent from the Gulf to the Arctic and still is widely distributed over North America. Beaver dwell in water habitats, usually lakes and streams but sometimes swamps. They construct dams, where necessary or possible, to give stable water levels (Fig. 15.2). In some of our national parks, where the beaver are undisturbed, they build dams across very swift mountain streams. Evidently the beaver find the streams to be marginal habitat or nearly so, and it is evident that the belief that beaver do not use swift mountain streams comes in part from their low numbers over most of the continent; because of this low population, they are present only in relatively good beaver habitat and absent from marginal habitat found in swifter streams. Probably their appearance in swift streams is a gauge of their abundance. Beaver build new dams mostly in the spring and summer, though they repair them at all seasons when they can get about. They also build their own homes, of which they have two types: lodges in the water and burrows in the bank.

Fig. 15.2. A beaver dam thrown across an abandoned drainage ditch. Beaver render important service by impounding water for fish and waterfowl and for flood control.

Food. The beaver feeds primarily upon bark, though it also eats many other plant parts, chiefly of aquatics. It uses many species of trees for bark food, especially the aspens, with which the beaver is largely associated throughout its range, as well as willows and many softwoods (Fig. 15.3). Conifers are eaten little. The annual growth of an acre of aspen seems sufficient to supply the year's needs of a beaver. Roots of aquatic and shore plants, along with buds, stems, and foliage, supplement the bark forage, especially in summer.

Management Operations. In new areas or those where beavers have eaten all available aspen or other trees, planting may be resorted to for establishing a new stand. It is doubtful that the expense is warranted under ordinary conditions. Fast-growing hybrid aspens might help somewhat. The consumption and yield of bark can be determined by setting up yield tables as for regular forest operations.[1]

FIG. 15.3. Stumps cut by beavers give evidence of beaver presence. The number of stumps, together with the age and growth of the trees, gives some idea of the rate of consumption in relation to tree growth.

Though beavers cut trees chiefly in the fall when they are storing food for winter, some cutting may be done during other seasons for

[1] Yield tables as given in cords can be used in beaver studies. *Technical Bulletin* 39, *Minnesota Agricultural Experiment Station*, gives such tables.

feeding or dam repair or lodge construction. The length of the canals that beaver construct for gaining access to distant trees depends upon topography; the canals may reach 200 yards or more, but they are usually fewer than 100 yards long. In the absence of canals beavers rarely haul wood overland more than 100 yards. The potential availability of trees can be judged roughly by the distance from water or the practicality of running canals to them.

When emergencies arise in the beaver colony, aspen bolts hauled to the water will supply food. A reasonably safe estimate of the need for winter is one to two cords for each member of the colony. If need be, bolts can be thrust through the ice to feed the beavers in winter.

Trapping and Control. A controversial matter in beaver work is the beaver-trout relationship. Beavers help or hinder trout production according to the region and topography. They almost always benefit trout in swift streams, but they can be inimical to trout in sluggish streams where the ponds collect silt, which in turn may smother spawning beds. Warming of water by stagnation is the most frequent allegation against the beaver by fishermen, but this has been shown by most studies to be of little importance because all the water rarely becomes warmer than trout tolerance and most of it is reduced in temperature in the open stream below dams.

Beavers occasionally attack shade or fruit trees, flood roads, or plug irrigation and drainage canals. The removal of dams is more successful with dynamite than by hand, for a colony of beavers can outstrip the man with a shovel. Persistent beavers can be discouraged from a location by noisemakers, such as a paddle wheel striking a tin can, or by an electric current running through the water. A cable stretched across the water where beaver encounter it in swimming is said to be effective also. Problem beaver can be live-trapped and transported elsewhere for release; beaver for restocking are also trapped and transported in boxes, cages, or tow sacks, which should be kept wet. Beavers in self-opening cages have been dropped into remote areas by parachute. Pack strings are also used to carry beaver into the back country for release.

Man sometimes wishes to maintain a constant water level, but this wish may not be in keeping with that of the beaver. Constant levels can be maintained, however, by tubes through the dam so that the opening on the pond side is remote from the dam, a condition that seems to be beyond beaver comprehension. This is especially true if the tube opens below water and slants up to the dam at an angle. Culvert pipe works well, but a tube can be made in the woods by three poles or logs fastened together or a plank laid the length of three logs.

All beaver trapping should be done by live-trapping so that immature or other animals can be returned to the pond if not in prime condition. Beaver are usually sexed during live-trapping, but sexing is difficult for the layman because the animals possess cloacae. The presence of an os penis that denotes a male is easy to detect. Beaver are marked by branding on the tail and by punching holes in the webbing of the hind feet (Fig. 5.6). Tags ordinarily do not stay securely.

Beaver require protection from poaching, which is usually most severe at ponds some distance from roads, but they need no protection against natural enemies. Systematic bootlegging of pelts, although it occurs irregularly, is an ever-present threat. Some state game departments prefer to have all beaver trapping done by share-crop or state-paid trappers and all fur marketed by the state. Although such a state monopoly does simplify law enforcement for the administration, control of trapping in the customary way has been just as effective or more so in other states in preventing overtrapping, because a state administrative body that profits from the sale of furs is reluctant to cut its own spending money.

Muskrat (*Ondatra zibethica*). The muskrat inhabits most of North America, where it lives in cattail marshes, streams, ponds, and lakes. It is not its own engineer like the beaver, though it may build its own houses in marshes and make channels throughout the thick aquatic vegetation. The muskrat uses burrows in the banks or marsh edge or its own houses of mud and vegetation, which make it possible for these animals of low mobility to inhabit marshes without hard ground for burrows. Muskrats breed with true rodent rapidity, and there is a high mortality rate in the young; in fact life is cheap in the muskrat marsh when populations are high.

The muskrat feeds upon a multitude of marsh and aquatic vegetation; it shows a preference, however, for cattail roots and the like.

Management Practices. There are fewer management procedures for muskrats than for beavers, but the biological knowledge of the muskrat and its life aids materially in proper administrative procedures.

Protection from enemies generally is not essential because predation troubles the muskrat population little, except when the animals have been exposed to it by grazing, drought, fire, or flood. The rodent breeding ability seems to require a heavy predation factor to keep it in bounds. Systematic overtrapping, on the other hand, takes muskrats irrespective of their security of habitat and can menace the existence of a capacity population.

The trapping season of muskrats, as with other animals, ought to be regulated to avoid needless catching of muskrats before the fur is prime or the young mature. Muskrats breed early in the season, in some areas as early as mid-February, so that trapping late in the winter may take pregnant females needed to maintain the stand. Setting traps close to houses also tends to catch a higher run of females than males. In order to prevent crippling—because trapped animals twist their way out—traps should be set to drown the animal.

Maintenance of stable water levels is desirable, for flood may drive out the muskrats, as drought will also. Dikes or dams are valuable in controlling the water level and maintaining a suitable depth, which should not exceed 4 feet for maximum suitability.

Stakes driven into the marsh at an angle, along with old stumps and logs, often furnish resting places for the animals or foundations for their homes where the water is deep or the bottom soft. Large willows, even in rather wet soil, may supply places for burrows.

SUGGESTED READING

Arthur, Stanley Clisby, 1928, "The Fur Animals of Louisiana," *La. Dept. Cons. Bull.* 18.

Bachrach, Max, 1946, *Fur*, Prentice-Hall, Inc., New York.

Bradt, G. W., 1947, *Michigan Beaver Management*, Michigan Department of Conservation, Lansing.

Cahalane, Victor H., 1947, *Mammals of North America*, The Macmillan Co., New York.

Chase, Warren W., and Elizabeth B. Beard, 1948, *Teaching Aids in Wildlife Management; Outline of Management of Fur Animals*, Edwards Bros., Ann Arbor, Mich.

Chittenden, H. M., 1935, *The American Fur Trade of the Far West*, 2 vols., The Press of the Pioneers, Inc., New York.

Gerstell, Richard, 1937, "The Pennsylvania Bounty System," *Penn. Game Comm. Res. Bull.* 1.

Grinnell, Joseph, Joseph S. Dixon, and Jean M. Linsdale, 1937, *Fur-Bearing Mammals of California; Their Natural History, Systematic Status, and Relations to Man*, 2 vols., University of California Press, Berkeley.

Hamerstrom, F. N., Jr., and James Blake, 1939, "A Fur Study Technique," *Jour. Wildlife Management*, 3:54–59.

Hamilton, W. J., Jr., 1939, *American Mammals*, McGraw-Hill Book Co., New York.

Hamilton, W. J., Jr., 1943, *Mammals of Eastern North America*, Comstock Publishing Co., Ithaca, N. Y.

Innis, Harold A., 1930, *The Fur Trade in Canada; an Introduction to Canadian Economic History,* Yale University Press, New Haven, Conn.

Miller, J. Paul, and Burwell B. Powell, 1942, "Game and Wild-fur Production and Utilization on Agricultural Land," *U.S.D.A. Circ.* 636.

Murie, Adolph, 1936, "Following Fox Trails," *Univ. Mich. Mus. Zool. Misc. Publ.* 32.

Murie, Adolph, 1940, *Ecology of the Coyote in the Yellowstone,* Nat. Park Serv., Fauna Ser. 4.

Ogden, Adele, 1941, *The California Sea Otter Trade, 1784–1848,* University of California Press, Berkeley.

Seton, Ernest Thompson, 1925–1929, *Lives of Game Animals,* 4 vols., Doubleday, Doran and Co., Garden City, N. Y.

Sperry, Charles C., 1941, "Food Habits of the Coyote," *Fish and Wildlife Serv., Wildlife Res. Bull.* 4.

Stuewer, Frederick W., 1943, "Raccoons: Their Habits and Management in Michigan," *Ecol. Monographs,* 13:203–257.

Warren, E. R., 1927, *The Beaver, Its Work and Its Ways,* Williams and Wilkins Co., Baltimore.

Yeager, Lee E., 1941, "A Contribution toward a Bibliography on North American Fur Animals," *Ill. Natur. Hist. Surv. Biol. Notes* 10.

16

Wildfowl Management

Although several species of wildfowl other than waterfowl will be mentioned in this chapter, the main emphasis will be upon the waterfowl, not because the other wildfowl are less important or less interesting but because hunting pressure and consequent need for waterfowl management are far greater. Our knowledge of waterfowl management is also far greater than it is for other species.

Waterfowl belong to the order Anseriformes, composed of two families, the Anhimidae restricted to South America and the Anatidae of world-wide distribution.[1] The waterfowl of North America divide into five natural groups composed of 47 species native north of the Rio Grande. Because they are hunted, three species of Rallidae are frequently allied by man with waterfowl. These species are shown in the tabulation.

Swans and Geese

Mute swan [2]
Whistling swan
Trumpeter swan
American brant
Emperor goose (accidental)
Snow goose

Ross goose
Canada goose
Black brant
White-fronted goose
Blue goose

Tree Ducks

Black-bellied tree duck   Fulvous tree duck

[1] Lexicographers differ in the use of the term *waterfowl*. Some hold that they are any web-footed bird, others any aquatic bird hunted by man, and others only members of the order Anseriformes. The Migratory Bird Treaty defines *waterfowl* as members of the Anatidae family. In this book *waterfowl* will be used to mean members of the order Anseriformes, and *wildfowl* to mean collectively waterfowl and other water birds, such as coots, grebes, or gallinules.

[2] Feral in parts of North America.

Dabbling Ducks

Mallard	Wood duck
Black duck	Pintail
New Mexican duck	Green-winged teal
Mottled duck	Blue-winged teal
Gadwall	Cinnamon teal
European widgeon	Shoveller
Baldpate	

Diving Ducks

Redhead	Steller eider
Ring-necked duck	American eider
Canvasback	Pacific eider
Greater scaup	King eider
Lesser scaup	Spectacled eider
American goldeneye	White-winged scoter
Barrow goldeneye	Surf scoter
Old squaw	American scoter
Harlequin	Ruddy [1]

Mergansers

Hooded merganser	American merganser
Red-breasted merganser	

Non-waterfowl Species

Purple gallinule	Florida gallinule
Coot	

Waterfowl Areas and Flyways. The chief original waterfowl breeding grounds of interior North America extended from the middle of the United States north to Alaska and the adjacent Arctic islands; the continental margins where important numbers bred included the general Arctic coastal areas from the Mackenzie Delta east to Labrador, and took in also the shores of Hudson Bay. Special concentrations of note are known for this region, such as those on Baffin Island, in the Maritime Provinces, and the St. Lawrence area (Fig. 16.1). Waterfowl no longer breed in numbers at all near their former abundance in the middle and northern United States and the southern part of Canada, especially in the prairie states and provinces. The chief breeding areas were limited to the glaciated regions of North America, now covered by both prairie and forest. Glaciation, by disturbing the drainage pattern, made many poorly drained areas that resulted in innumerable marshes, sloughs, ponds, lakes, and sluggish streams.

The area reaching northward from Nebraska and Iowa to northern Saskatchewan and Manitoba constituted the "heart" of waterfowl

---

[1] In a strict sense the ruddy probably should not be classed as a diving duck.

Waterfowl Areas and Flyways

breeding range in North America, once one of the world's great waterfowl areas. The northern part still is important, though less so than

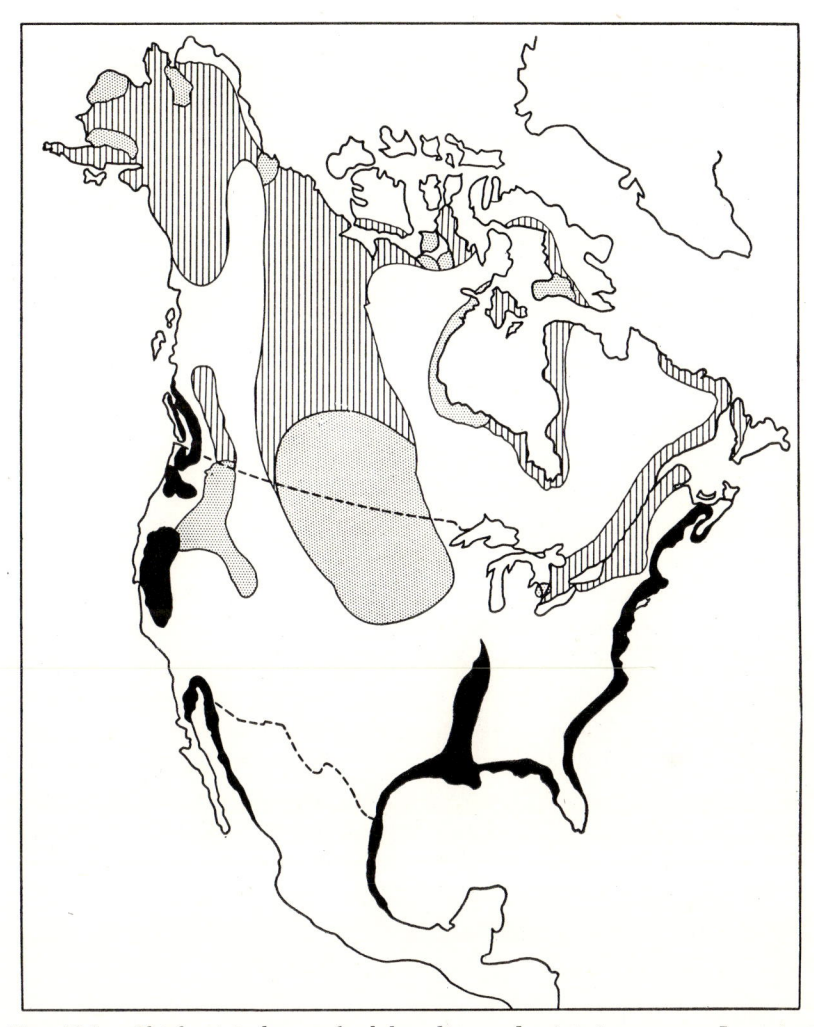

FIG. 16.1. Chief original waterfowl breeding and wintering areas. Important wintering waterfowl concentrations occur in the black areas, though waterfowl winter wherever open water occurs. The chief breeding grounds are shaded, and the more important parts are indicated by dotting.

in its former state. Cultivation and grazing, combined with shooting and some drought, have been mainly responsible for this decline in waterfowl range. About 85 per cent of the waterfowl nest in Canada, for the most part north of the "drought area," while 75 per cent of the hunting is done within the United States.

The winter range of wildfowl extends as far north as open water. Wildfowl winter in great numbers in the marches along both coasts, in the marshes of the Gulf coast, and in the lower Mississippi Valley. Some migrate farther south into Mexico and Central America, and some cinnamon teal, blue-winged teal, and shovellers may reach South America. Areas south of the Rio Grande play a most unimportant part in providing hunting pressure on waterfowl. Some shorebirds winter regularly as far south as southern South America.

"*Flyways.*" The concept of "flyways" grew out of the idea that waterfowl followed four lines of migration that merge into one another as broad belts; they are better administrative units, however, than biological actualities. The four "flyways" are: the *Atlantic flyway*, between the Atlantic Ocean and the Allegheny Mountains, bending eastward at the northern end; the *Mississippi flyway*, between the Allegheny Mountains and Saskatchewan, Nebraska, and Texas; the *Central flyway*, between the Mississippi flyway and a line through Utah and New Mexico; and the *Pacific flyway*, extending from the central flyway to the Pacific Ocean.

Changes in Status of Waterfowl. Profound changes have resulted from a number of causes, but it cannot be denied that the chief one is overshooting. There are approximately 2 million or more hunters bagging no fewer than 10 million ducks annually. The cripple loss is nearly as great; this loss, added to the natural mortality incumbent upon any creatures in the wild, gives a heavy total annual drain upon the waterfowl stand. Thirty to thirty-five per cent of the stand seems to be somewhere near the actual drain; wild populations seldom seem able to withstand a consistent drain exceeding 20 per cent. The lack of sufficient breeding pairs upon northern breeding grounds seems to reflect the overdrain upon the brood stock.

The most fundamental change of all those due to settlement has resulted from drainage of marsh and lowland. An estimated 77 million acres have been drained since the Swamp Land Act of 1850. The 1940 census gives the land area of the United States as 2,977,128 square miles as against 2,973,776 in 1930, an increase of 3,352 square miles (2,145,280 acres) attributed in a large measure to decrease of inland water area. The majority of the drainage projects have failed to provide land as good as or better than surrounding high land; often lake bottoms and marshes are but a thin layer of humus soil over sand. Peat of a marsh decomposes upon exposure to air, and the consequent lowering of the surface may result in loss to crop land and even a return to fairly wet conditions. Changes in the ecology of a marsh follow upon the heels of drainage work to the detriment of water birds. Often these changes encourage the encroachment of brush and other cover of little use to water birds.

Mosquito control likewise has been a serious factor in some areas in reducing the suitable waterfowl habitat, especially in the East.

Fig. 16.2. Drainage for mosquito control may destroy waterfowl areas along coastal marshes without eliminating breeding places for mosquitoes.

Drainage work has been especially active along the salt-marsh coasts (Fig. 16.2), where it has sometimes failed to eliminate or to reduce the mosquitoes. In some parts of the country destruction of emergent vegetation is required by mosquito control regulations. Although it must be granted that the control of mosquitoes is necessary for health and convenience, rational operations have a less adverse effect upon waterfowl than untried and uncontrolled work.

Continued deficiency of rainfall in many parts of the continent has aggravated the situation on the waterfowl breeding grounds. The effect of drought cycles is most serious on water levels in the continental interior, where the area along the dry margin stretches from Texas north into the prairie provinces. The effect has been noticed elsewhere, but the greatest drying of waterfowl marshes has occurred in the interior, particularly from the Lake states to the High Plains. It appears that either little deficiency of rainfall has occurred in the

254   *Wildfowl Management*

Far North or that undisturbed marshes are better able to maintain themselves in the face of rainfall decline, for reports indicate that northern waterfowl breeding areas are substantially full of water during drought farther south. Highs of long cycles mean wet periods with short droughts; lows mean dry periods with short-time relief by wet years (Fig. 16.3). The precipitation that the marshes need thus fluctuates in definite cycles of both long and short periodicity. Periods

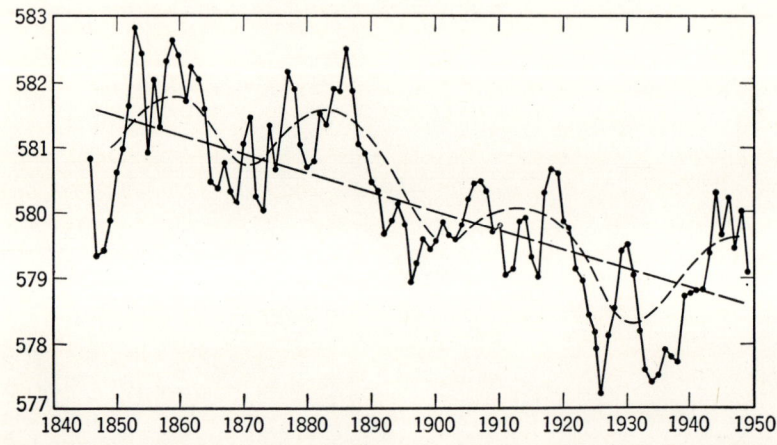

Fig. 16.3. A century of water levels. The elevations above sea level of Lake Michigan at Milwaukee (1846–1949) show a long rainfall cycle of about 152 years, and two shorter ones of about 11 and 9½ years. The highs of long cycles mean wet periods with temporary drought; lows mean dry periods with temporary relief by wet years.

of lessened rainfall tend to encourage invasion of normally wet areas by farmers and stockmen; increase in drainage projects seems to accompany drought also.

Drought in the breeding season causes loss of young; earlier drought may reduce nesting attempts. The loss of food and cover plants through drying of the marshes and lakes is especially serious; most aquatic plants are rarely able to stand exposure for any length of time and may require many years to re-establish themselves upon the return of water.

Enemies of Waterfowl. Overemphasis is universally placed upon predator control as a means of increasing desired species, even though it has yet to be demonstrated technically that control of natural predators has increased or will increase appreciably the number of waterfowl. (Man is still the chief predator, and all others fade into

Effect of Pollution upon Wildfowl

insignificance beside him.) Few hawks or owls can do more than consistently catch the weak, sick, exposed, crippled, or insecure ducks. In summer some predation loss may occur from exposure of molting ducks, such as mottled ducks, in dry or burned-over marshes. Because of the year-round shooting in predator campaigns, usually by unreliable gunners, greater loss may occur from disturbance than from the predators themselves.

Where turtles are excessive, they may be controlled by the use of live traps baited with meat. In some areas turtles are trapped commercially.

Mammalian predators may prey upon water birds in breeding areas by catching nesting birds and young and occasionally by breaking up nests. Live trapping is the recommended method of dealing with such predators if the habitat is strong; otherwise the habitat should receive first attention. Live-trapped animals may be released elsewhere.

The crow has been reported to be a factor in nest destruction under special circumstances in areas where the bird has increased its range since settlement. The highest figure reported is a possible loss chargeable to crows of 31 per cent of the nest destruction during drought years in the prairie provinces, which are not normal crow range. On the normal crow range, crow destruction of waterfowl nests is slight at most, and that occurring in the prairie provinces is unusual. Only when water levels drop does crow predation become significant.

Grazing cattle expose duck nests by eating the nesting cover. They may also cause some loss by trampling. Trampling, eating, and puddling of the vegetation or bottom in prairie sloughs reduce the desirability of the land for waterfowl.

Carp may destroy vegetation, particularly wild rice, where conditions are unusual. The destructiveness of carp or other fish to waterfowl areas or vegetation seems to be largely a local problem. The muskrat occasionally destroys vegetation that could be used by water birds, but the muskrat is a strong ally of the water birds because of its work in opening channels, building houses, and the like.

Effect of Pollution upon Wildfowl. Chemical pollution poisons both aquatic plants and aquatic animal life upon which waterfowl depend; the destruction of vegetation means the destruction of habitat, always more drastic and longer lasting than the direct killing of animals. Aquatic plants and most invertebrates are smothered by the sludge that creeps along the bottom of many sewage-choked streams. Sewage interferes with light transmission, causing a marked reduction in photosynthesis by plants. On the other hand, a small amount of sewage, organic in nature, may have a fertilizing effect upon the water and increase animal life. An excess uses up dissolved oxygen.

Oil pollution kills many ducks. The oil not only destroys emergent vegetation but it also mats the birds' feathers, both body and flight, so that birds covered with oil may be unable to fly. Matted feathers also reduce the insulation factor, and oil-soaked birds may become chilled and may perish from exposure, pneumonia, starvation, or even drowning. Oil reaches the water from many sources, such as industrial wastes, filling stations, refineries, oil wells, and mosquito-control work. Along navigation routes and on the high seas, oil pollution is caused chiefly by boats that give off oil in the exhaust, in the bilge water, or in ballast water from empty fuel tanks. Tankers are notorious offenders. Oil is sometimes discharged into waters by accidents and from damaged ships also.

Oil pollution in inland waters is being brought under control by application of restrictive laws, even to motor boats. Emptying crankcase drainings into a lake has been known to kill ducks in an arm of the waters. Restrictive laws and cooperative efforts among shipping nations have also brought some success in control of oil pollution in coastal waters and on the high seas. The four main methods of reducing oil pollution fall under these four headings:

> Removal of oil by separators in exhaust and bilge lines.
> Discharge of ballast at least 50 miles offshore.
> Prevention of accidents that might release oil.
> Disposal of oil wastes in places other than sewers or connections to waterways.

Disease. Many diseases affect different waterfowl, but only those which are important in general management practice or for which management procedures have been devised will be treated here. These three chief diseases are botulism, alkali poisoning, and lead poisoning.

Botulism.[1] Botulism affects many water birds and land birds. It has been reported attacking grebes, herons, gulls, shore birds, and other frequenters of the marsh, shore, and water. More than three score species are known to have been susceptible. Man is not susceptible to duck botulism, and no danger occurs in handling dead or ailing birds.

[1] Botulism and alkali poisoning are often confused; many of the epizootics attributed to alkali poisoning may have been botulism. It is also called *duck sickness* or *western duck sickness.*

Disease

Botulism is caused by bacteria (*Clostridium botulinum*, Type C), which produce toxins in decaying organic matter. They are not active in living tissue, and botulism is not contagious; it is contracted through ingestion of the toxins in the food or water. The conditions that favor botulism may be listed as:

> Abundant decaying organic matter.
> A suitable medium (pH of 7.1 to 10.0).
> Oxygen deficiency.
> Shallow water (usually less than a foot deep).
> Still water.
> Warm water (optimum about 98.5° F).

Though botulism is indigenous, and perhaps endemic also, to the arid and semiarid parts of western North America, it occurs over a wide area. It appears that only when conditions are suitable do the bacteria become a serious factor. The problem has been intensified by drainage, irrigation, and reclamation, which, by changing water levels and alkalinity, have sometimes brought about conditions favorable to botulism.

Diagnosis of botulism is relatively simple, and the presence of botulism can be detected by cursory examination as well as by isolating the causative organism. Manifestations of the disease are:

> Paralysis of wing, then legs, and finally neck.
> Breathing difficulty.
> Eye and nostril discharge; tends to become cheesy.
> Greenish diarrhea; may block cloaca.
> Lowering of body temperature.

Remedies are best applied as preventives rather than as treatments after the disease becomes epizootic; the methods that have been tried or used are:

> Frightening birds from contaminated areas.
> Treatment of sick birds, especially with fresh water, but also by "shots."
> Elimination of mud flats by flooding or drying.
> Change of water levels.
> Construction of devices for draining affected areas.
> Circulation of water.
> Sanitation by cleaning shorelines, disposal of organic debris, disposal of dead and dying ducks.

Alkali Poisoning. Under normal conditions, alkali poisoning is not serious, and it does not occur where continuous flow provides fresh water. Alkali is concentrated by evaporation of water, as in the arid and semiarid West. The disease results from the toxic action of alkali salts, particularly chlorides of calcium and magnesium. The symptoms are similar to those of botulism but can be distinguished, it is said, by the lack of a well-defined "air hunger" during advanced stages of disability. Also, the fluid discharge from the eyes does not become cheesy. The salts cause diarrhea and severe irritation of the intestinal tract.

Lead Poisoning. Lead poisoning menaces waterfowl in those areas that have been subjected to heavy and continued shooting. Lead accumulates on lake or river bottoms in front of some blinds, and the bottom may become filled with lead shot after some years of shooting. Waterfowl swallow the shots when feeding, perhaps through mistaking the hard pellets for seeds. The top opening of the gizzard assures that pellets will remain inside and be ground up for assimilation by the body. Six No. 6 pellets, and perhaps fewer, can cause the death of a duck. Lead is a cumulative poison, which greatly increases the likelihood of poisoning.

Paralysis sets in first in the leg muscles, progresses to the wing muscles, and finally reaches the neck. Sick birds usually go ashore; otherwise they are subject to drowning. The nictitating membrane is unaffected and the appetite is unimpaired, but food may clog the esophagus. Lead poisoning causes a green diarrhea, and a regurgitation of a greenish fluid may take place.

No practical methods are known for treating sick birds, but lead can be removed from individual birds by a tube into the stomach. There are no practical methods of removing lead from the bottom. It is possible that reduction in shooting over hard bottoms, where the lead pellets will not sink in the mud, may reduce the lead available, but we must remember that more ducks die from forcible lead penetration than from lead ingestion. Experiments with disintegrating alloys promise much; the only disadvantages of these alloys seem to be the lower efficiency and the slightly higher cost over lead shot. Hunters appear unwilling to pay the price voluntarily, and the force of law may be needed to bring disintegrating shot into general use.

Food Habits. Waterfowl generally take any available food that fits the framework of their instinctive food selection. Some are more vegetarian than others, however, but nearly all aquatic vegetation, foliage, seeds, root stocks, and tubers, as well as aquatic animal life, are taken by some water bird. But to the wildlife manager there is no substitute for experience in learning how widely local conditions may differ and how seemingly disdainful of available foods birds frequently show themselves to be.

Food Habits

Stomach analysis tends to overemphasize the hard foods, as soft material disappears quickly or rapidly becomes a mass of indistinguishable pulp. Study of food habits requires a combination of field observation and laboratory analysis for best results.

Waterfowl Food Plants. Although local abundance of vegetation generally determines its use, a number of aquatics are sufficiently dis-

Fig. 16.4. *Saggitaria* is an important food and cover plant for waterfowl. (Mississippi River bottoms, near LaCrosse, Wisconsin.)

tributed over the continent and so widely used as to be important or even key food plants (Fig. 16.4). Chief among these are:

Pond weeds (*Potamogeton*).
Rice (*Zizania*, eastern North America).
Celery (*Vallisineria*, eastern North America).
Wapato, duck potato (*Saggitaria*).
Nut grass (*Chufa*).

Bulrush (*Scirpus*).
Widgeon grass (*Ruppia*).
Smartweed (*Polygonum*).
Eel grass (*Zostera*, coastal zone).

Feeding Habits. The dabbling ducks, geese, and swans feed chiefly upon plant foods, whereas mergansers feed almost wholly upon animal matter. The proportion varies and has been reported as follows among the diving ducks in percentage of animal foods (after Cottam):

Northern eider	99.37	Bufflehead	79.02
Harlequin	98.32	Barrow goldeneye	77.66
American eider	96.31	American goldeneye	73.91
Pacific eider	95.26	Greater scaup	53.48
King eider	94.49	Lesser scaup	40.45
White-winged scoter	94.12	Ruddy	27.59
American scoter	89.66	Canvasback	19.41
Old squaw	87.93	Ring-necked duck	18.53
Surf scoter	87.90	Redhead	10.34
Steller eider	87.14		

Diving birds seek vegetation in deep water but bring it to the surface for consumption. A fixed ratio exists in general between the depth of the water and the time submerged. If the time of three successive dives is averaged, the depth of water can be determined with bottom feeders by allowing 20 seconds for the first fathom (6 feet) and 10 seconds for each fathom thereafter. This is known as the 20:10 ratio and holds for most water birds; the time-depth ratio for the coot, however, is 10:10. The old squaw, loon, and some other water birds dive to depths of 200 feet at times. The specific volume of the body is lowered in preparation for the descent by *exhaling* the breath, compressing the body, and compressing the feathers. The pneumaticity of the bones is low in diving birds, which also aids in making the deflated body heavier than water. The extended neck of the diving bird produces apnoea. Oxygen present in the oxyhemoglobin and oxymyoglobin supplies the needs when submerged.

Dabbling ducks, in contrast to diving ducks, feed upon materials found in shallow marshes and waters. But, if **driven out from shore** by shooting or excess disturbance, they will feed upon floating vegetation torn loose from the bottom by the diving ducks, coots, muskrats, and other animals. In a sense this feeding is a form of symbiosis.

Time of Feeding. Waterbirds feed regularly throughout the daylight hours, but when disturbed by excessive hunting they may shift their feeding time in order to feed chiefly in the early morning hours, at dusk, or at night and but slightly during the day. Geese and some ducks will feed during moonlight nights when they even fly to wheat fields, rice fields, or pastures.

General Waterfowl Range Improvement. The general needs of waterfowl can be listed as:

> Clean water.
> Relatively stable water levels.
> Food.
> Protective cover on land and water.
> Freedom from disturbance.

Sterile lake bottoms can no more produce adequate food and cover for water birds than poor upland can produce food and cover in sufficient amounts for upland game animals. Rich bottom soils produce rich aquatic life, and waterfowl conditions are best where soils are best.

The improvements that benefit water birds in general are determined by circumstances and the ingenuity of the man in control. The chief operations fall under the following headings:

General Waterfowl Range Improvement

Control of water levels.
Construction of nesting and resting islands.
Installation of nesting and resting structures.
Construction of bars and shallows.
Digging canals and lagoons.
Increasing shorelines.
Installing improvements for aquatic animal life.
Plowing and seeding bottoms subject to flooding.
Sowing quick-growing vegetation on exposed bottoms.
Clearing debris.
Clearing shorelines and beaches.
Planting shores to cover or food plants.
Planting aquatic vegetation.
Increasing water area.

Waterfowl, especially geese and dabbling ducks, prefer grassy slopes to timbered ones. Clearing a strip around the shore provides better feeding and resting grounds and is sometimes a means of increasing the usefulness of marshes, lakes, and ponds in forested regions. Because tall timber around small woodland ponds and marshes may interfere with free flight, clearing small flight ways between adjoining woodland ponds may increase their use.

Dabbling ducks prefer water not more than 2 or 3 feet deep because they are tippers in feeding. Diving ducks use deeper water, but, unless it is clear, water deeper than 10 or 12 feet produces little vegetation. Some deep water is needed in times of drought, however, to protect the birds.

Suitable waterfowl area is related to the amount of shoreline, which can be increased by coves, indentations, lagoons, bars, and islands. Islands need not be more than a few feet in diameter; in fact the same amount of island area in small units is more valuable than in one. Waterfowl, especially swans, geese, and dabbling ducks, require rocks, bars, or dry shore for preening, sunning, or resting. These resting places may be logs, rocks, or even muskrat houses, and they can be increased by artificial rock or crib work.

Suitable vegetation may vary with the species of water birds. Some prefer beds of rushes, rice, pond lilies, and wapato, though they may use a wide variety of aquatic vegetation. Heavy emergent vegetation is almost essential for dabbling ducks, and some is also advisable for diving ducks, even though they will live out in the open water.

Some water birds, such as grebes, build floating nests of vegetation, often on a spar or other support. Most ducks nest on land, but some use holes in trees. Hollow trees or nest boxes near shore benefit hole nesters, chiefly the wood duck, goldeneye, bufflehead, and hooded merganser. Most of the nesting occurs close to the water, but mallards, wood ducks, and mottled ducks, for example, may nest more than a mile from water.

The density of nests among some Arctic water birds seems to vary with the cover, but among many, space demands limit the population to available territories. This demand may be a more universal biological factor of the duck than has been presumed.

Control of Water Levels. Changes in water level after nesting begins may have serious consequences. Rising waters flood nests, and

Fig. 16.5. An earthen dam for impounding water.

receding ones leave broods stranded. Exposure of the bottom may kill aquatic vegetation and animal life. Stable water levels are generally best for ducks.

There are several types of dams, varying in construction: masonry, earth-fill, rock-fill, and crib. The type to build depends upon materials at hand, the site, strain to be expected, and the money available. Masonry dams are often too expensive, and earthen dams, which generally prove to be cheapest, are usually satisfactory (Figs. 16.5 and 16.6). Lasting material, such as concrete, may be required in the spillway. The usual mixture suggested for work around dams is 1 part Portland cement, 2 parts fine aggregate, and 4 parts coarse aggregate, with the minimum of water to mix.

Dams tend to leak, and often an impervious core of clay, concrete, wood, or steel is needed to reduce leaking. Leakage can also be controlled by "puddling" the face of the dam or bottom of the pond. Commercial preparations have been successful, but common clay generally works as well and is cheaper. The action of silt alone tends to seal ponds and dams in a few years anyway.

Dams must be merged into the adjacent higher grounds to prevent water from working around the ends. The upstream face varies in slope from 3 to 1 to as much as 6 to 1, and the downstream face between 1 to 1 and 6 to 1. The height above the water may reach as much as 6 feet, and the part above water needs to be given a gentle

Fig. 16.6. A dam constructed to hold water. The upstream side (to the left in the picture) is much more gently sloped than the downstream side.

slope in order that the dam will serve as a resting and feeding area. Generally the top of the dam is sowed to grasses, but sometimes trees and shrubs are needed to anchor the soil. The water side of the dam, if exposed to wave action, may be covered with riprap; otherwise vegetation is preferred.

Marsh Control. Control of water levels is no less important in marshes than in lakes and ponds. In tidal marshes dikes and water gates can stabilize water levels despite changes in tides. Stabilizing structures may be built also in fresh-water marshes to retain spring flood water, as well as to regulate the depth of water where needed, as for botulism control. Control in marshes may be achieved with dikes, impervious cores, diversions, and even pumping. Low earthen dikes, sometimes several miles in length, have been used. When financially possible, it may be advisable to construct an impervious core in a trench across the outer fringes of a marsh in order to reduce seepage through coarse soil. The water supply can be increased also by diversion of water from elsewhere or by obtaining it from wells, springs, and reservoirs. Pumping water into marshes is often too expensive, but occasionally a hydraulic ram has been used locally.

Improving Food and Cover. The first step in improvement is a survey of the existing food and cover and their condition. This is particularly needed for long-time programs. Aquatic plants have environmental preferences no less than land plants have. The major ones are:

> Climate.
> Soil type.
> Soil condition (firm, fertile, stable, etc.).
> Suitable pH (some have wide, some have narrow, tolerances).
> Sunlight.
> Suitable water.
> Stable water levels.

Planting. The results of introducing exotic plants are not predictable; planting stock should come from local sources. Alien plants may become pests even though apparently satisfactory in other regions. Planting programs that take seed and stock from local areas may be delayed thereby, but in the end the results usually justify the caution. A mistake once made can be costly. As a rule commercial and unknown seeds and stock should be avoided.

The species to select will vary with the region and local conditions. The vegetation already present is another factor. There are many species of aquatics that may be planted, and selection will have to be made for each area individually.

Aquatic plants propagate from seeds, tubers, root stocks, whole plants, cuttings, or buds. Generally seeds and vegetative parts may be gathered at the appropriate time and kept until planting season in moist or water storage. The storage of aquatic material requires more care than that of terrestrial plants. Damp and cool storage may be enough for some, but underwater storage may be needed for others. The natural method used by the plants in the wild to carry seed over to the sprouting season is a good indicator of the method to choose.

Planting procedures vary with the species of plant as well as with the area. Planting may be done from a boat or from shore or by wading. Plant parts that will not sink to the bottom can be weighted or staked down. Weights may be needed also when planting in a current. Clay balls, mesh bags with weights, or weights tied to the plant will hold the plants down.

Control of Plants. Algae sometimes create a problem by choking a stream, lake, or pond, especially those containing sugary organic pollution, as from mills. Copper sulphate distributed at the rate of 1 pound to each million gallons of water generally eradicates the algae, but in quantity it may kill fish. The usual methods employed for weed control include poison sprays like 2,4-D. Mechanical methods are also used. The general methods fall into eight types:

Drainage	Cutting
Flooding	Digging
Burning	Smothering
Grazing	Poisoning

Nest Boxes. The ducks that nest in holes and cavities in trees may use nest boxes put out for them. A satisfactory box can be made easily from old boards. Slabs make boxes that are more natural in appearance, and those built of boards may be covered with bark. Nail kegs and hollow tree sections have also been used. A nest box of suitable size measures 10 by 15 inches inside and 15 inches high. The entrance holes should be about 4 by 2½ inches in size and not more than 3 inches above the floor. A cleat of rough material fastened below the entrance hole aids the bird entering the nest. Boxes usually are placed 10 to 40 feet above the ground.

Protection. The greatest single need of waterfowl in general is still more protection from hunters. Excessive drain on the waterfowl population has been materially speeded up by the advent of the automobile, increase in number of hunters, increased gun power, increased leisure time, and decline in waterfowl habitat. Curtailment of hunting pressure has been sought by various means, chiefly the bag limit and shorter seasons, but the high license fee still may be the only feasible way to reduce the kill to the biological surplus. Yet there is no biological surplus of ducks when the desired population level is not in sight. The number of waterfowl, coots, and gallinules in North America was estimated at 27 million at the opening of the 1935 nesting season. The January 1940 population was reckoned at 65 million, the increase being credited variously to refuge programs or to "duck factory" improvement. During the mid-forties, however, the number of waterfowl and other associated water birds declined.

Protection needs are greatest in the United States, where about three-quarters of the kill takes place, in consequence more drastic curtailments than those in Mexico or Canada are logical. The kill in Mexico is insignificant and does not equal in a season a good day's hunting in the United States.

A number of species have suffered more from overshooting than others, as well as from differences in breeding-ground loss. Differential protection is the recommended practice, though this makes it necessary for the hunter to distinguish different species, a requirement not yet invoked. In 1947, for example, two-thirds of the American brant along the Atlantic coast disappeared, though the number did increase a little during the next two seasons.

A number of hunting practices have been prohibited permanently or temporarily in the evolution of regulations. Among these should be mentioned:

>Spring shooting.
>Night hunting.
>Shooting over baited areas.
>Early morning and late evening hunting.
>Use of sink boxes or sneak boats.
>Use of live decoys.
>More than three shells in the gun.
>Automatic guns.
>Shooting from automobiles, power boats, and aircraft.

Cripple Loss. The loss from crippling varies between 10 and 75 per cent of the total bag, depending upon the method of hunting and the equipment, skill, and conscientiousness of the hunter. The greatest crippling is done by novice hunters, the lowest by veteran hunters. The heaviest losses occur in pass shooting. It seems entirely conservative to estimate that, for every 10 birds actually retrieved, the hunter leaves 2 or more cripples in the marsh, most of them to die. Seven cripples for each 10 seems the best all-round estimate. How many deaths will occur among those birds carrying lead shot in the body is not known. Fluoroscope and X-ray studies indicate that perhaps 1 out of 4 have shot in the body.

Sex Ratios. Under normal conditions the sex ratio is about evenly balanced in nature. Among polygamous animals deferred maturity or mortality may change the sex ratio. Differential hunting loss may upset the sex ratio. Differential sex migration and flocking habits may bring about differences in the hunting-season effect. No suitable regulations are known that will change the sex ratio, but a closed season will restore a sex ratio out of balance from hunting.

Refuges. Refuges play an important part in waterfowl administration and management; their primary purpose is to assist in the return of an adequate breeding stock to breeding grounds. A substantial number of waterfowl may breed also on refuges. Their principal function is to protect waterfowl from hunters and to protect the environment from destruction. If neither adverse effect is likely to occur, an organized refuge is not needed.

Though refuges are intended to protect the waterfowl, it is possible for an isolated refuge actually to increase the kill in its neighborhood, just as a section of duck-club property is closed to hunting in order to increase the number to be killed on the open area. Public shooting grounds near a refuge may make the refuge completely valueless as an aid to waterfowl increase or survival or as a protection to the waterfowl brood stock. Refuges established in connection with shooting grounds likewise may have an adverse effect. It is probable also that some existing refuges have a negative value because the increase in the number of waterfowl killed in the neighborhood is greater than the number escaping death because of the refuge operation.

Unless a refuge offers food and resting opportunities of the kind needed, it is a refuge in name only, and from the administrative standpoint it is better to abolish such a refuge and to work elsewhere. Good sites are often occupied by hunting clubs and other private owners, and usually such properties have too high a value for refuge purchase. The small amount of money available to public agencies can provide little except land that is poor or unmarketable. Since private property is the fundamental policy of democracies, and placing land on the tax rolls the fundamental policy of our states and their citizens, a very high degree of justification is necessary before such private lands may be taken over by public and thereby non-taxable agencies. Extra effort is required on low-value sites to make them attractive to waterfowl, but low-value land is usually all that can be had. The size of an area is not the measure of its effectiveness as a refuge. On the contrary, effectiveness is measured by the number of birds the refuge serves.

To be successful refuges need to operate together, as far as possible, rather than operating as isolated units. A well-defined program of refuges, as along the Mississippi River in its upper reaches, works best in returning an adequate breeding stock to the nesting grounds themselves. Refuges function best as a part of a program that includes hunting restrictions.

There are a number of criteria for measuring the probable usefulness and success of a refuge. The major ones may be listed as:

Nearness to heavily used flight routes.
Nearness to other refuges.
Adequate water.
Adequate food and cover.
Freedom from disturbance.
Satisfactory hunting restrictions.
Adequate patrol against poachers.
Large size.

Public activities in refuges—such as recreation, trapping, logging, grazing, farming, digging gravel, fishing, or upland game hunting—may be permitted if they will not interfere with the primary purpose as refuges for waterfowl. It is easy, however, to reduce the refuges' attractiveness to waterfowl by these practices unless they are carefully watched.

Refuges vary in size as well as in purpose. Federal waterfowl refuges have been classified as *super refuges* (e.g., Upper Mississippi), *primary refuges* (e.g., Upper Klamath), and *secondary refuges* (e.g., Turnbull Slough). There are also *special refuges, easement refuges,* and *bird rocks.*

Trapping, Marking, and Censusing. Duck traps are of many designs, which depend upon the material at hand and the situation in which they are used. Although successful trapping requires skill, experience, and care, ducks are easily caught and marked with aluminum bands during migration and in the winter. In addition to regular bands, ducks can be feather-marked for individual studies. Day-old ducklings can be marked by punching holes in the webbing on the foot or attaching clips to the patagium. "Cannons" have been used to fire projectiles attached to the leading edge of folded nets, which thus casts the net over birds at baited grounds. Young can be caught on nesting grounds as can adults also when molting. The birds can then be herded into corrals or, if in the water, directed into corrals on shore by means of drift fences.

Direct counts of water birds are made on foot or from airplanes, boats, and canoes during all seasons of the year. Flocks in flight or rafted on the water are counted individually or estimated by counting a segment and applying this factor to the flock. Successive doubling of an initial block count (such as 5, 10, 20, 40, etc.) is very useful for flocks in the air. Rafts can be counted sometimes by estimating the area covered and allowing a square yard for each bird; the total of birds is thus the total of the yardage.

Nest counts are made in the field by hard field work. Sometimes the number of nesting birds can be determined from the number of territories. Brood counts are best made in early morning or immediately before dark, when the young are out feeding. By this method, not only the number of broods and the young can be determined but also the apparent age of the young. A good pair of binoculars and a high point of vantage are helpful in brood counting.

The "Lincoln index" was devised originally as a means for estimating waterfowl numbers from banding returns.

SUGGESTED READING

Anonymous, 1947, *Malaria Control on Impounded Water*, U. S. Public Health Serv. and Tenn. Valley Authority, Washington, D. C.

Beard, Elizabeth B., and Warren W. Chase, 1947, *Teaching Aids in Wildlife Management; Outline of Waterfowl Management*, Edwards Bros., Ann Arbor, Mich.

Bennett, Logan J., 1938, *The Blue-winged Teal, Its Ecology and Management*, Collegiate Press, Ames, Iowa.

Bent, Arthur Cleveland, 1923, 1925, "Life Histories of North American Wild Fowl," *U. S. Nat. Mus. Bulls.* 126, 130.

Cottam, Clarence, 1939, "Food Habits of North American Diving Ducks," *U.S.D.A. Tech. Bull.* 643.

Day, Albert M., 1949, *North American Waterfowl*, The Macmillan Co., New York.

Fassett, Norman, 1940, *A Manual of Aquatic Plants*, McGraw-Hill Book Co., New York.

Gabrielson, Ira N., 1943, *Wildlife Refuges*, The Macmillan Co., New York.

Hochbaum, H. Albert, 1944, *The Canvasback on a Prairie Marsh*, American Wildlife Institute, Washington, D. C.

Kalmbach, E. R., 1934, "Western Duck Sickness: A Form of Botulism," *U.S.D.A. Tech. Bull.* 411.

Kortright, Francis H., 1943, *The Ducks, Geese, and Swans of North America*, American Wildlife Institute, Washington, D. C.

McAtee, W. L., 1939, *Wildfowl Food Plants, Their Value, Propagation, and Management*, Collegiate Press, Ames, Iowa.

Martin, A. C., and F. M. Uhler, 1939, "Food of Game Ducks in the United States and Canada," *U.S.D.A. Tech. Bull.* 634.

Phillips, John C., 1922–1926, *A Natural History of the Ducks*, 4 vols., Houghton Mifflin Co., Boston.

Pirnie, Miles David, 1935, *Michigan Waterfowl Management*, Mich. Dept. Cons., Lansing.

Theroux, Frank R. (and others), 1943, *Laboratory Manual for Chemical and Bacterial Analysis of Water and Sewage*, McGraw-Hill Book Co., New York.

Wing, Leonard William, 1937, "Cycles of Water-levels," *Trans. Second N. A. Wildlife Conf.:* 346–379.

17

Lake Fish Management and Improvement

This discussion will be limited to fresh-water game fish. Both commercial and salt-water fish work and its biology are different from operations in fresh water and warrant more extensive treatment.

General Management Methods. Fish-management operations can be separated into three major over-all divisions: artificial propagation, protection, and lake or stream improvement and control. The main emphasis here will be upon improvement and control.

In many ways the early history of fish work parallels that for game birds and mammals. When protection failed to maintain conditions at the levels desired, artificial restocking came into vogue. Early fish work has been described as little more than "dumping" fish into lakes and streams, with success measured by the millions or billions of fry and fingerlings planted. Hatcheries naturally expanded in numbers and capacity during this period, and exotics were imported and released. Likewise, many native species were transplanted from one region to another and thereby became exotics in the new environment. It has been remarked that a characteristic of this era was repeated planting of fish in waters where nature never intended them to live. The original emphasis on fry changed to emphasis on fingerlings and even larger fish. In some places the practice was established of releasing full-grown fish but a few hours ahead of the hook.

Although the past tense has been used here, these practices are still carried on to some degree in a few states.

Improving the environment for lake fish involves four practices that may be called major ones, as well as a number of lesser ones:

> Manipulation of shelter conditions.
> Increasing the available food supply.

Regulation of the water level and extent.
Regulation of the fish populations.

Most management procedures have been based on studies made in cold northern waters. The longer growing season and higher temperature of water and air, along with other important considerations, make management methods for southern waters different. In general southern waters are far more productive of fish poundage than northern waters. In many southern waters, for example, emergent vegetation is not permitted, in marked contrast to the North, where vegetation may be more completely encouraged.

Fish Culture and Planting of Fish. In farm fish ponds and in some other waters stocking may be advantageous, but in most waters it will do little good. It has considerable effectiveness, however, in small ponds where game fish, like bass, must compete with prolific bluegills and their allies. Artificial propagation for most waters is based upon thinking in terms of animals having few offspring. But fish are prolific; female trout lay hundreds of eggs, others thousands. Adding small fish to a lake or stream would be equivalent to adding calves to a pasture where cows had thousands of calves apiece each year. Adding catchable fish in quantity does improve fishing, but the costs are prohibitive (usually several dollars per pound of fish caught).

The requirements for fish propagation vary with the species as well as with the region and general conditions. A fish hatchery requires buildings and grounds properly equipped with ponds, troughs, and an adequate supply of water of the right temperature and purity. Other requirements are traps, machinery for growing or handling food, and transplanting equipment.

Lake Surveys. In many ways lakes are more difficult to work during survey operations than streams; the size of streams and ease of access to all parts make for convenience. Yet travel over lakes in a boat is an advantage. In the North travel over the ice favors some operations.

The data obtained in lake surveys depend upon many factors besides the time available and conditions existing. Temperature readings are made of both air and water; likewise, the clearness of water (e.g., as indicated by Secchi discs) is important. The nature of the lake bottom, its soil and slope, and the depth of the water are easily determined. Chemical analysis at various depths throughout the lake is an important phase of the work. Studies of fauna and flora go along with physical and chemical studies.

A seemingly limitless variety and volume of data—some of great importance, others local or minor—may be obtained. Some data taken cannot yet be interpreted in terms of fish management, but they are gathered in hopes that later correlations may be useful. The usual data collected fall into one or another of the following groups:

Tributary streams.	Chemical conditions of water.
Water levels.	Physical conditions of water.
Areas of various depths.	Fishing pressure.
Water volume.	Wind.
Spawning grounds.	Springs.
Shore conditions.	Altitude.
Amount of shoreline.	Topography.
Shore vegetation.	Access to lake.
Weed beds.	Land ownership.
Aquatic organisms.	Pollution.

Maps aid in recording data and are generally of a size that can be conveniently handled in the field. Standard symbols facilitate entering data and simplify the map for others. Maps may be obtained from existing sources, or they can be made in the field when need be. Mapping may be done easily with a plane table, and standard methods work well. The area of all or part of the lake can be determined by means of a planimeter or cross-section paper.

Chemical analysis of water is made either on the spot by portable or moving laboratory facilities or by samples transported to indoor laboratories. Because transporting samples is far from satisfactory, even when the samples are kept cool, many states use laboratory boats or laboratory trucks for such work. The dissolved oxygen and carbon dioxide and the pH of the water are the data most frequently obtained. The standard procedures for analyzing water are available in many publications, which also give modifications that may be needed for testing water in warm regions or waters that are turbid. Organic and inorganic compounds in the water may interfere with tests for dissolved oxygen and carbon dioxide. In all such chemical tests as are needed or desirable, it is advisable to run standardization tests to obtain correction factors; otherwise the results may be unreliable.

The pH determination may be made with standard colorimetric sets obtainable from scientific supply houses. Directions accompany the sets.

Supplying Shelter. Fish require shelter for escape from enemies and for resting, in some ways analogous to the shelter needs of land game. It should be borne in mind that fish, like other organisms, avoid so far as possible places that are unsatisfactory to the instinctive needs of their security pattern and life habits. Like land animals, fish have many well-developed senses—smell, taste, hearing, sight, and touch. Some, like the sense of smell, may be weak, but others, like the sense of hearing, may be more acute than we think, even though the ordinary noises that disturb us (such as those from power boats) may not disturb them. Fish even have some ability to produce sounds.

The natural shelter of fish is present in the form of weed beds and other aquatic plants, sunken logs or stumps, overhanging banks, and the like. Where adequate natural shelter is available for the species concerned, the policy should be to leave conditions alone unless improvement measures are reasonably sure of success. Supplementary cover is needed only in waters of deficient natural cover, particularly in cold-water lakes and ponds. Cover of itself, however, will not substitute for other needs, such as the food supply.

Aquatic vegetation is frequently planted in the North to give permanent shelter where suitable aquatics can live. More plantings will fail from lack of proper selection on the basis of ecological conditions than from any other cause, and so due consideration must be given to soil, exposure, depth, and turbidity, as well as the pH.

Often there will be conditions that must be corrected before plants will grow successfully. Raising the water level may prevent ice or wave action from destroying aquatic vegetation, and shorelines may need protection to prevent erosion and consequent turbidity, as well as mechanical destruction. Sometimes waters deficient in organic material can be fertilized successfully, and, under special circumstances, those too acid can possibly be rendered less acid with lime additions. Jetties and windbreaks may control excessive wave action.

Beds of aquatic vegetation frequently become overgrown, especially in the South, and impede fish life. One of the pond-management problems in the South is control of vegetation; cold-water lakes and ponds of the North present this problem less often. Excessive vegetation may interfere with spawning and may also rob the water of oxygen by decay of dead vegetation, even though it is the action of live vegetation that aids the oxygenation of waters. Vegetation growth is controlled by poisoning, cutting, and pulling, as well as by changing the water levels. In northern waters some vegetation may be controlled by lowering the water so that the ice freezes to the vegetation; subsequent raising of the level tears the vegetation loose. Some success has been obtained in killing excess vegetation with poisons, like sodium arsenite, copper sulphate (for algae, 0.5 to 1.5 parts per million), and 2,4-D

(5 per cent to 15 per cent sprayed), all of which may be toxic to animal life. Some vegetation has also been controlled by means of dyes added to the water, which kill the vegetation by shutting out their life-giving sunlight.

Tree tops have been added for protective cover, but they need small twigs attached in order to serve best as refuge for small fish. Tree tops and other shelter may be floated in place in the summer or dragged over the ice in winter. Attached weights cause the shelter to sink and to stay down until waterlogged. Those placed in position over the ice may be dropped through by cutting the ice or by allowing them to sink through with the spring break-up. If the ice shifts in the spring, the shelters are not permitted to melt through. Shelter may be placed in position ahead of impounded water by staking to the bottom. Shelters under water will last much longer than similar shelters for upland game in the open air (Fig. 17.1).

Brush piles are utilized best by fish if in shallow water, though they can be used in deeper water. The best results for small fish accrue to brush piles in water less than 6 feet deep (unless ice destroys the shelter), though good results have been obtained with adult fish by placing brush piles in water as deep as 20 feet.

Brush mats of woven brush and wire can be placed to cover bare bottoms or silt deposits and sometimes to protect eroding banks. They are sunk in shallow water by weighting.

Where fluctuating water levels make fixed structures impossible, floating devices, such as platforms suspended below the surface from floats, may be effective. Gravel for spawning as well as for escape cover may be placed upon the platform. Floating structures are anchored to the bottom by long lines that allow the structures to shift position as the water level changes. Ice subjects them to destruction in the North, where they are little used, although they are suitable for seasonal operation if taken ashore in the fall.

Shelters may be used to attract adult fish so that they may be caught more readily by fishermen. Such shelters have especial value as aids to "pan-fish" fishing in reservoirs and other bodies with deep water, deep shores, or fluctuating water levels.

Spawning Beds. Most fish spawn on beds in shallow water, and spawning beds are sometimes provided artificially by placing small quantities of gravel where needed. A bushel of gravel will generally make a bed 2 to 5 feet in diameter. The greatest satisfaction is given by material varying from 0.5 inch to 2 inches in diameter. It can be dumped overboard from boats, poured through holes in ice, or scat-

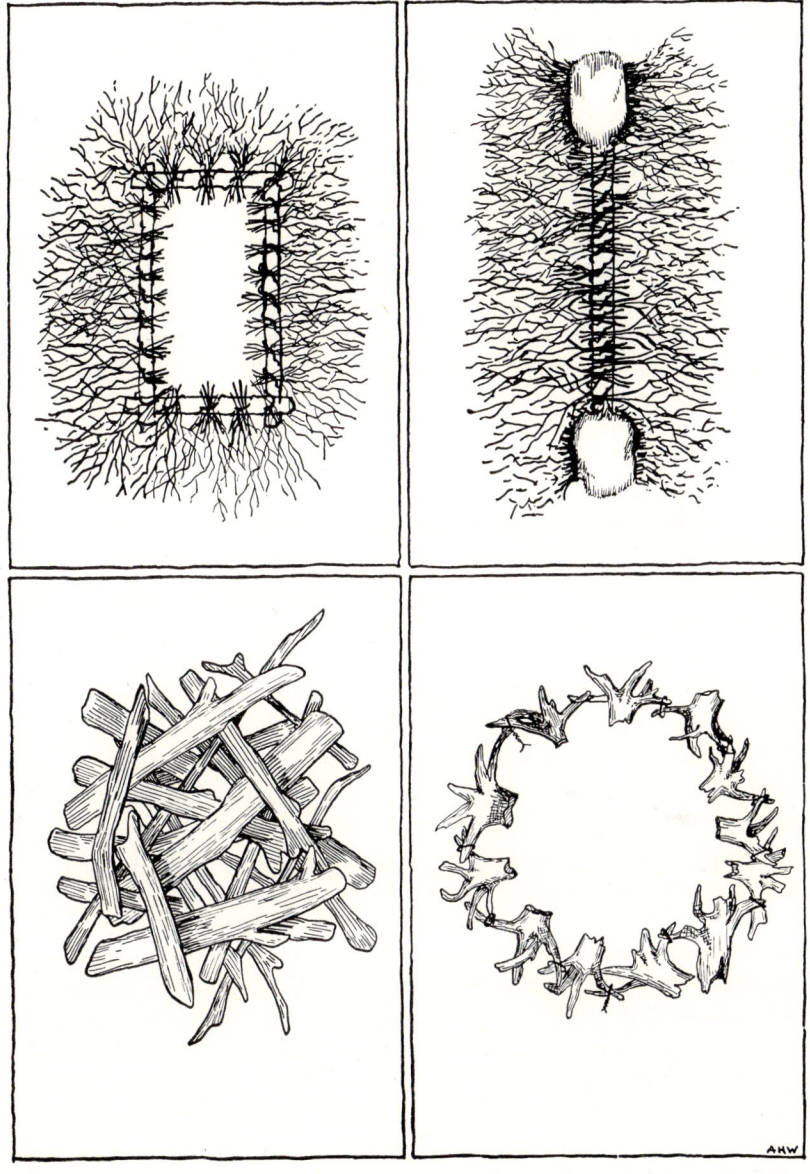

FIG. 17.1. Examples of fish shelters. Upper left, hollow square brush shelter. Upper right, single log shelter with brush. Lower left, deadhead shelter of waterlogged tree branches. Lower right, deadhead shelter of waterlogged stumps. (After Hubbs and Eschmeyer, 1938.)

tered over ice and allowed to melt through. Gravel piles are generally spaced at intervals of 5 to 10 feet, according to the species for which they are intended. Where the bottom is soft, gravel may be supported on brush piles or gravel boxes 2 to 3 feet square.

Some fish spawn upon roots of pond lilies or other aquatic vegetation, which can be planted as desired. Boards and other fixed material may be dropped in for minnows and bullheads.

Food Supply Improvement. Fish growth, which is indeterminate, varies with the food supply, and the amount of food varies with the water temperature. In fact temperature of the water is probably the most important single factor in production of fish food and production of fish in turn. Southern waters, even comparatively poor waters in areas of sterile soil, produce far more poundage of fish than northern waters, because of the long growing season and the warm waters, both reflecting high energy reception from the sun. Because fish feed chiefly on aquatic animal life, any increase in aquatic organisms directly increases the food supply of fish and thereby improves fishing.

The fertility of water and soils of lakes are controlling factors in the production of fish foods. Experiments have shown some possibilities for improving food production through application of commercial fertilizers in waters where low fertility is a limiting factor. The cost of this practice, however, prohibits its application to large bodies of water. Organic fertilizers have been found successful in hatchery ponds.

Shallow waters lead in production of food, although rich plankton sources may be found in deep lakes. Raising or lowering water levels, whichever course is indicated, will increase the usable food-producing water. Owing to soil infertility, wave action, or other factors, however, not all bottom has food-production possibilities.

"Forage fish" are smaller species, generally of low appeal to fishermen, upon which larger ones depend for food. These prolific and fast-growing fish form intermediate links of the food chain between plankton and larger fish. Like any fish, they increase with better cover, better food supply, better habitat, and the removal of inhibiting influences. Forage fish often spawn in thick vegetation, upon sticks, or upon stones, and spawning can be aided by regulating the vegetation or providing better spawning conditions.

Control of Water Levels. The control of water levels for water birds has already been discussed. Constant levels are best for fish life, just as for water birds, and the practices for water birds usually serve as well for fish life. Fishermen frequently agitate for raising water levels

Miscellaneous Techniques

in lakes in the belief that increased surface area, water volume, or shoreline automatically means a proportionate increase in fish life. This does not necesarily follow, however, and raising water levels may actually do far more harm than good. Raising water levels is such a drastic action that it should be done only after long and careful

Fig. 17.2. Constant-level dam for holding water in an arm of a reservoir during the "drawdown" at the main dam.

Fig. 17.3. Aquatic plants cannot survive under conditions of extreme fluctuation as in some reservoirs.

analysis of the situation; little harm results from delay while studying the matter, but haste may prove costly to fishing (Figs. 17.2 and 17.3).

Miscellaneous Techniques. Wave action can be brought under partial control by several means. Windbreaks on shores of small lakes help by breaking the force of wave-generating wind; their value is slight on large waters, though they may reduce waves in their lee near shore. Wave breakers break the force of waves and are made of stones or logs placed under water. Beds of heavy vegetation, once established, break the force of waves, but temporary control measures may be needed to start the vegetation. Jetties have also served to control wave action.

Silt fills lakes and covers spawning beds of fish and may even smother vegetation; it may also increase the turbidity of the water, with consequent harmful effects upon vegetation, as well as possible algae increase. The best action against silt is to prevent it from reaching the lake. Good soil erosion control on the land is good fish practice because it keeps the soil on the farms and out of the water. Eroding shores may be protected by vegetation, riprap, mats, and shrubs or trees. An eroding shore may sometimes be drowned to stop its eroding. Scouring action of ice on the bottom can be reduced by deepening the water.

Little control of natural enemies of fish is needed. The complexity of the problems of fish life makes it impossible to judge conditions with any certainty. Desire for predator control arises from lack of knowledge of fish ecology, as well as from a clash of interests and programs. "Overpopulation" with pan fish may become a serious problem for the fish manager; in holding down the numbers of such fish the predators not infrequently serve a useful purpose in fish management. Often it has been deemed advisable to control "rough fish," such as carp and gars. Bottom feeders, like carp, roil the water so that commercial fishing for them may aid sport fishing. "Rough fish" are usually controlled by commercial fishing, though poisoning them, as well as poisoning stunted fish populations, has been tried in small waters with some success. Farm fish tanks or ponds are usually drained to eliminate a fish population that has got out of control. The waters upon returning again to normal levels are restocked.

The temperature of some lakes can be lowered by reducing the amount of shallow water and raised by increasing it. Windbreaks may help to warm waters by breaking the force of cold winds. Both the amount of shade and the circulation of water may play a part in affecting temperature.

Untreated organic pollution, especially domestic sewage, is obnoxious from the health and esthetic view as well as for its harmful effects upon fish life. Quantities of pollution destroy fish life and its oxygen; pollution may make "rough fish" dominant. Other organic matter may also reduce the oxygen, and means for improving the oxygen should be applied. The removal of some of the organic debris may help, for turbid water may not let enough sunlight through for adequate photosynthesis in plants. In winter a lake with snow covering the ice may become oxygen-deficient because little photosynthesis can be carried on.

Aeration of water has been accomplished by running power boats to agitate the surface so that oxygen may be taken in from the air. Removal of deep snow over ice allows light to reach plants, and thinning of heavy vegetation growth may help in summer. Water can be pumped from below or from under ice and shot into the air for aeration. In general any method that churns the water surface will cause air to be dissolved, and anything that will increase photosynthesis in plants will also increase oxygen.

Gathering Population Data. Regulation of the season, size limits, and other factors of fishing depend upon adequate data if it is to be properly handled. Fishing may be poor because there are too many fish present and therefore too few able to reach legal size because of pressure on the food supply. The effectiveness of any operations or regulations can be tested only by means of carefully collected data.

On big waters four important studies are recommended:

Creel census. A creel census will reveal trends in the catch and show whether or not fishing is satisfactory.

Population studies. By seining, netting, and local sampling by poisoning with derris root, the fish biologist can note whether reproduction and survival of young has been satisfactory.

Catch studies. By tagging fish and observing the percentage of tagged fish recovered by fishermen, the extent to which fish population is caught can be learned.

Growth studies. Growth studies give important evidence of the sufficiency of the food supply for the fish stand.

Creel data are obtained extensively from reports transmitted by fishermen or taken by wardens and biologists in connection with their regular duties, and are obtained intensively by means of volunteer labor or hired labor. These censuses, as they are called, tend to contain systematic errors due to enthusiasm or lack of it on the part of the census takers, lack of time, or press of other needs, as well as concentration of effort near heavy fishing. Censuses obtained by intensive work on definite lakes by paid workers are the most reliable; voluntary creel census data are not reliable.

The accuracy of the work can be checked roughly and quickly by observing the sizes of species as reported by various census takers. Those for each lake should be similar. Likewise, the number of measurements reported in half and even inches should be equally abundant. The general data by all should agree on each lake, and any that differ markedly from those taken by others should be looked upon with suspicion.

The data to be obtained vary from area to area as well as with the expected uses. The most frequently obtained data fall into the following classes:

Date.	Sex of fisherman.
Weather.	Age of fisherman.
Name of lake.	Size of fishing party.
Location of lake.	Method of fishing.
Location of fishing.	Bait used.
Time of fishing.	Number of fish and species.
Name of fisherman.	Size and weight of fish.
Home address of fisherman.	

Scale Samples. Fish scales remain the same in numbers throughout life, though the body continues to grow; the scales increase in size to cover the body. The growth of the fish slows up during cold weather, causing a "winter check" to appear on the scales of many fishes. The number of such checks or "rings" gives the age, and the distance between them indicates the proportionate growth, so that age class and growth curves can be constructed from the scales and other body measurements.

Scale samples may be obtained as part of the creel census, or they may be transmitted to the fish biologist by interested fishermen. A minimum of about 50 specimens is best for each lake. Scales may be stored indefinitely and readings made during the winter when work is slack. Scales are mounted on microscope slides and measured directly with the microscope or by means of scale-reading machines that project the image of the scale upon a ground-glass or other screen. An impression of the scale in softened Celluloid or other plastic sometimes gives better readings than the scale itself.

Population Counts. Biologists obtain population counts by various means, usually by taking samples with seines, nets, and traps. The numbers may be indicated in terms of relative abundance or of absolute abundance, according to the method used and extent of operations. The fish in small lakes or ponds can be counted by poisoning with derris root or its derivatives and gathering them from the surface. Ponds may be drained for a complete count and perhaps also counted by complete netting, though this is seldom possible. Fish may also be counted on spawning beds and in shallow water. Another method of calculation is to catch a portion of the fish population, mark the fish by clipping a fin or tagging, and release them for subsequent catching in netting or seining operations; the total marked fish caught will bear the relationship to the total marked fish in the water that the captured unmarked fish will bear to the total unmarked population. The marked fish being known, the total population is quickly computed. As the distribution of marked fish in a large lake will influence the retake, care must be taken to get a random distribution of marked fish. If fishermen's creels are used for gathering the data of retakes of marked fish, a summation of the daily catches will aid in adjusting for the decline in total numbers with fishing.

Fish may be marked for subsequent identification by the clipping of fins and tagging. Number tags may be attached to the jaw or to the gill covers. Plastic tags may be inserted into the body cavity, where they will remain for life, though a few may migrate from the point of insertion or be lost altogether. In some waters the incision made for inserting the tag may be subject to infection.

Protection. Although fish may require protection from man, natural enemies may be ignored except under some conditions. The usual purpose of regulations is to prevent destruction of the breeding stock and excessive depletion of the fish numbers by closing seasons during breeding periods, by reducing the length of seasons, by reducing the bag limits, and by increasing the size limits. The general practice of closing the season during the spawning period needs sufficient flexibility to assure protection during late spawning seasons or seasons otherwise disturbed by weather. Catch limits are a favorite device for reducing fishing pressure, as are also legal limits on the size. But the size limit is not necessarily a good practice because some waters may produce an excess of undersized fish owing to food deficiencies or stunted populations. Growth rates and age-class studies are needed to determine stunted fish populations, those that are below the average for the lakes of the region.

The policy in the United States and Canada has eliminated many methods of fishing, either generally or in most areas. Among these may be mentioned "jack lighting" (night spearing with a light), and "gigging" (spearing). The use of dynamite and other explosives, along with poisons, is universally prohibited. Likewise, nets, fish traps, and multiple lines or gear have been outlawed in most areas. Because "sport fishing" is considered the highest form of "use," methods that are "unsporting" are generally frowned upon and tend to be displaced or prohibited. Fishing derbies and other promotions that offer prizes are discouraged in most progressive areas on the ground that fishing should be for sport and not for automobiles, refrigerators, or other rewards.

Formerly, and largely still in some areas, fishing regulations paralleled the general practice of hunting regulations because it was not appreciated that the hook and line is a very inefficient machine compared to a shotgun or rifle. The trend is toward relaxing regulations for sport fishing. Many "fished-out" lakes are merely lakes where fishermen cannot compete with the natural food for the attention of the fish, rather than lakes without breeding stock. In small ponds of the South, at least, a high fishing pressure may play an essential part in maintaining fish numbers by holding the population in bounds. It may also play a part in keeping such ponds from becoming dominated by a few large fish of voracious species.

Disease as a factor in fish management is easier to prevent than to treat. Epizootics are prevented by breaking up concentrations and maintaining clean waters. Hatchery stock is frequently a potential source of disease that may be introduced into healthy fish populations by restocking. Parasites of fish are common but ordinarily do little harm. Since fish parasites often require an alternate host, it may be possible to combat them by reducing the numbers of such alternate hosts.

Farm Fish Ponds. The sound engineering principle of keeping the water in the upper reaches when possible and using it there to fullest advantage, instead of rushing it down to the main stream and lower drainage, has increased the interest in fish ponds, both for themselves and as water-control agents. The Soil Conservation Service especially has been a forward-looking advocate of the farm pond. Hundreds of thousands of ponds have been constructed. Farm fish ponds serve not only to hold the water back and provide fishing space but also to provide water for stock, maintain ground-water levels, and provide stored water for dry periods.

Standard procedures are available for constructing and stocking fish ponds on the basis of watershed, soil, vegetation, and regional experience. In general a pond must hold water at a suitable depth. It must be protected against silt and turbidity. The proper vegetation must be used. In the South precautions are essential against mosquitoes.

The usual practice is to plant the vegetation and then to introduce aquatic organisms if needed. Although many fish have been used in the past, usually one species of predatory fish and one of forage fish are customarily planted. These are usually large-mouth black bass and blue gill (bream), respectively. Both can be taken on the hook, which is not true of the smaller species of forage fish. Careful watch of the pond is needed so that the proportions will remain in balance; otherwise a few large fish may dominate the pond and the fishing will become poor. Heavy fishing of blue gills is sometimes needed to prevent them from outbreeding the bass and destroying the bass's eggs and young. Seining the pond and removing the excess or large fish of either species may be necessary to preserve good fishing.

Fish ponds yield from 150 to 200, and sometimes more, pounds of fish per acre. Ponds yield more in the South than in the North because the growing season is longer. It is probable that by use of several non-competitive species rather than the customary predator-prey fishes, several times as many pounds can be produced.

SUGGESTED READING

Allan, Phillip F., and Cecil N. Davis, 1941, "Ponds for Wildlife," *U.S.D.A. Farmer's Bull.* 1879.

Anonymous, 1939, *Problems of Lake Biology*, Am. Assoc. for the Advanc. of Sci., Lancaster, Pa.

Anonymous, 1947, *Malaria Control on Impounded Waters*, U. S. Public Health Serv. and Tenn. Valley Authority, Washington, D. C.

Curtis, Brian, 1949, *The Life Story of the Fish: Its Manners and Morals*, Harcourt, Brace and Co., New York.

Davis, H. S., 1938, "Instructions for Conducting Stream and Lake Surveys," *Bureau of Fisheries Fishery Circ.* 26.

Dobie, J. R., O. L. Meehean, and G. N. Washburn, 1948, "Propagation of Minnows and Other Bait Species," *Fish and Wildlife Serv. Circ.* 12.

Eddy, Samuel, and Thaddeus Surber, 1947, *Northern Fishes*, University of Minnesota Press, Minneapolis.

Edminster, Frank A., 1947, *Fish Ponds for the Farm*, Charles Scribner's Sons, New York.

Fassett, Norman, 1940, *A Manual of Aquatic Plants*, McGraw-Hill Book Co., New York.

Gabrielson, Ira N., and Francesca La Monte (Editors), 1950, *The Fisherman's Encyclopedia*, Stackpole and Heck, Harrisburg, Pa.

Hubbs, Carl L., and Karl F. Lagler, 1947, *Fishes of the Great Lakes Basin*, Cranbrook Institute of Science, Bloomfield Hills, Mich.

Hubbs, Carl L., and R. W. Eschmeyer, 1938, "The Improvement of Lakes for Fishing," *Inst. for Fisheries Res., Bull.* 2.

Lagler, Karl F., 1949, *Studies in Freshwater Fishery Biology*, Edwards Bros., Ann Arbor, Mich.

McAtee, W. L., 1939, *Wildfowl Food Plants, Their Value, Propagation, and Management*, Collegiate Press, Ames, Iowa.

Morgan, Ann Haven, 1930, *Fieldbook of Ponds and Streams*, G. P. Putnam's Sons, New York.

Noble, G. Kingsley, 1931, *The Biology of the Amphibia*, McGraw-Hill Book Co., New York.
Norman, J. R., 1948, *A History of Fishes*, A. A. Wyn, Inc., New York.
Schultz, Leonard P., and Edith M. Stern, 1948, *The Ways of Fishes*, D. Van Nostrand Co., New York.
Smith, Gilbert M., 1933, *The Fresh-water Algae of the United States*, McGraw-Hill Book Co., New York.
Tiffany, Lewis Hanford, 1937, *Algae, The Grass of Many Waters*, Charles C. Thomas, Springfield, Ill.
Ward, Henry Baldwin, and George Chandler Whipple, 1918, *Fresh-water Biology*, John Wiley & Sons, New York.
Welch, Paul S., 1935, *Limnology*, McGraw-Hill Book Co., New York.
Welch, Paul S., 1948, *Limnological Methods*, The Blakiston Co., Philadelphia.
Whipple, George Chandler, 1927, *The Microscopy of Drinking Water*, John Wiley & Sons, New York.

18

Stream Improvement and Management

Stream and Lake Management Relations. The philosophy and many of the procedures for artificial propagation and restocking are substantially the same for both lake fish and stream fish. Stocking in streams has had about the same success and lack of success as stocking in lakes. Many stream fish require cooler water than the fish we ordinarily consider lake fish. Although taxonomically lake and stream fish may be the same, the development, life history, and ecological requirements often are entirely dissimilar because of physical differences in the respective media (Table 18.1).

Oxygen supply is rarely a problem in unpolluted streams, for surface agitation assures absorption of oxygen and turbulence assures proper distribution. Some trout, however, have too high an oxygen requirement for many streams. Temperature changes may or may not be of the same importance in streams and lakes.

The principles of protection and regulation of stream fish and fishing vary but little from those for lakes, though the problems themselves are widely different. Predators and competitors seem to cause little general worry in stream management except under unusual or local conditions. Where tributary streams harbor young migrants, it may be desirable to close these "feeder" streams against fishing in order to protect fishing in the main stream.

Because streams have a high recreational value, it is sometimes worthwhile to spend more effort per unit of surface area or fish yield in streams than in lakes. Fly fishing is generally considered the "highest" recreational use of fish resources; hence larger expenditures may be warranted for trout work than for work with pan fish and other sport fish.

TABLE 18.1

COMMON FRESHWATER FISHES

(Contributed by Frank T. Knapp)

Species	General Range *	General Food Habits	Chief Spawning Season	Principal Spawning Place
Sturgeons	Middle (anadromous on coasts)	Bottom organisms	Spring	Rivers
Gars	South, Middle	Omnivorous, scavenger	Spring–summer	Bayous
Bowfin	South, Middle	Piscivorous	Spring	Lakes
Lake trout	North, Middle	Piscivorous	Fall	Lakes
Eastern brook trout	North, Middle	Insectivorous	Fall	Streams
Rainbow trout / Steelhead trout	West, North (planted Middle)	Insectivorous and piscivorous	Spring–fall	Streams
Pacific salmon	West Coast	Insectivorous and piscivorous	Spring–summer–fall	Streams, lakes
Atlantic salmon	East Coast	Insectivorous and piscivorous	Spring to fall	Streams
Whitefish	North, Middle	Bottom organisms	Spring	Lakes
Suckers	North, Middle, South	Bottom organisms	Spring	Streams
Carp	South, Middle (introduced)	Insectivorous and planktivorous	Early spring	Lakes
Catfishes and bullheads	Middle, South	Omnivorous	Spring–summer	Lakes, rivers
Pike	North, Middle	Piscivorous	Spring	Lakes
Muskellunge	Middle	Piscivorous	Spring	Lakes
Pike-perches	Middle	Piscivorous	Spring	Lakes
Crappies	South, Middle	Piscivorous	Spring	Lakes
Bluegill sunfish	South, Middle	Planktivorous and insectivorous	Spring–summer	Lakes
Other sunfishes	South, Middle	Planktivorous and insectivorous	Spring	Lakes, rivers
Small-mouth black bass	Middle	Piscivorous	Spring	Lakes, rivers
Large-mouth black bass	Middle, South	Piscivorous	Spring	Lakes
Spotted black bass	South	Piscivorous	Spring	Lakes, rivers
White bass	South, Middle	Piscivorous	Spring	Rivers
Striped bass	Middle coasts	Piscivorous	Spring	Streams

* North, Middle, and South continental latitudes.

Water Fluctuations. Floods and high water occur with the melting of snow on the watershed and the coming of spring rains. Runoff varies in different areas. It is most rapid in areas of high relief and those with complete drainage patterns; it is lowest in flat areas and those with poorly adjusted drainage patterns. Streams with headwaters in distant mountains (like the Snake River) may experience a local spring high, followed by a greater high when the snow water from the higher country hits the lower reaches in early summer. Glaciation is responsible for poorly drained areas where lakes and marshes abound; these store water during rainy periods and feed it out slowly during the rest of the year.

The vegetation cover plays a part in controlling runoff and the seasonal regimen of streams; forested areas, for example, have less variable stream flow than unforested or deforested ones. Runoff is greater from crop land than uncropped land and greater from overgrazed than from ungrazed or properly grazed land. Destruction of the cover on the watershed contributes to the flood problems by increasing seasonal runoff. Drainage and flood-control operations usually increase the seasonal fluctuations by rushing the water downstream from the upper watershed; keeping the water in the upper reaches and paying it out later, however, is itself good flood control. The ideal stream for local fish would be one having an even flow throughout the year, but no such stream exists in our region; probably migratory fish would find it less suitable than a stream with a seasonal high.

Floods bring destructive effects to the water course by eroding the bed, covering spawning sites, and filling pools and retreats, as well as by destroying important weed beds. Floods may change the course of a stream, excavate new holes, and create new sand or mud bars. Unless anchored securely, improvement devices may be washed out by floods.

Intermittent streams rarely have much fish life because they go dry, which kills fish or restricts them to deep pools. The yearly possibility of any stream of intermittent or seasonal variation is determined by the conditions of its poorest period.

Erosion and Silt Control. The best way to control silt is to keep it from getting into the streams; erosion control on the watershed is a necessary prelude to the control of damage to water courses lower down. Any soil erosion control practice will help to stabilize stream flow if it serves to slow up the water or to reduce the amount of silt reaching streams.

Silt not only harms fish but also affects their food supply. Turbidity of the water and the deposition of silt reduce and may even destroy aquatic vegetation; it may also evict aquatic animal life. Photosynthesis in plants is inhibited by turbid water, with consequent reduction of the oxygen supply. Silt may change a stream from a game-fish stream to a "rough-fish" stream; we have seen thousands of examples of this action in Canada, the United States, and Mexico.

Pollution. Both the United States and Canada have made open sewers of many streams. Complete destruction of nearly all forms of life in streams results from large-scale dumping of industrial pollutants and domestic wastes into streams. The organic refuse not only ruins the water as a life-supporting medium but may even cause a sludge to form and to creep along the bottom, overwhelming all except the hardiest of aquatic life. The obnoxious conditions that result from pouring pollution into streams ruins them for fishing purposes as well as for all other recreation.

Mine waters generally run high in acids, which destroy fishing in the streams into which they flow. Abandoned mines may be sealed. The water from active mines may be run through crushed limestone, which generally neutralizes the harmful acids. Mine debris dumped into or permitted to enter stream courses destroys the stream usefulness by a flood of dirt. Likewise the "rock flour" from stamping mills and the debris from gold mining may contain toxic compounds, which, along with the fineness of the material, may ruin the stream for fish miles below the point of origin. The concept that extractive exploitation, like mining, has priority over other activities is a hangover from pioneer days of the West and has no justification in the West of today.

Sources of pollution of serious nature exist in operations of paper mills, refineries, chemical plants, tanneries, canning factories, and woodworking mills. One mill or factory alone can be as harmful to a stream as a city of several hundred thousand people. The wastes of industrial plants destroy fish life if run untreated into fishing waters, though often they may be capable of yielding by-products that sometimes can pay the cost of treatment and more.

The Stream Survey. Stream survey data can be recorded on a well-constructed map that indicates the location of all important features, devices, and sampling stations. Since it generally is not feasible to work the entire length of larger streams, sample stations customarily are set up at frequent intervals. The data obtained by stream surveys vary in different parts of the country and with the purpose of the

The Stream Survey

survey, but the data most valuable can be divided into the following classes:

Geological conditions.	Temperature.
Topography.	Shade.
Stream gradient.	Pools and shelters.
Stream velocity.	Bottom character.
Volume of flow.	Aquatic vegetation.
Width and depth.	Aquatic animal life.
Existing dams and diversions.	Spawning grounds.
Springs.	Fishing pressure.
Tributaries.	Recreational features.
Color and turbidity.	Economic uses of water.
Alkalinity.	Improvement operations.
Chemistry of water.	Physical condition of water.

Bottom samplings are usually made to determine the production of fish foods. A stream-bottom sampler suitable for such work consists

Fig. 18.1. Fish counting houses at a fishway. Bonneville Dam, Columbia River. (Photograph by R. L. Webster.)

of two brass frames, each a foot square, set at right angles to one another, the vertical frame covered with netting, the horizontal one open. The sampler is placed on the bottom with the net stretched downstream, and the square foot of bottom within the horizontal frame is stirred, causing organisms present to float into the net, from which they can be removed for study.

Data on the stream's fish population are collected in about the same way as those for lake populations. The techniques for marking are also the same.

It is sometimes possible to sample migrating fish numbers moving in shallow water by direct count and to count those in deeper water from a darkened blind suspended over the stream. Funnel gates permit movement one way in the stream and prevent movement in the other direction. Migrating fish may also be counted as they pass through fishways (Fig. 18.1).

Improving Food Conditions. Usually riffles produce more important quantities of food than quiet pools do. Clean bottoms, such as bed rock, produce the least food, and gravel bottoms and weed beds the most. Sticks, stones, and other objects that make attachment possible for many organisms increase food production. In some streams the major fish foods during some periods may be largely of terrestrial origin.

Devices may be used to control the current and to increase food resources of streams by uncovering gravel bottoms and establishing conditions suitable for weed beds. Many gravel bottoms and possible weed beds exist but are covered by silt or sand. Deflectors, when properly handled, remove the covering sand or silt. They may also prevent destruction of rich muck bottoms by diverting the force of the current.

Providing Shelter. Shelter problems for stream fish are about the same as those for lake fish. In cold climates, however, the problem of ice is less severe in streams than it is in lakes, but, because of the current, improvement structures in streams must be anchored to prevent them from being washed out. *Unless they are built on sound engineering principles,* improvement structures may be destroyed. Brush and log shelters can be placed where needed in streams, whether the water is deep or shallow; often they may be combined with other devices. Brush hanging over the bank sometimes can be trained down over the water by weights or stakes, and it will then supply good cover. In fact the cover along the stream bank may need attention before any devices are built in the water itself.

Shade trees and shrubs planted along the banks provide shade for the water and thereby reduce its temperature; shade may be an especially important addition to streams flowing through open meadows, and lack of it may mean no fish. So-called flood-control work may completely destroy such shade trees and shrubs along streams.

Use of Dams. Dams long have been constructed to form pools and even lakes, as well as to control water flow. They extend the available water area, and sometimes the stored water alone keeps aquatic life alive during summer droughts by preventing drying of lakes and streams below the dam. By spreading the water, dams will warm lakes or streams that are too cold for some fish, but the warming effect of large impoundments in some areas may reduce the productive capacity of the streams below the dams. This may be averted somewhat by withdrawing cooler water from the bottom of the dam, rather than taking the warm surface water. Dams remove silt from the water, but in so doing they may destroy the storage capacity unless some cleaning arrangement is made. But removing silt from ponds and passing it on downstream is hardly likely to help fishing. Since dams may on occasion actually reduce the fishing quality, judgment should be exercised in putting them in. They also impede the free movement of fish in streams.

Stone dams are constructed by placing large boulders across the stream and filling in with smaller ones. Brush and earth piled over the stones on the upstream side make a water-tight job. Logs may also be used, alone or in combination with other material, but they generally require heavy staking or setting in both banks to prevent water from running around the ends. Crib work is also effective.

Deflectors. The purpose of a deflector is to make the current dig the bottom or sides and to maintain holes or bars. In essence the deflector is a barrier that concentrates the force of the current where wanted. Deflectors may create and enlarge pools, uncover gravel beds, remove silt, or even protect the banks. They are built of boulders, logs, or other handy material. Although there are several different types of deflectors, the simplest and the least likely to be destroyed by flood is a log partly or wholly submerged and fixed in each bank. This type is more common than any other.

Wing deflectors reaching out from one or both banks have also been used, but they are subject to easy destruction. Channel guides at the end of the "V" formed by the two deflectors carry the force of the stream farther down, in a "Y" shape. Quiet water is provided alongside the timbers (Fig. 18.2). A deflector built like the letter "A" has been used in the middle of streams (Fig. 18.3).

Surface Cover Devices. Covers in quiet pools may provide shade and hiding places for fish, somewhat as a low bridge does. They may also be used, like a vertical deflector, to throw a current against the bottom for digging. Floating covers will float on the surface until waterlogged enough to sink. After that stones and stakes will hold them off the bottom. The "boom" is a cover made of logs suspended across a bend with the inside corner filled with stumps, or other floating debris, which may be wired together. The "raft" is similar, except

292   Stream Improvement and Management

Fig. 18.2. "Y" deflector and digger log in a mountain meadow brook. A rock cover device appears in the foreground. (Photograph by Clarence Tarzwell.)

Fig. 18.3. An "A" deflector in a forest trout stream. (Photograph by Clarence Tarzwell.)

that it is constructed of logs fastened together. Booms and rafts may be placed at bends in streams or even along an eroding bank. Other covers have also been devised, such as triangle covers, square covers, submerged covers, and tepee covers.

Obstructions to Free Passage of Fish. The principal artificial obstructions to fish movement in streams are dams too high for fish to pass over; high waterfalls form natural barriers. Fishways have been rather generally installed for passing fish over dams; they are most

Fig. 18.4. Fish ladder 1200 feet long and consisting of 75 pools having rises of 1 foot. (Photograph by R. L. Webster.)

effective with migratory species having strong migratory instincts. Such fishways allow fish to pass upstream with some success, but they are not so successful as downstream passages. Fishways rarely improve fishing below dams, though they may improve it above the dam at the expense of the fishing below. Most states require fish-passing devices as a part of the construction of dams.

The fish ladder consists of a series of pools having low differences in level, usually under 12 inches. The fish ladder is essentially a stream of low gradient formed by increasing the distance that the water travels by means of zigzags and curves (Fig. 18.4). The fish conveyor works on the principle of an endless belt with buckets that haul fish up for subsequent release. Devices like this that catch fish make it possible to sort out "undesirable" species. Fish elevators have also been used to lift fish up over a dam (Fig. 18.5).

Fish have been trapped below a dam and transported to the higher waters by tank trucks. It has proved feasible to catch fish below the

294   Stream Improvement and Management

dam and to use them for artificial hatching of their eggs rather than to use them for natural spawning by releasing above the dam.

Preventing Fish Movement. It may be desirable to prevent fish from passing from one body of water to another. Many fish are lost by passing down irrigation diversions in the West and floundering in

Fig. 18.5. Fish elevator in background and fish ladder in foreground for getting fish over a dam. (Photograph by R. L. Webster.)

farm fields. Screens of various types prevent passage of fish. An electric one works by setting up a charged area of water that keeps out the fish, but electric devices have generally been discarded in favor of mechanical ones. Brush and rock filters may be suitable where current is slow and the size of the stream small. The laws of most western states require screening of diversions. Rotary screens have found favor in irrigation projects, where they successfully prevent much loss of fish (Fig. 18.6). The rotary screen is used in large irrigation canals. It is turned by a chain from a water wheel and automatically carries debris over the top. Unless some such device is provided, trash may accumulate and the screen be washed out. Stationary screens may be hinged at the top and the bottom held in place by springs or counterweights. Pressure from the trash causes the screen to swing open and empty; it returns to its position automatically.

Overpopulation. Streams, like lakes, may sometimes suffer from an excess number of small or stunted fish in relation to the space and

Fig. 18.6. These rotary screens are self-cleaning and keep fish from passing out of the Yakima River into irrigation canals. (Photograph by R. L. Webster.)

food supply. The mass of fish that a stream produces is relatively fixed, and fishing will be poor if it is spread over large numbers of small fish. The proper remedy is a reduction of pressure on the food supply, either by providing more food or reducing the number of mouths for the stream to feed. Fish that are small because of genetic reasons will not grow large unless new stock is added or unless they are replaced with stock of better genetic composition. Opening the stream to increased fishing reduces the number of stunted fish. Providing pools for larger predatory fish has also been effective, as has removal of retreats that protect the small fish from the large ones. Some states allow unlimited year-round fishing in some streams to improve fishing.

SUGGESTED READING

Anonymous, 1936, *Standard Methods for Examination of Water and Sewage*, Am. Health Assn.

Anonymous, 1949, *Limnological Aspects of Water Supply and Waste Disposal,* The Science Press, Lancaster, Pa.

Curtis, Brian, 1949, *The Life Story of the Fish: Its Manners and Morals,* Harcourt, Brace and Co., New York.

Davis, H. S., 1938, "Instructions for Conducting Stream and Lake Surveys," *U.S.D.C. Fishery Circ.* 26.

Eakin, Henry M., 1936, "Silting of Reservoirs," *U.S.D.A. Tech. Bull.* 542.

Eddy, Samuel, and Thaddeus Surber, 1947, *Northern Fishes,* University of Minnesota Press, Minneapolis.

Ellis, M. M., B. A. Westfall, and Marion D. Ellis, 1946, "Determination of Water Quality," *Fish and Wildlife Serv. Res. Rept.* 9.

Gabrielson, Ira N., and Francesca La Monte (Editors), 1950, *The Fisherman's Encyclopedia,* Stackpole and Heck, Harrisburg, Pa.

Hubbs, Carl L., John R. Greeley, and Clarence M. Tarzwell, 1932, "Methods for the Improvement of Michigan Trout Streams," *Inst. for Fisheries Res. Bull.* 1.

Lagler, Karl F., 1943, *Studies in Freshwater Fishery Biology,* Edwards Bros., Ann Arbor, Mich.

Morgan, Ann Haven, 1930, *Fieldbook of Ponds and Streams,* G. P. Putnam's Sons, New York.

Needham, Paul R., 1938, *Trout Streams,* Comstock Publishing Co., Ithaca, New York.

Schultz, Leonard P., and Edith M. Stern, 1948, *The Ways of Fishes,* D. Van Nostrand Co., New York.

Welch, Paul S., 1935, *Limnology,* McGraw-Hill Book Co., New York.

Welch, Paul S., 1948, *Limnological Methods,* The Blakiston Co., Philadelphia.

Ward, Henry Baldwin, and George Chandler Whipple, *Fresh-water Biology,* John Wiley & Sons, New York.

19

Songbird and Non-Game Conservation and Management

Protection of song and insectivorous birds has long been traditional in the United States and Canada. The esthetic appreciation of bird song and sight also dictated protection of most songbirds other than insectivorous ones, and all are protected for their own sake, rather than for economic returns. Because of the tradition instilled in the mind that the harmless ought not be destroyed, violation of such protection for smaller non-game animals seldom occurs and for larger ones only by irresponsible segments of the population.

Among the lower vertebrates, protection is extended to include some reptiles, such as "harmless" turtles, as well as alligators; many states also have laws regulating the hunting of frogs or prohibiting it altogether in the public interest. The protection of game and food fish automatically assures protection for all except so-called "rough fish" and bait minnows, because few people can tell non-game and non-food fishes from game or food ones. Commercial shellfishes like the oyster and shrimp are protected or their gathering is regulated because of economic value; in most states, however, non-commercial shellfish are protected also. As a general rule non-game or non-commercial animals that may be confused with game or commercial ones are protected in order to reduce illegal taking under claims of identification.

Protection for many non-game mammals, such as the flying squirrels and bats, follows as a natural sequel to protection of non-game birds.

The migratory bird treaties among Canada,[1] the United States, and

[1] See footnote in Chapter 22, page 335, for explanation of the terminology involved in the treaty between His Majesty (as the King of Canada) and the United States.

the United Mexican States set a pattern for international protection, and such protection will undoubtedly be extended among progressive nations, especially in the western hemisphere where the movement is strongest. Many international conferences have touched upon this subject in its exploratory phases. Among non-governmental organizations that are most actively interested in promoting international protection should be mentioned the National Audubon Society, International Zoological Congress, International Ornithological Congress, Committee for International Wild Life Protection, and the American Wildlife Conference. The Conservation Section of the Pan-American Union has likewise been active internationally.

General Requirements of Non-Game Species. The ecology of non-game species differs in principle not at all from that of game or other species. The practices for game species usually help non-game ones as well. More bird species are found in the South, where habitat and climate throughout the year are more suitable than elsewhere, and along the coasts (Fig. 19.1). This is particularly noticeable when winter comes and migrants retire to the southern states.

Colony nesting species require rookery grounds near sources of food. Topography plays an important part in the establishment of bird rocks and gull islands. The rocks must provide security for the young, especially from four-footed animals, and must enable many of the water birds to launch into the air from heights. Gull islands need enough water around them to keep four-footed enemies from reaching them in the breeding season. Vandal fishermen sometimes destroy the nests of gulls, terns, and herons in the belief that the birds compete with the fishermen unduly for game or food fishes. Visits of well-meaning people may result in disturbance that raises havoc with the colony by exposing eggs and young to sun, enemies, trampling, or other destruction. Many nesting sites are being purchased, leased, set aside, or otherwise protected by public and quasi-public agencies. Publicly owned lands used by colonies have frequently been set aside for bird reservations, a practice that is gaining in favor.

Regulating the Environment and Plant Composition. Management operations for non-game species may be general in nature, bettering conditions for any and all species of an area, or they may be specific and designed for a single species. Considerable study is required to devise management techniques for a single species, though general practices are easier to apply.

Heavy grazing has a definite influence on the composition in a grazed woodlot or other area. The most palatable species go first, and the

Regulating the Environment and Plant Composition 299

less palatable ones multiply. Often heavy grazing and attendant disturbance change the composition over thousands of square miles, as in the Edwards Plateau brush country, which was formerly largely grassland. *Light grazing* may have a beneficial effect for some species

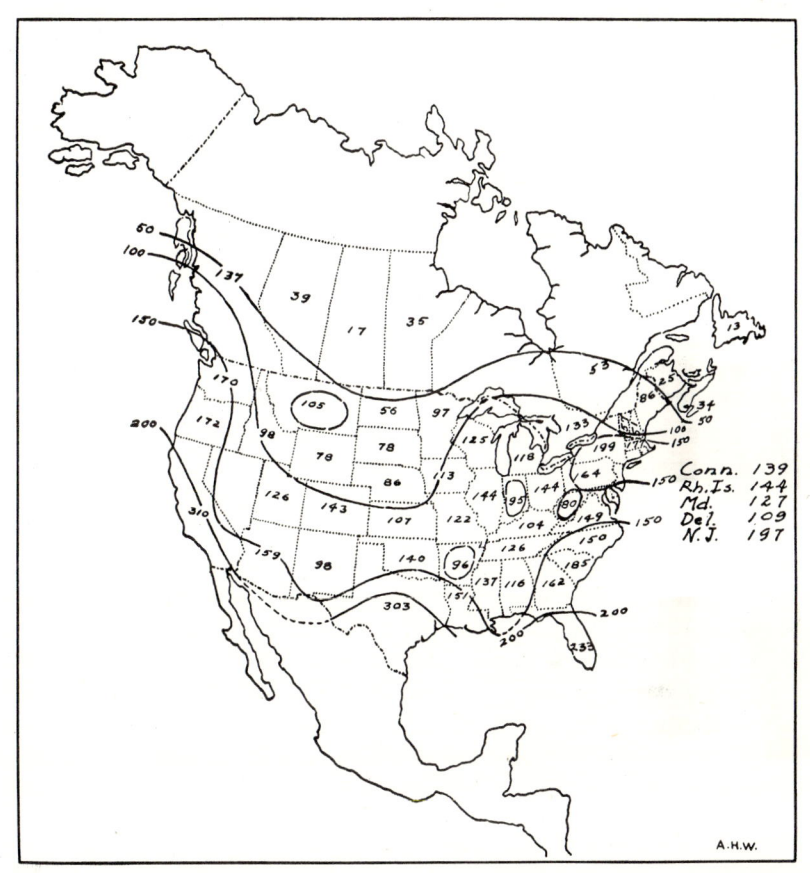

Fig. 19.1. Isopleths of winter species abundance show the increase in numbers southward and oceanward. (Data from Christmas Censuses, 1900–1939.)

by breaking up the understory, just as *heavy grazing* may aid others by destroying it and *no grazing* may benefit still others by restoring it. Grazing, for example, tends to make *Crataegus*, hazel, and similar pasture shrubs grow in small clumps or patches favored by many birds. Woodlands can be kept in a brush state by cutting at intervals, usually fewer than 20 years apart. Burning will accomplish the same result with less effort. Cutting and burning may also be invoked to preserve open spaces, as in a gull or tern colony subject to eviction by encroaching vegetation, or to keep a low canopy locally.

Some discretion is always necessary. Junipers, for example, play host to the apple rust that also may attack *Crataegus*, but it is reported that the Ozark cedar, *Juniperus ashei*, is immune to apple rust. Many species of *Berberis* are host to wheat rust, and *Ribes* of some species harbors white pine blister rust. All these plants may be valuable wildlife food or cover plants, but they must be used with caution where they could harbor agricultural diseases.

Supplying Cover. Clumps of conifer supply excellent cover in winter and are regularly used to provide windbreaks around feeding stations and to supply warm night roosting cover. "Living snow fences" have proved valuable also for birds in treeless and open country. Small thickets of hawthorn, plum, and other thorny or close-growing shrubs are often sought by birds, especially when plentiful supplies of foods are nearby. Tangles of grape and vines have proved satisfactory for roosting and resting cover, as have also brush piles, though brush piles for songbirds must usually be larger than those for game birds in order to satisfy the songbirds' desire to be higher above the ground.

Songbirds like the chickadee, nuthatch, and titmouse like to roost in holes at night and will inhabit bird boxes for winter roosts as well as for summer nesting. But the boxes should be cleaned of old nests before winter sets in.

In summer birds need adequate cover where they may find the seclusion that they prefer for nesting and for the young during the critical period after leaving the nest. *Facing down* the edge often helps, and it can be accomplished by planting low-growing shrubs to cover the break between the ground and higher shrubs.

Migration cover varies, and it is impossible to do more than to generalize. The migration cover tends to follow the cover preferences of nesting time (i.e., open, marsh, brush, forest, etc.), but the food need seems a disproportionately greater attraction. During migration, birds tend to pile up on the outgoing sides of woods and at the far ends of peninsulas. They favor south-facing sites in fall and north-facing ones in spring. Food-bearing plants could be planted accordingly, though each site would need its own shrubs. The same plants would thus serve for both cover and food.

Food Plants for Birds. The species of food plants for birds should be the same as for a game species, that is, hardy, productive, adapted, and attractive to birds. A wide variety of plants will increase the food choice, and presumably the available insect supply, for other birds

Winter Feeding

than fruit eaters. Birds also feed extensively upon weed seeds, crop remnants, and hibernating insects in fall and winter. As soil always seems to have an abundance of weed seed, the quantity left in fallow fields or cultivated crops seems unlikely to influence the amount of seed growing the next year.

Though adequate lists will be found in several books and published information, the twelve leading bird foods suitable for most parts of the country are:

Mulberry	Service berry
Blackberry	Sumac
Rose	Holly (*Ilex* sp.)
Mountain ash	Grape
Cherry (*Prunus*)	Dogwood
Elderberry	Viburnum

Winter Feeding. Winter feeding implies temporary methods of putting out food rather than permanent methods such as planting of food-producing shrubs. Among the many devices that will attract birds by feeding are:

Window shelves	Tree shelves
Suet containers	Revolving feeders
Stationary feeders	Hoppers
Scattered food	Fountains

Food patches serve admirably for songbirds in winter; even a few plants, such as sunflower, will be much used. Food-patch plants for game birds also serve well for songbirds, although corn will be eaten by few songbirds other than jays, cardinals, and grosbeaks. There are also many kinds of food that attract birds at feeding stations; Table 19.1 lists several foods and examples of birds known to use them.

TABLE 19.1

EXAMPLES OF BIRDS ATTRACTED BY VARIOUS FOODS

(After McAtee, 1940)

Species	Small Grains	Raisins	Suet	Cracked Nuts	Cracked Corn	Whole Corn	Sunflower Seeds	Bread Crumbs	Cut Apples
Woodpeckers			x	x	x	x			
Blue jay	x		x	x	x	x	x	x	
Chicadee, Nuthatch, Titmouse			x	x	x		x	x	
Robin, Thrasher, Mockingbird, Catbird	x	x		x	x		x	x	x
Cardinal	x			x	x	x	x	x	x
Native sparrows	x			x	x		x	x	

Bird Houses. Bird houses have long been supplied for hole-nesting species, but the maximum number that will be satisfactory is not known. It might be that as many as 25 units on an acre of home grounds will not be too many where concentration is desired.

Houses need to be durable, heat proof, cleanable, roomy, and, when possible, natural in appearance. Wood is the best material, though others can be used. The houses may be unpainted, painted, or covered with bark. Wood should be treated with a preservative. (Creosote-treated wood should be allowed to weather before being put out for birds. Some of the newer preservatives are better.) The simplest design is best; many of the simple designs lend themselves to mass-production and economy of effort. Hollow limbs and hollowed-out sections of trees make more natural-looking houses than those made of boards. Tin is not advised, nor is other material that is subject to heating excessively. Ventilation holes at the top make the house cooler, and drainage holes at the bottom assure dryness. Although the size of the box and hole is not important, houses designed for a species are better than a series of standardized houses that attempt to catch all birds.

The recommended height above the ground is variable, as is the direction of the entrance. Martins prefer houses in the open away from trees. Other species favor shade or partial shade, whereas still others want full sunlight. Table 19.2 lists the size of opening, size of box, and height above ground recommended for various species.

Nesting Material and Nesting Sites. Certain species, especially robins, barn swallows, and cliff swallows, require mud for nests, which can be supplied by flooding a favored spot or perhaps by placing mud where birds can find it. A binder like straw may also be needed.

Soft yarn or string in short lengths (6 or 8 inches) scattered throughout the shrubbery will be found by birds that weave nests. The goldfinch and phoebe use down in the nest and take cotton or wool put out for them; often an entire nest will be made of the offering. Sticks, which may be at a premium in an egret or heron colony, can be supplied artificially by placing them on rafts or on the ground.

Suitable whorls for nest sites are formed by repeated pruning or by tying together branches and twigs. Dense thickets suitable for nesting sites also result from severe pruning or dwarfing, a practice that also gives spreading shrubbery for a time. Cleats nailed to the walls of buildings may be supplied for phoebes and cliff swallows. Rough spots in masonry under bridges and in culverts (Fig. 19.2) serve the same purpose.

Bird Houses

TABLE 19.2

SIZES OF NEST BOXES AND RECOMMENDED HEIGHT ABOVE GROUND

(After Kalmbach and McAtee, 1925)

Species	Floor of Cavity	Depth of Cavity	Entrance above Floor	Diameter of Entrance	Height above Ground
Kestrel	8 × 8	12–15	9–12	3	10–30
Barn owl	10 × 18	15–18	4	6	12–18
Saw-whet owl	6 × 6	10–12	8–10	2½	12–20
Screech owl	8 × 8	12–15	9–12	3	10–30
Hairy woodpecker	6 × 6	12–15	9–12	1½	12–20
Downy woodpecker	4 × 4	8–10	6–8	1¼	6–20
Red-headed woodpecker	6 × 6	12–15	9–12	2	12–20
Golden-fronted woodpecker	6 × 6	12–15	9–12	2	12–20
Flicker	7 × 7	16–18	14–18	2½	6–20
Crested flycatcher	6 × 6	8–10	6–8	2	8–20
Phoebe	6 × 6	6	*	*	8–12
Violet-green swallow	5 × 5	6–8	1–5	1½	10–15
Tree swallow	5 × 5	6–8	1–5	1½	10–15
Barn swallow	6 × 6	6	*	*	8–12
Purple martin	6 × 6	6	1	2	15–20
Chickadees	4 × 4	8–10	6–8	1⅛	6–15
Titmouses	4 × 4	8–10	6–8	1¼	6–15
Nuthatches	4 × 4	8–10	6–8	1¼	12–20
House wren	4 × 4	6–8	1–6	1	6–10
Bewick wren	4 × 4	6–8	1–6	1	6–10
Carolina wren	4 × 4	6–8	1–6	1⅛	6–10
Bluebirds	5 × 5	8	6	1½	5–10
Robin	6 × 8	8	*	*	6–15
House finch	6 × 6	6	4	2	8–12
Song sparrow	6 × 6	6	†	†	1–3

* One or more sides open.
† All sides open.

Protection from Enemies. The natural enemies of songbirds form an unimportant part of the environment so far as management practice goes, except under special conditions. Cats and dogs are the most serious enemies of birds around cities, settlements, and farms. Cat licenses have long been advocated for control of cats, and some parlor cats have been belled to protect birds. Trapping and shooting still seem to be the surest methods for controlling stray cats and dogs.

304 Songbird and Non-Game Conservation

Cat-proof fences have been erected at some bird-banding stations. A 6-foot fence with an overhang and an underground outward-projecting ledge is usually cat-proof. On many oceanic islands and bird rocks, cats, dogs, rats, goats, rabbits, and hogs have been destructive factors threatening the existence of many marine birds, especially hole-nesting ones like petrels (Fig. 19.3). No doubt some removal measures could reduce or eliminate these alien enemy additions to the fauna of nesting islands and rocks.

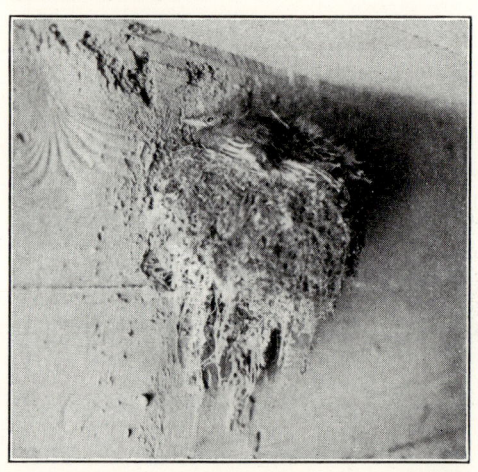

Fig. 19.2. Rough spots in the masonry or cleats make it possible for some birds like the phoebe to nest on man-made constructions.

The house sparrow and starling are formidable competitors and sometimes enemies of native birds, particularly of those that nest in holes. They can be controlled locally by persistent shooting and continued trapping. It is not convenient for a house sparrow to enter a nest box with a hole less than 1 inch in diameter or for a starling to enter one much less than 1⅝ inches in diameter. Wrens and chickadees readily pass through 1-inch holes, and martins can use one of 1⅝ inches, though larger ones are preferred.

Crop Protection and Damage Control. Non-game wildlife occasionally may cause damage, sometimes real but usually overrated. Any damage claim needs careful examination to determine what control measures, if any, need be initiated. Minor and transitory damage needs no control; control measures elsewhere may prove too expensive. Destruction of birds or other animals should be undertaken only as a last resort. Generally, destroying the wildlife can be con-

Crop Protection and Damage Control 305

strued as evidence that other methods have not been perfected or are not applicable. Repellents are satisfactory in preventing much damage to farm seeds at planting time, and they have little effect upon germination. Coal tar, kerosene, and naphthalene have been effective when mixed into a batch of seeds. Some of the commercial repellents satisfactorily protect seeds and other crops.

FIG. 19.3. Oceanic birds often seek islands for protection during nesting seasons, but hole-nesting species may be wiped out by cats, dogs, and rats. Petrel nest hole on Green Island, Maine.

The scarecrow is an ancient repellent supplemented in recent years by glass and tin flashers. The flash gun (acetylene exploder) makes a sharp explosion at regular intervals and has proved valuable in driving robins, starlings, and crows from roosts and orchards. The electric fence has been installed sometimes for control of small mammals, as well as larger ones, but it works only where the ground remains damp. Some success has been had in controlling starlings and pigeons, and sometimes other birds, by means of stuffed, artificial, or mechanical horned owls. Sometimes luminous paint applied to them increases their effectiveness. Other methods tried have been fire hoses, Roman candles, noisemakers, and tree shakers.

Occasionally damage may be reduced by diverting the interest of birds. One of the best ways to divert birds is to plant preferred fruits, like the mulberry, among orchard trees.

Wires stretched over the waters of ponds, and sometimes other devices, have been useful in excluding large birds from fish ponds and reservoirs. Such wires will also aid in preventing gulls from roosting on boat masts, posts, and houses.

Elimination of Unwelcome Species. Wildlife managers may be called upon to advise on the elimination or dispersal of unwelcome birds and mammals or other species around buildings. Though many species may become problems under some circumstances, only bats, flying squirrels, domestic pigeons, starlings, and house sparrows regularly make themselves unwelcome. Most of the pests are alien introductions. The majority of attempts to introduce or transplant birds have failed; only a few have been successful (Table 19.3). Pests like the rat and mouse were not introduced purposely.

TABLE 19.3

SPECIES OF BIRDS SUCCESSFULLY INTRODUCED OR TRANSPLANTED IN NORTH AMERICA

Valley quail
  Washington, Oregon, Idaho, Utah, British Columbia
Bobwhite
  Washington, Idaho, Colorado, Wyoming
Hungarian partridge
  Lake States, Prairie Provinces, Oregon, Idaho, Washington, British Columbia
Ring-necked pheasant
  Connecticut, Massachusetts, Rhode Island, New York, Pennsylvania, Michigan, Ohio, Indiana, Illinois, Wisconsin, Missouri, Iowa, Minnesota, North Dakota, South Dakota, Washington, Idaho, Oregon, Ontario
Starling
  West to the Pacific Coast States
Crested mynah
  British Columbia
House sparrow
  Settled parts of North America
European tree sparrow
  Missouri
Chinese spotted dove
  Los Angeles

The surest way to eliminate nuisance bats and flying squirrels is to plug openings through which they gain admittance to buildings. Repellents must be used where plugging cannot be done. Naphthalene or other moth repellents scattered in attics and partitions have been successful in driving out intruders (even mice as well as bats). As a last resort poisoning, trapping, or even poison gas (such as cyanide) may be used.

Pigeons, starlings, and house sparrows may become pests around houses, barns, and city buildings, where they nest in holes, projections, vines, or other suitable places. In the warmer parts of the country house sparrows will nest in trees, often several nests to a tree. The removal of vines where starlings and house sparrows congregate is usually necessary for permanent elimination. Birds may also congregate on window ledges or other perches, especially on buildings that have much "gingerbread" in the design. Walls, eaves, columns, and other such places can be covered with hardware cloth, small-mesh poultry netting, or fish netting (Fig. 19.4). Good results have been obtained by eliminating the perching ledges, the simplest method being the addition of a triangular strip of wood to the top of the ledge. The wisest way to prevent such unwanted concentration of birds around buildings is to simplify the outside design so that no nesting and perching sites are available for the unwanted birds. The architecture of public buildings usually provides a paradise for pigeons, starlings, and house sparrows.

Wildlife and the Highway. Considerable destruction of wildlife occurs along the highway from collisions with fast automobiles. Mortality is especially high in young birds. Red-headed woodpeckers, robins, bobwhites, house sparrows, pheasants, screech owls, rabbits, and skunks are the leading sufferers. In parts of the West, the jack rabbit also suffers heavily.

The greatest mortality occurs along paved roads with fast traffic and the lowest along country roads. Many birds are killed as they come to the highway for food, such as insects, but the majority are killed as they cross the open space in going from one side to the other. The question naturally arises as to whether or not the mortality is greater than the number of birds and other wildlife produced by the highway habitat. The total acreage of roadside in the United States and Canada is very great indeed, although the roadsides themselves are but narrow belts; they aggregate many millions of acres of good wildlife habitat. In farmed areas and settled regions, the highway strip may be a very significant part of the total cover. The amount varies with the type of roadside; it is greatest along modern parkways and least along "slick and clean," debrushed, mowed roadsides.

Mortality can be reduced by rounding off sharp points or projections in the cover, because birds often work their way along the face of the

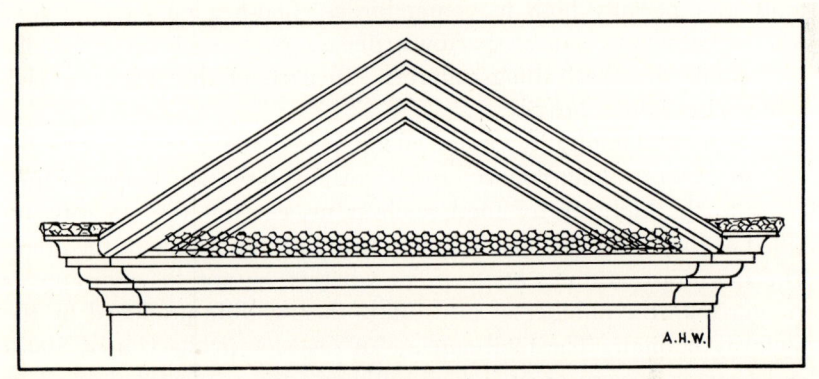

FIG. 19.4. Preventing house sparrows, starlings, and pigeons from nesting by covering with screen or netting.

cover to a point or perch sticking out from the main cover line before launching across the open space. Smoothing the face by a curving front removes some shuttling back and forth. Straight-line fronts to the shrub mass, however, are not good practices from the standpoint of landscape design, and so the curving front is a satisfactory compromise.

Yearly cutting and burning of roadsides is a practice entrenched in the minds of highway engineers, though it is not good ecologically. Left undisturbed, shrubs or other vegetation relatively high in the ecological succession would form permanent cover needing little maintenance, an important economy. Disturbance by cutting and burning

FIG. 19.5. Living snow fences along highways and railroads supply important winter cover, especially in the prairies. (Photograph by Great Northern Railway.)

sets the succession back. Native shrubs are to be recommended, even though planting horticultural varieties is easier. Native vegetation, however, generally gives superior results because it is better adapted to the sites. "Living snow fences" serve as nesting cover in summer and shelter in winter (Fig. 19.5). Along some roadsides local clubs have put out nest boxes and also winter feeding stations.

Re-establishing Extirpated Species. Extirpated species may spread back into vacant range if given the necessary protection, though it may be necessary to rebuild some of the habitat before it will be reoccupied permanently. Needless to say, protection of remnant species or remnant populations is of first importance because they serve as centers for natural restocking.

Extirpated species have been restocked successfully in a few recolonization experiments by taking stock from the nearest remnants. The nearest remnant is recommended because of possible racial and subracial adaptations to the climatic environment. The movement of stock over long distances should be avoided and should not be undertaken at all if it involves the introduction of different races or jumping of the range of another race. Live-trapped gulls, deer, and other species have been recolonized. Eggs have been moved experimentally and placed in the nests of closely related species.

SUGGESTED READING

Baker, John H. (Editor), 1941, *The Audubon Guide to Attracting Birds*, Doubleday, Doran and Co., Garden City, N. Y.

Henderson, Junius, 1927, *The Practical Value of Birds*, The Macmillan Co., New York.

Henderson, Junius, and Elberta Craig, 1932, *Economic Mammalogy*, Charles C. Thomas, Springfield, Ill.

Jackson, C. F., and Philip F. Allan, 1931, "Experiment in the Recolonization of the Common Tern (*Sterna hirundo*)," *Auk*, 48:17–21.

Kalmbach, E. R., 1930, "English Sparrow Control," *U.S.D.A. Leaflet* 61.

Kalmbach, E. R., 1940, "Suggestions for Combating Roosts of Birds with Special Reference to Those of Starlings," *Fish and Wildlife Serv. Wildlife Leaflet* 172.

King, Ralph T., 1942, "Is It Wise Policy to Introduce Exotic Game Birds?" *Audubon Mag.*, 44:136–145, pp. 230–236, 306–310.

Linsdale, Jean M., 1931, "Facts Concerning the Use of Thallium in California to Poison Rodents—Its Destructiveness to Game Birds, Song Birds and other Valuable Wild Life," *Condor*, 33:92–106.

McAtee, W. L., 1940, "A Venture in Songbird Management," *Jour. Wildlife Management*, 4:85–89.

Pearson, T. Gilbert, 1937, *Adventures in Bird Protection*, D. Appleton-Century Co., New York.

Phillips, John C., 1928, "Wild Birds Introduced or Transplanted in North America," *U.S.D.A. Tech. Bull.* 61.

Silver, James, 1935, "Eliminating Bats from Buildings," *U.S.D.A. Leaflet* 109.

Van Dersal, William R., 1938, "Native Woody Plants of the United States, Their Erosion-Control and Wildlife Value," *U.S.D.A. Misc. Pub.* 303.

Wight, H. M., 1931, "The Effect of Pole Traps on Harmless and Beneficial Species," *Wilson Bull.*, 43:282–292.

Wing, Leonard, 1943, "Spread of the Starling and English Sparrow," *Auk*, 60:74–87.

20

Treatment of Rare, Threatened, and Persecuted Species

Of the many species of wildlife now reduced in numbers, some must be classified as *rare*, others as *threatened*, and still others, we regret to say, reduced to zero abundance and now *extinct*. To these we must add another group whose present treatment is deliberately destructive and that therefore are called *persecuted species*.

Causes of Decline. As has been noted earlier, probably the most misunderstood and therefore the most controversial matter in the whole wildlife field is the relation of predators to prey—and indirectly to the sportsmen. It is not the purpose of this text to go into the pros and cons of predator campaigns but to give the foundation material and measures of true management. The student is referred for fuller treatment to the many recent writings that have covered with varying judiciousness the different predator-prey relationships and predator control.

Biological Eclipse. Natural extinction of species is the rule in nature, just as the death of the individual follows a natural law. Species have arisen and have fallen in the geologic past, some to become extinct and to leave no descendants behind, some to evolve into other, and different species that have carried on the protoplasmic torch.

Biological eclipse, i.e., natural extinction, moves so slowly that it really is not measurable in terms of human observation. There can be no doubt that biological eclipse goes on today just as it has in the past, even though we cannot see its slow-motion procedure. We have many species that have become adapted to narrow environmental conditions; like oldsters in the decline of life, they are excessively intolerant of changes in their habitat and find it difficult or impossible to adapt themselves to the disturbances, changes, or pressures wrought by ecological changes. It is logical to assume that many of these narrowly restricted species are on their way to oblivion, to oblivion from biological eclipse.

Among the forms that express evolutionary age by intolerance and low vigor may be noted the California condor, ivory-billed woodpecker, Kirtland warbler, and manatee. Though we are justified in reaching the conclusion that these species are headed for the end, we are not thereby justified in assuming that they will of necessity disappear in our times. If left unshot or if given help by man to ease the human pressure, they could continue to exist for thousands and perhaps millions of years. Although the process of their extinction can be speeded up by man, there is no warrant for believing that we are wholly incapable of preserving them from immediate dangers of extinction.

Extinction Threshold. The extinction threshold is allied to *renewability,* namely, the power of a species to re-establish itself from near-zero abundance. The extinction threshold is actually the lower limit of renewability. The passenger pigeon, for example, probably reached its extinction threshold when its number and population assortment were too few for the massed breeding necessitated by its behavior habits and low breeding potential. The heath hen perhaps reached its extinction threshold about the year 1915, and the Michigan grayling before 1910.

Inroads of Settlement. The inroads of settlement need little comment. It was inevitable that man's occupation of the land would work hardships upon many species of wildlife. The inroads were sometimes accompanied even by deliberate destruction of wildlife under the guise of disease control, as in the history of the Florida deer herd. In destroying wildlife the settlers were sometimes attempting to cut off the food resources of unruly Indian tribes who, when their bison supply was lost, had to submit or starve.

Hunting for Sport and Trophies. Some wildlife has been hunted zealously for trophies, especially the largest, the best, the rarest, or the last. The desire for rarities causes such a persistent pursuit, usually without realization of the destruction thus wrought, that it differs enough from ordinary hunting to merit comment.

Few egg collections are made any more for scientific purposes; the real motive is the desire of possession, just as the stamp collector desires rare stamps. The pursuit of rarities has placed a fictitious value

Rare and Threatened American Birds 313

on the eggs of some birds, and "postage-stamp" egg collecting has been especially hard, along with other pressures, on the ibis, condor, kites, falcons, and limpkins.

Pursuit for Plumage, Fur, and Other Products. The pursuit of birds for their plumage has been eliminated over most of the Americas, but many mammals of the sea—seals, sea otters, sea lions, and whales—have been pursued with increasing pressure in order to obtain valuable pelts or valuable products. The list would be too large to include here.

Wanton Destruction. Ignorance and maliciousness beget wanton destruction; both are difficult to overcome, and both testify to the need for education. It is the habit of a thoughtless group of people to shoot at any live or unusual animal merely to see it closely or merely to try to hit it. Even men in the high position of President of the United States have succumbed to the seemingly uncontrollable temptation to shoot the unusual.

Along some ocean cliffs accessible from highways, people have maliciously thrown objects or fired guns at nesting sea birds and even at the rare sea otters. Only warden patrols seem at present a sufficiently educational force to stop the practice. Hunting elk for their teeth was formerly remunerative; the rest of the animal went to rot. Waste of whales has occurred in the past, and perhaps still occurs, because of wasteful or crude processing methods. Kingfishers, hawks, owls, and many other predators are pursued relentlessly both from ignorance and maliciousness. Because they are almost always conducted indiscriminately, poison campaigns have killed many harmless birds and mammals, and many forms of wildlife are also destroyed by pole traps. Both practices have been outlawed or severely controlled in some states. More rigid control will doubtless be the future trend.

Extinct Species. Fourteen species or subspecies of American birds are known to have become extinct since the arrival of the white man. To these we must add one species of fish, five of mammals, and undoubtedly several subspecies. Perhaps several other subspecies or even species became extinct before taxonomists recognized them, which may explain some puzzles like the sea mink and Townsend bunting. The fact remains, however, that at least 20 forms must be reckoned as extinct (Table 20.1).

Rare and Threatened American Birds. The threatened birds (Table 20.2) are those reduced in numbers and distribution. The wood duck has made a splendid comeback with the expected hunter-pressure for open seasons, indicating one of the effective advantages of the closed season and the attendant public enlightenment that must go with it for success as a measure for re-establishing reduced species. Several other birds have shown some increase in numbers under the same closed season.

TABLE 20.1

EXTINCT NORTH AMERICAN ANIMALS

Species	Probable Date of Extinction
Michigan grayling	1930?
Great auk	1853
Pallas cormorant	1852
Labrador duck	1878
Guadelupe caracara	1900
Black-capped petrel	1912
Heath hen	1931
Passenger pigeon	1898 (1914)
Carolina paraquet	1904
Louisiana paraquet	Unknown
Cuban tricolored macaw	1864
Gosse macaw	1800
Guadeloupe macaw	Unknown
Eskimo curlew	1930?
Townsend bunting *	1832
California grizzly	1900?
Sea mink	1860?
Arizona elk	1901
Dawson caribou	1908
Steller sea cow	1768

* Townsend bunting has puzzled taxonomists. Its characters are not those of a hybrid, and it may have been a species that became extinct before a second specimen was collected.

Active measures for the protection and increase of the trumpeter swan show what can be done to save birds. Other measures for the great white heron and roseate spoonbill are proving helpful, but efforts for the whooping crane show no such results, though the possibilities are still hopeful for its eventual recovery of numbers to a safe margin. The sandhill crane, however, is a species that lives both in settled regions, although in the more remote marshes, and in wild areas. Some management opportunities exist for it.

The members of the Falconiformes and Strigiformes, especially the kites and others equally harmless, have been reduced in numbers through unwarranted persecution. Their role in the biota is an important one, and their place in the nature epic distinct. All need more than just legal protection, often a fact on paper only.

The peregrine falcon nests on ledges and cliffs, and a pair usually returns to the same eyrie year after year. Some eyries have been occupied for centuries by generations of falcons. Publicly owned cliffs probably can be protected by official action, though private ones used as eyries must have leases or other means for preventing intrusion. The marking of falcon eggs with indelible ink destroys their "postage-stamp" value and protects the eggs near centers of population without harming the embryos. "Scrapes" consisting of a shallow box of sand placed on skyscraper window ledges have been used by falcons for nesting. The peregrine is an active pigeon-control in cities, and it is an ally of health authorities in the reduction of such pigeons found to harbor psittacosis.

TABLE 20.2

RARE AND THREATENED SPECIES (North America)

Great white heron	Aleutian tern *
Glossy ibis *	White-crowned pigeon *
Ross goose	White-winged dove *
Trumpeter swan	Florida burrowing owl
California condor	Ivory-billed woodpecker
White-tailed kite *	Kirtland warbler
Swallow-tailed kite	Sutton warbler
Mississippi kite	Cape sable seaside sparrow
Everglade kite *	Grizzly bear
Red-bellied hawk	Black-footed ferret
Sennett white-tailed hawk *	Sea otter
Short-tailed hawk *	Kit fox
Harris hawk *	Wolf
Mexican black hawk *	Cougar
Peregrine falcon	Elephant seal
Aplomado falcon *	West Indian seal
Attawater prairie chicken	Carolina beaver
Sage hen	Desert bighorn
Masked bobwhite	Sierra bighorn
Whooping crane	Manatee
Sandhill crane *	Woodland caribou *
Roseate tern *	

* At least north of the Rio Grande or in the United States.

Several special concentration areas of migrating hawks have been protected from gunners by official closure or by private means, such as the famed Hawk Mountain Sanctuary. The method is one that offers opportunity for action in a number of areas.

Rare and Threatened Mammals. Several mammals reduced generally throughout the range still survive in remnants. Others may be of local reduction. The bison decline is a classic example of the reduction on a general scale (Fig. 12.1).

The desert bighorn and Sierra bighorn have been extirpated over most of their range. It is doubtful that the introduction of any foreign relative can substitute for either of these animals. The reduction has been brought about by the inroads of settlement, along with excessive shooting and poaching. The preservation of these sheep seems to be largely a problem in land use and tolerance; tolerance is obtainable only through education.

The mountain lion or cougar has been relentlessly pursued over most of its range. The damage claimed to be caused by mountain lions is customarily grossly exaggerated. The oft-quoted statement that the mountain lion kills a deer a week has no basis in known fact, and its appearance should be taken as evidence of irresponsible, non-biological writing. Mountain lions today are not known to affect the game supply, though they may affect the domestic stock on big-game range.

The timber wolf has less protection than even the mountain lion, and even Congressional Acts have failed to get protection for it in our national parks. It is not a factor in the game supply, though, like the mountain lion, it may affect domestic stock on the game range.

The mountain goat has been reduced locally in parts of its range, especially in the United States. The chief causes seem to be human disturbance, hunting (legal and illegal), and some adverse affect of domestic stock in a few places. Rigid protection has shown the most success in increasing its numbers.

Rare and Threatened Sea Mammals. The sea mammals in the categories of rare and threatened animals may be divided into four groups:

> Whales, porpoises, and other cetaceans (Order Cetacea).
> Seals, sea lions, and walruses (Order Pinnipedia).
> Sea cows (Order Sirenia).
> Sea otters and polar bears (Order Carnivora).

The protection of some, such as the cetaceans, requires international action especially. The several treaties for whaling regulation seem likely to have continued success if they are conscientiously followed. The protection of sea lions and sea elephants seems to be dependent largely upon public opinion. The tradition for their protection seems not yet fully developed.

Little action for the increase of sea mammals, other than added protection, is available at the present time except in a few isolated or minor cases.

SUGGESTED READING

Allen, Glover M., 1942, *Vanishing Marine Mammals of the Western Hemisphere,* Am. Comm. for Int. Wild Life Protect.

Allen, Ropert Porter, 1942, "The Roseate Spoonbill," *Nat. Audubon Soc. Res. Rept. 2.*

Beard, Daniel (Editor), 1942, *Fading Trails,* The Macmillan Co., New York.

Bent, Arthur Cleveland, 1919–, *Life Histories of North American Birds,* U. S. Nat. Mus.

Cahalane, Victor H., 1939, "The Evolution of Predator Control Policy in the National Parks," *Jour. Wildlife Management,* 3:229–237.

Cahalane, Victor H., 1944, "Restoration of Wild Bison," *Trans. Ninth N. A. Wildlife Conf.:* 135–143.

Cahalane, Victor H., 1947, *Mammals of North America,* The Macmillan Co., New York.

Henderson, Junius, 1927, *The Practical Value of Birds,* The Macmillan Co., New York.

Henderson, Junius, and Elberta Craig, 1932, *Economic Mammalogy,* Charles C Thomas, Springfield, Ill.

Hornaday, William T., 1913, *Our Vanishing Wild Life,* New York Zoölogical Society, New York.

Imler, Ralph H., and Hosea A. Sarber, 1947, "Harbor Seals and Sea Lions in Alaska," *Fish and Wildlife Serv. Spec. Sci. Rept.* 28.

May, John Bichard, 1935, *The Hawks of North America,* National Association of Audubon Societies, New York.

Mershon, William Butts, 1907, *The Passenger Pigeon,* Outing Publishing Co., New York.

Murie, Adolph, 1940, *Ecology of the Coyote in the Yellowstone,* Nat. Park Serv., Fauna Ser. 4.

Murie, Adolph, 1948, "Cattle on Grizzly Bear Range," *Jour. Wildlife Management,* 12:57–72.

Pough, Richard H., 1937, "An Inventory of Threatened and Vanishing Species," *Trans. Second N. A. Wildlife Conf.:* 599–604.

Seton, Ernest Thompson, 1925–1929, *Lives of Game Animals,* 4 vols., Doubleday, Doran and Co., Garden City, N. Y.

Tanner, James T., 1942, "The Ivory-billed Woodpecker," *Nat. Audubon Soc. Res. Rept. 1.*

Trippensee, Reuben Edwin, 1948, *Wildlife Management,* McGraw-Hill Book Co., New York.

Walkinshaw, Lawrence, 1949, *The Sandhill Cranes,* Cranbrook Inst. Sci., Bloomfield Hills, Mich.

Young, Stanley P., and Edward A. Goldman, 1944, *The Wolves of North America,* American Wildlife Institute, Washington, D. C.

Young, Stanley P., and Edward A. Goldman, 1946, *The Puma, Mysterious American Cat,* American Wildlife Institute, Washington, D. C.

21

State Powers and Controls

The original thirteen American colonies received their governmental powers in the form of charters and grants from the Crown. The American courts hold that the colonies revolted from the Crown not as one nation, since there was none in existence at the time, but as individual colonies, and when the Revolutionary War was over, they possessed all the powers of independent governments. They thereupon created a federal government to which they *delegated* certain powers to be exercised in the interest of all. The colonies became states and as such still possess all the powers of sovereign nations, except those that have been delegated to the federal government and those that have been prohibited to them by the states themselves. The American system differs from others in that power comes from the *state*, not the federal government, and the state is the unit of government and source of power. This fact should not be overlooked, even though the current trend is to ignore its existence.

The framers of the Constitution provided for the admission of additional states to the Union.[1] The courts universally hold that the Constitution intends a nation of equal states and that states admitted later automatically obtain all the rights and prerogatives of the original thirteen states and must be on an equal footing with other states in all respects.

It is obvious that the jurisdiction of each of the thirteen original states still reaches to all points within its borders, unless the state ceded jurisdiction over specific areas to the federal government for legitimate purposes; such purposes must be related to proper functions of the federal government. Newer states have these same jurisdictional rights unless exemptions for proper purposes are specifically made by the act of admission. The areas that have been so exempted in the form-

---

[1] Constitution, Article 4, Section 3.

ing of new states or over which jurisdiction has been ceded by established states are such areas as Indian reservations, national parks, and military reservations. Unless full jurisdiction over their included area was received, new states would not have equality with the original states.

Ferae Naturae and State Ownership. All animals may be placed in one of two legal classifications: domesticated or *ferae naturae* animals. *Ferae naturae* means literally "animals of nature." The question of which animals are or are not *ferae naturae* has been the subject of numerous court decisions, and universal agreement has resulted. All animals "wild by nature" are *ferae naturae*, the governing point being the status of the species, not whether an individual animal is wild or captive. Thus deer are *ferae naturae* even when they are raised in captivity and the offspring of captives.[1]

The distinctions between domesticated and *ferae naturae* animals are too well known to require discussion. Everyone knows that cattle, horses, and other stock are not wild by nature, despite the fact that they have descended from wild ancestors. But the distinction may become narrow, as in the case of *feral* animals (domestic animals gone wild). Generally speaking, animals that have reverted to the wild and thus become feral are considered to have become once more *ferae naturae*. The mute swan, now wild in some of the eastern states, is an example of a feral animal, like the wild horse of the early West.

Game and food animals are those animals *ferae naturae* that are commonly taken for food or sport, and the term includes a wide variety of fishes, birds, and mammals, as well as some lower forms such as oysters and shrimps. Whether an animal is a game or food animal is more or less immaterial in the legal view. In actual practice we find that the use of animals for game is a "higher" form of use than for food, and the latter use invariably gives way to the former when conflicts arise.

In addition to the control of animals *ferae naturae* through *police power*, a power exercised by the states in common with all other civilized sovereign nations, the states derive power over animals *ferae naturae* from another source—the ownership of all animals *ferae naturae* within the boundaries of the states. For most purposes the police power alone is enough to control people in their relations with wildlife, just as it controls them in their relations with domestic animals.

---

[1] A discussion of *ferae naturae* will be found in the case of **Geer** v. **Connecticut**, 161 U. S. 519.

The doctrine of state ownership of wildlife comes to us through a long chain of circumstances, principally by reason of events that occurred in England, the mother country. It appears that hunting was communal in England at the "dawn of civilization" and that animals *ferae naturae* had no owner other than the man who brought them within his power (i.e., slew them). This situation continued in England even after the Anglo-Saxon people subjugated the previous inhabitants and themselves had taken to agriculture. Some historians believe that the Anglo-Saxons still had ownerless game status in that animals belonged to the hunter, not the landowner or ruler.

The Normans brought feudalism to England, and with it apparently came the king's claim to all things and people within his domain as *Lord Proprietor*. William the Conqueror asserted ownership of all game upon the assertion that the Anglo-Saxon kings (whom he also claimed to have succeeded as legitimate heir) owned the game as proprietors. Nebulous though his claims seem to have been, William and his successors established them by the code of the times, when might counted for more than legal precedent. But England changed as time went on, and the king ceased to be the Lord Proprietor; thenceforth the *Crown* existed in a dual status: *sovereign capacity* and *proprietary capacity*. The venerable Magna Charta was an early breakdown of the single status of proprietary capacity, and the heavy-handed actions over hunting played an important part in bringing it about.

As stated previously, the American Revolution transferred the sovereign power of the Crown to the people, as represented by the individual colonies. Their successors, as represented by the states, are now sovereign in the same manner as the Crown, and so wildlife now belongs to the people, represented by the states in their capacity as the sovereign power of the people of the respective states. Strictly speaking, the animals *ferae naturae* belong to the people themselves, and the states (not the federal, county, city, or town governments) act as trustees, in effect, as the sovereign power of the people and not in the proprietary capacities of the states.

State laws invariably contain provisions that all wild animals within the boundaries of the state belong to the state. Such laws are merely statements of fact, because the state, as the representative of the people who are the owners-in-fact, owns the wild animals whether or not the laws assert the ownership.

Police Power and State Controls. *Police power* is the authority of a government to control people within its jurisdiction in their relations with one another, as in matters of public health, safety, protection, or morals. Although it has not been judicially determined, it is accepted in legal circles that police power is not possessed by the national government because no delegation of such authority occurs in the Constitution. Enforcement of federal statutes is the enforcement of laws coming under delegated authority; no other kind is constitutional. Control of hunting in the best interests of the public comes under police power, not only of foreign governments but also of the states of this country as well. Foreign governments commonly regulate seasons, hunting, and manner of hunting, as well as other actions concerned with wild animals in the public interest, even though the animals may be the property of the landowner upon whose land they dwell. Under police power, foreign and state governments also regulate people in their dealings with their own domestic animals as evidenced by humane laws. It is obvious that in any society no one landowner could exercise enough control to protect wildlife adequately, and it is certain that much wildlife would have disappeared from many countries long ago if the governments had not had sufficient power to control hunting. Our courts have held that police power alone is sufficient basis for all regulatory powers that the states exercise over wildlife.[1]

Though animals *ferae naturae* are property common to all citizens of the state in the United States, in almost all other countries the game belongs to the property owner upon whose land it lives for the time being. But for all practical purposes the end result is the same whether the game is the property of the landowner or of the state (the people being the owners-in-fact) because police power is such that seasons and other hunting relations may be controlled by the state just as effectively under private as under public ownership. In the United States the ownership of hunting rights by the landowner as a part of ownership of the soil is just about as effective a private control as private ownership of the game elsewhere. The "American system" (which might equally well be called the "Canadian system") of state ownership of animals *ferae naturae* differs little from the "European system" as far as the individual landowner or hunter, himself is concerned. His hunting activities are subject to police power of the state in either system.

Unless some revolutionary court decisions are handed down in the future, state ownership of animals *ferae naturae* appears to remove

[1] *Geer* v. *Connecticut,* 161 U. S. 519.

any possibility that the federal government might regulate seasons on federal lands counter to state laws. (As a landowner the federal government can reduce the season within limits of the state law by denying use of its land for hunting for all or part of the season.) The fact that only the states may set seasons is an important factor in placing federal lands in the same category as other lands in the state as far as the state's jurisdiction goes. If we were not under the "American system," it might be possible for seasons on federal lands to run counter to state laws. Whether the police power of the state could operate successfully would not be clear, as control over federal property is vested in Congress,[1] and game might be a "property" by court interpretation. Without state ownership, game law control would be a patchwork pattern rather than the uniform application of state laws to all lands within the jurisdiction of the state, be they state, federal, or private lands.

Legal authorities hold that it is not possible for the state to transfer title to animals *ferae naturae* to the federal government, were the federal government constitutionally authorized to act as the sovereign power of the people directly rather than as the collective power of the sovereign states, because the state is but the trustee of its people, who are the owners-in-fact. For the states to transfer title thus would be to abrogate this trust in behalf of the people, and this, the courts hold, cannot be done except by the people (which means a constitutional amendment in each state). The rule of the courts also is that rights of sovereignty cannot be taken away by implication;[2] thus an implication that the states delegated sovereignty over animals *ferae naturae* in any way seems hardly worthy of consideration. This, of course, is not the same as federal activities in accordance with federal powers duly delegated by the states when they established a federal government.

Discriminations against Non-Residents. State ownership of all animals *ferae naturae* permits differences in the rights of citizens and non-residents or non-citizens. Among the earliest decisions covering the subject of animals *ferae naturae* was one upholding the right of the state to discriminate against non-residents. In 1842 the Supreme Court held that ownership of the soil from the low-water mark to the 3-mile limit passed from the Crown to the colonies individually.[3] The

---

[1] Constitution, Article 4, Section 3.

[2] *People* v. *Godfrey*, 17 Johns 225.

[3] *Martin* v. *Wodell*, 16 Peters 367. But see also *U. S.* v. *California*, 332 U. S. 19, in which the Court created the term "paramount rights."

Discriminations against Non-Residents

colonies did not surrender this land to the federal government when they created it, and the title to the land is held by the states that succeeded the colonies, both the original thirteen and the later ones. The states own all animals *ferae naturae* inside the territorial limits and may make all needful regulations to preserve them for the exclusive use of the citizens of the respective states in the same way as land animals are preserved. Non-residents may be required to purchase non-resident licenses or may be prohibited entirely from taking such animals in these waters.

That the states may require non-residents to purchase special licenses or even forbid them to hunt was affirmed by the Supreme Court in 1876 when it held that game within the state was the property of the people of that state and that the state could legally grant its citizens the privilege of taking a portion of the common property for private use without thereby being obligated to grant the privilege to citizens of other states.[1] It was held that this did not conflict with the constitutional provision [2] that states must give equal protection to citizens of other states with their own because it was not a matter of legal protection and only citizens of the state could have an interest in the public ownership of game.

Prohibition of out-of-state shipping of game was upheld by the Supreme Court in a famous decision.[3] The matter in question was the authority of the state to prohibit transporting out of the state game *legally* taken within the state. This prohibition was claimed to be an interference with interstate commerce, a federal field of activity.[4] The Court held that the state owned all animals *ferae naturae* in its sovereign capacity as the representative of the people and that it might permit the taking of such animals subject to their remaining within the state. This did not interfere with interstate commerce because the state had granted only a *qualified ownership,* that is, subject to the game's being used within the state. The game in question could not become an article of interstate commerce in the normal sense because the shipper had ownership for use within the state only. Hence, when he tried to ship it, the game was not his but the state's.

The right of the state to retain title to animals *ferae naturae* until such time as qualifying restrictions should be met was likewise upheld.[5]

[1] *McReady* v. *Virginia,* 94 U. S. 395.
[2] Constitution, Article 4, Section 2.
[3] *Geer* v. *Connecticut,* 161 U. S. 519.
[4] Constitution, Article 1, Section 8.
[5] *LaCoste* v. *Department of Conservation,* 263 U. S. 545.

The Court sustained a law of Louisiana that provided that peltries were the property of the state until a required severance tax had been paid. The Court held that this action of the state was a valid exertion of its police power to conserve and protect wildlife for the common benefit and that the state had the power to impose a tax as a condition to its giving up title and permitting the acquiring of private title.

Courts look with favor upon restrictions of out-of-state shipments of game when the restrictions aim to preserve wildlife or to reserve it to the use of its owners, the citizens of the respective states. But such restrictions are unconstitutional interference with interstate commerce *if promulgated for other purposes;* this was the opinion of the Court in the case of a Louisiana restriction on out-of-state shipment of shrimp not partially processed. Because the shrimp could be shipped if partially processed, the purpose of the restriction clearly was not to protect the shrimp, nor to restrict their use to the people of the state, but to force packing plants to move into the state and thereby to bring more wages to local people.[1]

In the course of preserving to its people the benefits of their ownership of the game, a state may prohibit an alien from hunting without violating constitutionally authorized treaties granting equal protection to citizens of other lands along with ours because people in the sense of owners means citizens. The authority to prohibit aliens from hunting in preserving the use of game to its owners, the citizens, carries with it the authority to prohibit aliens from owning guns with which they might hunt illegally,[2] even though citizens may not be so prohibited.[3]

Spheres of Influence, State and Federal. The type of government existing within the United States makes for a division of authority and for definite spheres of influence. It also makes for a dimness of distinction and the inevitable conflict in this shadow zone, as well as the inevitable pressure from within to expand the walls of the sphere.

These spheres are not mutually exclusive, because the national government acts as the concerted authority of the states, which are the sovereign power of the people, so that the power from the people feeds up from the bottom through the states. The sphere of the federal government overlies, but rarely reaches beyond, that of the states; that of the states, on the other hand, overlaps most of the federal

[1] *Foster-Fountain Packing Co.* v. *Hoydel,* 278 U. S. 1.
[2] *Patsone* v. *Pennsylvania,* 232 U. S. 138.
[3] Constitution, Amendment 2.

sphere and reaches far beyond as well. Other than for the few isolated exceptions being noted, the activities of the federal government are limited to those wherein it can serve as a function of the states collectively. The activity of the states as the sovereign power of the people embraces all functions common to independent nations less those delegated to the national government or prohibited entirely; inasmuch as the people of the state own the animals *ferae naturae* within their borders, the state sphere partakes of that of an owner as well as that of a government.

It is but natural that laws and regulations by either federal or state governments do not necessarily agree in the severity or liberality of their restrictions. Federal laws and regulations cover only those portions of wildlife regulations that properly fall within federal jurisdiction. The *most restrictive combination* of federal and state regulations determines what is permitted, and within the sphere of joint influence neither may be invoked as authority for an action prohibited by the other.

The establishment of game refuges and sanctuaries upon federal land is generally a cooperative venture on the part of both the state and federal governments. The authority of Congress to control federal property is undoubtedly sufficient for the federal government, like any landowner, to prohibit entrance for hunting and fishing purposes and thus to establish a refuge in actuality. The federal government, however, may in the course of regulating the use of federal land invoke criminal laws for violation of duly established prohibitions, which no landowner himself may do except as provided by the state under the state criminal code. The laws of Congress, however, may not interfere with the operations of state game officials in accordance with state laws, for the state has jurisdiction over federal lands other than those where its jurisdiction has been ceded away.

It has been the rule that, before land may be purchased within a state by the federal government, the state must pass an enabling act authorizing such purchase. It appears doubtful that federal control may be exercised legally over lands purchased in the absence of, or not in accord with, such an enabling act.

The Right to Hunt. The discussion thus far has been concerned chiefly with the authority of government; the right to hunt, to which the discussion now turns, concerns the right of the individual.

"Free hunting" is almost a byword, and the loose term implies to some that everyone has the right to hunt as he pleases, without cost and without restrictions. On the contrary, the *right* to hunt is a political freedom, and free hunting means only that in the eyes of the law every citizen has as much right to hunt as any other citizen. It is not an economic or social freedom. It does not grant anyone the free use of the property of another on which to do the hunting assured to him as a political right.[1]

The right to hunt, like almost any other right, is not without some limitations. It is subject to the police power of the state to impose legal limitations deemed best in the interest of the public. A hunter can acquire no property rights in game save such rights as the state laws permit; the person upon whose land the game lives possesses a qualified interest, at best, through his ownership of the soil; the person who owns no land has no interest other than that in common with all the citizens of the state. A man who has hunted for the past 50 years, for example, has no more claim upon the game resources of his state on the opening day of the hunting season than a new-born baby in the nearby hospital; in fact the new-born baby has a claim upon his elders to protect his interests until he grows up. In a state of five million people, each hunter has only one-five-millionths of a claim on the game.

No person has any ownership claim, except that of his citizenship, as long as animals *ferae naturae* remain free and unconfined. Ownership is acquired only when the animal in question has been brought within the power and custody of the hunter *in accordance with laws and legal regulations;* no property interest may be obtained in game that has been taken illegally. In the eyes of the law, bringing an animal under control of the hunter means actually *reducing it to a state of possession.* The long-acknowledged woods rule that the man who draws the first blood obtains the game is not sustained by law and the courts; it is a rule of etiquette among sportsmen and gentlemen, not a rule of law. Merely wounding an animal does not deprive it of liberty and bring it within the custody of the hunter. Consequently, in some areas, the fastest runner with a tag in his hand gets the deer first!

But once game has been reduced to possession by legal methods, private ownership cannot be lost as long as the animal remains in the owner's possession or bears evidence of ownership recognized by law. The judiciary has held that marking dead game in the customary manner is enough to establish the fact of ownership and to enable the lawful owner to regain his property if lost; for another to remove

---

[1] *Diana Shooting Club* v. *Lamoreaux,* 114 Wisconsin 44.

the marks and take possession constitutes theft, and it is punishable under the criminal laws of the states.

The courts generally agree that private ownership of live game is maintainable only when the animal is within the legal and physical control of its captor. Should the animal escape, the title of its owner is lost and that of the state resumed unless the animal clearly shows evidence of ownership. As might be expected, variations occur in the opinions of various courts, and the determination of the moment when a captive animal becomes wild again often is a matter of nice judgment. Some courts hold that, if the control of the owner can be detected, title is not lost, as, for example, when an animal remains near the pen wherein it had been confined. Generally speaking, courts do not distinguish between wild native animals in confinement and wild exotics when ownership of escapees is under consideration.

The right to hunt and fish in lakes and streams is a matter of difference between landowners and the public and among the judicial opinions of the various states. It is the general rule that private waters are exempt from fish laws, but just what distinguishes private from public waters is not always agreed upon; usually isolated waters are considered private waters. States refrain from planting fish in private waters, but the mere planting of fish cannot make public waters of private ones. Private property may be taken for public purposes only by due process of law and just compensation.[1] In some states the courts have held that the right to pass along streams or other waters in a boat, like the right to pass over easement highways, is not enough to authorize shooting where the land under the stream or the adjacent banks is private property. The right to fish upon navigable waters is universally a public right, although just what constitutes navigable waters is not of such universal agreement.

Property and Hunting Rights. Ownership of property gives the owner exclusive use, and the courts have long upheld the right of the landowner to exclude others from his property or to qualify its use by others as he chooses. In actual fact the basis of our civilization is the ownership of property and the exclusive rights that go with this ownership of property, be it real property, like land, or personal property, like a shirt on a man's back.

The right to hunt is no exception to exclusive rights of ownership, and the exclusive right to hunt is vested in the owner of the soil.[2]

[1] Constitution, Amendment 5.
[2] *Ohio Oil Co.* v. *Indiana,* 177 U. S. 190.

Hunting is a use of the land, like growing a crop or grazing cattle, and the use of land for hunting is a right of the owner only. No one has any more right to trespass upon the premises of another in order to hunt than to trespass upon it for some other purpose. None but the owner or person in legal control may grant permission to another to enter upon any property for the purpose of hunting. The common law, the Constitution of the United States, and the constitutions of the various states protect the owner in his property rights, and no legislative act can deny the owner any of his rights of exclusive use, such as hunting. The fact that the owner must obey the game laws like anyone else is not an abridgment of his rights of ownership.

A hunting license issued by a state does not grant permission to hunt upon the lands of another; granting such permission is not within the powers of the state but within the power of the landowner or his legal representative only.[1] The hunting license authorizes the hunter to hunt only as far as the state laws and lawful regulations of the state are concerned. It authorizes him to convert public game to private use. It licenses him to hunt if, as, and when he can find something to hunt; the actual taking of any game for which he is thus licensed depends upon his finding a place where he may exercise the privilege granted to him, as well as upon his skill as a hunter.

The maintenance of the exclusive rights of the landowner, as far as hunting is concerned, is generally dependent upon some distinguishing evidence of private ownership. The public has long been permitted to hunt upon "ownerless land," which no doubt is a condition retained from prehistoric times when man subsisted upon the fruits of hunting and when all land was ownerless. Although the means by which the owner legally indicates that he is holding the land to the exclusion of others varies from state to state, usually any means that adequately makes ownership evident is sufficient to prohibit entrance by hunters. The means may be a single strand of wire, a public notice, a brushed-out boundary, a creek, or a road, but the exact means depends upon laws and customs.

Trespass upon the property of another for the purpose of hunting is fundamentally a civil rather than a criminal matter, and injunctions may be obtained and suits instituted for damages.[2] In most states trespassing for the purpose of hunting is covered now by the criminal code, though the law may require posting of the land or other quali-

[1] *Diana Shooting Club* v. *Lamoreaux*, 114 Wisconsin 44.
[2] *Kellogg* v. *King*, 114 Cal. 378; *Diana Shooting Club* v. *Lamoreaux*, 114 Wisconsin 44.

fications before the criminal trespass act may be invoked. The lack of laws expressly prohibiting trespass does not authorize hunting on the lands of another, for trespass is always an illegal invasion of the right of the owner to the exclusive use of his property. Criminal trespass laws bring the police power of the state to the landowner's aid in maintaining his rights.

The fact that hunting rights are attributes of the soil makes it possible for a person to obtain hunting rights upon the lands of another by conveyance from the owner. The right thus obtained is an interest in the land and may be for a stated period or in perpetuity. As the grant of hunting and fishing rights is the grant of an interest in the land, it is within the *statute of fraud* and must be in writing. The owner of land who sells or leases the hunting and fishing rights upon his land does not, by this action, deprive himself of the customary uses of his land. He is not bound to maintain a shooting preserve for the owner of the hunting rights, which are subject to the landowner's regular operations, even though such operations be destructive of game and habitat.

Although private ownership of game is obtained by the hunter when he brings game under his control, such private ownership is not obtained in violation of the landowner's rights. It appears that game killed by a trespassing hunter belongs to the property owner just as though he had exercised the hunting right himself.[1] Apparently, if possession is not allowed by law, game killed in trespass remains state property, but if possession is legal, it belongs to the landowner. No property interest is obtained in game by an illegal act, and game so killed appears to remain the property of the state or become the property of the landowner; in any event it does not belong to the offending hunter.

Growth of State Controls. The warden system within the United States traces back to local wardens appointed by the Massachusetts Bay Colony in 1739. Because the colonies and the area now a part of Canada were British possessions, the start of the warden system for the provinces may be considered the same. In 1764 the colony appointed special wardens known as "deer reeves" to enforce the ordinances protecting deer. The same type of officer appeared in 1809 to protect fish in New Hampshire and as moose wardens in Maine in 1852. Other local enforcement, as by constables and county or township wardens, appeared from time to time in the years that followed.

[1] *Rexroth* v. *Coon*, 15 Rhode Island 35; *Schulte* v. *Warren*, 218 Illinois 121.

A new departure came in the lake states in 1887 when Michigan, Wisconsin, and Minnesota appointed state game wardens and thereby laid the foundations of the current system. Wisconsin first employed four state wardens but in 1891 changed to one warden with several deputies. A Michigan act of 1887 departed from the earlier fee system; it placed the state game warden on a straight salary basis and also made the office a separate department of the state government.

The union of game administration with other forms of conservation also seems to have started in the lakes states. In Michigan in 1907 the duties of forest-fire control were added to those of game and fish administration to form the office of State Game, Fish, and Forest Fire Warden, which later became the Department of Conservation, embracing most official conservation activities.

Other forms of administration rose and fell during the years, even as they do today. One of the commonest was the system of county game wardens appointed and controlled by the separate counties of a state, either by the regular governing body or by a county game commission. Perhaps the most unusual was the incorporation of the North Carolina State Audubon Society as the official state game department in 1903; it functioned for a number of years before being succeeded by a regular state agency.

The inefficient work of local and volunteer wardens and of game-law enforcement by fee-paid officers made it necessary to employ a staff of full-time officers. Regular peace officers could not be depended upon to enforce the game laws because to them the press of other duties seemed more important and game-law violations too petty for their attention. They were inclined also to consider game-law restrictions as invasions of the personal privileges of the hunter. During the nineteenth century game-law enforcement by a special body of police officers was exceptional, but the twentieth century finds this the rule and local law enforcement the exception.

Growth of the License System. Licensing hunters, trappers, fishermen, and others is quite universal throughout the United States and Canada and now serves chiefly to obtain funds for operating state game departments. The license as a means to control hunters and fishermen or to reduce their pressure on the wildlife is not so successful as its use for raising money. The limited license now is coming into favor, however, as a method of controlling hunting pressure on small areas. It seems likely that the hunting license as a means of reducing hunting pressure will be emphasized in the future, probably by raising its cost and requiring qualifying tests.

The license was not always intended as a money-raising device; it was first applied to control hunters and to discriminate against non-residents. The first license was called for by an act of Virginia colony (1691) requiring the "lycense and permission" of the authorities before "hunting remote from the English plantations."

In 1719 non-residents of New Jersey colony were prohibited from gathering oysters or shipping them on a vessel not wholly owned by a resident. In 1795 North Carolina required a certificate showing that a person "not possessed of a settled habitation" in the province had planted and tended a definite amount of corn before he could hunt deer.

Local licenses, both for non-residents and residents, exist in many states. The areas where the licensee may hunt on such a license vary from restricted areas to counties and even sizable portions of a state. In general, local licenses are designed to cheapen the cost to the "one-gallus" hunter, although sometimes they are used primarily to raise additional funds by mass sales of cheap licenses.

Licenses may be general ones that permit the holder to hunt all species of game during open seasons or specific ones that restrict the hunter's privilege to designated species, such as upland game, big game, fish, or trout, or that restrict the methods, such as by rod and reel, bow and arrow, and artificial bait.

No selectivity is yet exercised in granting licenses; any resident may take out a state license at almost any hardware store and may get a federal duck stamp at almost any post office. The qualifications of the licensee to know what he may or may not hunt and to distinguish legal game from protected game are immaterial in the issuance of a license. It seems logical that the next stage in the license system is an examination into the qualifications of the individual to hold a license. A start has been made in a number of states by denying a license to chronic offenders or those who have endangered the safety of others.

SUGGESTED READING

Anonymous [1935], "Wild Game—Its Legal Status," Dupont, Wilmington, Del.
Connery, Robert H., 1935, *Governmental Problems in Wild Life Conservation*, Columbia Univ. Studies in Hist., Econ., and Pub. Law 411
Graham, Edward H., 1947, *The Land and Wildlife*, Oxford University Press, New York.
Grange, Wallace B., 1949, *The Way to Game Abundance with an Explanation of Game Cycles*, Charles Scribner's Sons, New York.

Fields, H. R., 1936, "Jurisdiction over Nationally Owned Areas within the States," *Calif. Law. Rev.*, 24:573–593.

Palmer, T. S., 1904, "Hunting Licenses, Their History, Objects, and Limitations," *Biol. Surv. Bull.* 19.

Palmer, T. S., 1912, "Chronology and Index of the More Important Events in American Game Protection (1776–1911)," *Biol. Surv. Bull.* 41.

Rupp, John N., 1939, "Jurisdiction over Lands Owned by the United States within the State of Washington," *Wash. Law Rev. and State Bar Jour.*, 14:1–29.

Stevens, Ross O., 1944, *Talk about Wildlife for Hunters, Fishermen, and Nature Lovers*, Bynum Printing Co., Raleigh, N. C.

22

Federal Wildlife Controls in the United States

Federal controls over wildlife arise from four separate delegations by the *states* of powers enumerated in the Constitution:

Regulation of interstate, foreign, and Indian commerce (Article 1, Section 8).
Levying of taxes for general welfare (Article 1, Section 8); actually a tax-limiting provision.
Treaty making (Article 2, Section 2).
Control of federal property and territories (Article 4, Section 3).

The federal government does not own the animals *ferae naturae*, whether migratory or not, because public ownership rests in the states.[1] Even game or fur confiscated during enforcement of federal laws remains the property of the states except as the federal government may gain title legally as provided by state laws, even as the title of property that has been stolen or otherwise taken illegally remains in the rightful owner. The same may be said of animals taken by federal or other predatory animal hunters.

Early Federal Laws. The earliest federal interest in wild animals concerned fishing off the Grand Banks. But its purpose was to protect the rights of American fishermen in competition with those of foreign nations rather than to protect wildlife, and this early federal interest obtained a mention of fishing rights in the Treaty of Paris.

The act of May 19, 1796, prohibited citizens or residents of the United States from going into Indian country for the purpose of hunting. The boundary as described in the act ran from the site of Cleveland, Ohio, to the Altamaha River in Alabama. The act was amended March 3, 1799, March 30, 1802, and June 30, 1834, and each amending shifted the boundary farther west. The final re-enactment, that of

[1] *Geer* v. *Connecticut*, 161 U. S. 519.

June 30, 1834, remained in effect until the last of the Indian country entered the Union as Oklahoma (1907). Probably violating and ignoring the law were more common practices than observing it.

Federal Prohibitions. The first important federal restriction, other than those already mentioned, was a law enacted by the Congress in 1886 prohibiting the legislatures in the several territories from passing local or special laws for the protection of game and fish. The purpose of the act is not clear, but it may have been to protect settlers in their use of a much-needed food source or perhaps to end local discriminations. The Tariff Act of 1895 contained a clause prohibiting the importation of game bird eggs. The Lacey Act [1] of 1900, however, really marks the entrance of the federal government into wildlife work, and once this important matter of policy was established, the expansion of federal activity in this field multiplied. The principal feature of the Lacey Act is the control of "bootleg" game by prohibition of interstate commerce in game taken or possessed in violation of the laws in the place of origin or destination. Its purpose is to aid the states in their law enforcement in a spot where states are handicapped but where the federal government may very properly operate. An act of March 4, 1909, prohibited killing or disturbing birds and mammals upon federal refuges, both upon those established by law and those established by presidential proclamation. In effect this act validated earlier presidential actions.

The next major event in federal wildlife activity occurred through an addition to the Tariff Act of 1913.[2] Previously great quantities of egret plumes and bird feathers came from abroad for millinery purposes. Most of the states themselves already had laws protecting native birds, but large numbers continued to be killed and passed off as foreign birds. Among these were the egrets of the Gulf states. Efforts led by the Audubon Society and others obtained an amendment to the Tariff Act that prohibited the importation of wild-bird plumage. This far-reaching act shut off the United States market as a disposal ground for plumage taken in other countries and eliminated the subterfuges by which quantities of native plumage went to market. Some plumage, however, came in later through loopholes in the law that have since been plugged.

Some protection to wildlife beyond the 3-mile limit was given by a law of 1906 that imposed regulations on the size of sponges that could be gathered off the Florida coast and brought ashore. The owners

[1] 31 Stat. 187.
[2] 16 Stat. 144.

of a vessel that landed such a cargo challenged the law on the grounds that because the boat had only gone out and returned through the same port, it was not engaged in either interstate or foreign commerce and was therefore beyond federal control. They argued further that as it was not engaged in intrastate commerce, it was beyond state control. The Supreme Court solved the neat point by holding that the ship was engaged in foreign commerce, a Congressional matter, as soon as it passed out of the territorial waters, even though it touched no foreign port. Congress could constitutionally prohibit the importation of small sponges in the proper regulation of foreign commerce.[1] The law is important, as it protects the wildlife of the high seas from American overexploitation.

The Migratory Bird Treaties. The signing of the Treaty with Canada,[2] which was proclaimed December 8, 1916, was undoubtedly the most important step in the snowballing expansion of federal activities in the wildlife field. It also marked a new phase in dealings between nations, for it was aimed solely at the protection of wild birds. A similar treaty with the United Mexican States was proclaimed on March 15, 1937.

The treaty now in force describes three groups of migratory birds:

Migratory Game Birds

Anatidae or waterfowl
Gruidae or cranes
Rallidae or rails, coots, gallinules
Limicolae or shore birds
Columbidae or doves, pigeons

Migratory Insectivorous Birds

Bobolinks	Hummingbirds	Robins	Vireos
Catbirds	Kinglets	Shrikes	Warblers
Chickadees	Martins	Swallows	Waxwings
Cuckoos	Meadowlarks	Swifts	Whippoorwills
Flickers	Nighthawks	Tanagers	Woodpeckers
Flycatchers	Nuthatches	Titmouses	Wrens
Grosbeaks	Orioles	Thrushes	

"and all other perching birds which feed entirely or chiefly on insects."

[1] *"Abby Dodge"* v. U. S., 223 U. S. 166.

[2] A common error in the United States is the assumption that this treaty was concluded between the United States and Great Britain because His Majesty's ambassador carried on negotiations. His Majesty is also King of Canada, and in 1916 the same ambassador carried on for both Canada and Great Britain. The treaty is technically between His Majesty and the United States, which in ordinary language would probably be termed between Canada and the United States.

Other Migratory Non-Game Birds

Auks	Gannets	Herons	Petrels
Auklets	Grebes	Jaegers	Puffins
Bitterns	Guillemots	Loons	Shearwaters
Fulmars	Gulls	Murres	Terns

The treaty provided for closed seasons on many species and limited the length of the open season on migratory game birds to 3½ months.

The treaty between the United States of America and the United Mexican States defined but two classes of birds, using the scientific names of the respective families. In a sense this marked an evolution of thought from the earlier reliance upon insect control as the principal justification for including non-game birds.

Migratory Game Birds

Anatidae	Scolopacidae
Gruidae	Recurvirostridae
Rallidae	Phalaropodidae
Charadriidae	Columbidae

Migratory Non-Game Birds

Cuculidae	Mimidae
Caprimulgidae	Sylviidae
Micropodidae	Motacillidae
Trochilidae	Bombycillidae
Picidae	Ptilogonatidae
Tyrannidae	Laniidae
Alaudidae	Vireonidae
Hirundinidae	Compsothlypidae
Paridae	Icteridae
Certhiidae	Thraupidae
Troglodytidae	Fringillidae
Turdidae	

The treaty limited the hunting of migratory game birds to 4 months of the year. (This clause affects Mexico only because the treaty between the United States and Canada already limits hunting to 3½ months. But the Mexico restriction probably has little practical effect because of the low hunting pressure in Mexico.) The treaty prohibited hunting from aircraft and provided for permits for transportation of protected species across the international border. It further provided for permits covering international shipping of game mammals.

The Migratory Bird Treaty Act gave effect to the treaty with Canada and, by amendments, to the treaty with Mexico.[1] The constitutionality

---

[1] 40 Stat. 755 (1918), 49 Stat. 1555 (1936).

of the Act was sustained (1920) by the Supreme Court when it held that the matter of migratory birds came within the treaty-making powers of the federal government as delegated in the Constitution, for any one of the preceding colonies itself could have made such a treaty had it remained independent, whereas the federal government acts only as the agency of the present states.[1]

The Act authorizes the Secretary of Agriculture (in the course of governmental reorganization, the Secretary of the Interior replaces the Secretary of Agriculture) to make regulations to govern hunting of migratory birds. The regulations become effective upon receiving presidential approval. In accordance with the provisions of the Act the Secretary issues regulations such as those governing open seasons, bag limits, baiting, and gun size.

Migratory Bird Conservation Act. The Migratory Bird Conservation Act (1929) provided for the acquisition of refuge areas for migratory birds in order to carry out obligations in the Treaty.[2] It created a Migratory Bird Conservation Commission consisting of the Secretaries of Agriculture, Commerce, and Interior, two Senators, and two Representatives who pass upon all land for purchase or lease under the Act. The Commission was modeled after the Forest Reserves Commission that had functioned so well for a number of years in the purchase of lands for national forests.[3] The Act provided further that all areas purchased thereunder were to become inviolate sanctuaries, a marked contrast to the "public shooting grounds" feature of earlier bills.

Duck Stamp Act. The first general federal "game license" to be established was the migratory bird hunting stamp (1934), popularly known as the "duck stamp," required of everyone older than sixteen who hunts waterfowl.[4] The distinctively designed stamps are issued through the Post Office Department, which retains a portion of the receipts to cover costs of the stamps and their issuance. The stamps must be attached to the state hunting license or to a tag supplied by the Post Office Department in those states not requiring a hunting license for the applicant. The funds derived are earmarked for inviolate sanctuaries and for the enforcement of the Migratory Bird Treaty Act.

Federal Aid to States. The Pittman-Robertson Act granting federal aid to states for wildlife restoration projects is patterned after other acts providing money from the federal treasury for the construction of

[1] *Missouri* v. *Holland*, 252 U. S. 416.
[2] 45 Stat. 1222.
[3] Public Law 435, March 1, 1911.
[4] 48 Stat. 451; 49 Stat. 379.

highways and for forest-fire protection. It authorizes the appropriation of money, not to exceed funds accruing from a 10 per cent tax on sporting arms and ammunition, for distribution to the states. The return to the states is made for definite restoration projects approved by the Secretary of the Interior (formerly the Secretary of Agriculture). The states must contribute 25 per cent of the cost of such projects; the appropriated money reimburses the state for the remaining 75 per cent. Maintenance after completion is paid for by the state. Since the amount appropriated has never reached the total collected by the tax collector, a large unexpended accumulation builds up.

The fund available for distribution to the states is divided into two halves, one half allotted on the basis of land area in the state and the other on the number of hunting licenses. Thus a state with a large area but a small population would receive a small share on the basis of licenses but a large one on the basis of area. The bounty received by a thinly settled state conceivably could exceed the game fund of the state itself. Congress has, however, provided for both a maximum and a minimum amount that any one state may receive.

The act is interpreted to authorize projects falling into three general classes: purchase of land for wildlife restoration purposes; development and improvement of public land for the benefit of wildlife; and research.

Unlike the Duck Stamp Act or the Migratory Bird Conservation Act, this one permits the purchase of land for shooting grounds rather than requiring that lands so purchased with public funds be held as inviolate sanctuaries. It does not restrict funds to useful projects for migratory birds only, but authorizes use for non-migratory species as well. Although the act specifies "wildlife" without defining what Congress meant by the term, it is interpreted administratively to mean game birds and mammals. Fish are ruled out by such definition, but it is stated that projects for non-game species could be undertaken. A 1950 law (Dingell Act), however, provides for appropriations for fish projects similar to those of the Pittman-Robertson Act.

Hunting upon Federal Lands. Federal lands, which it seems appropriate to discuss next, may be divided into four classes: [1]

> Land owned by the United States as a proprietor but not devoted to any public purpose. Examples: Public domain, housing projects.

[1] *California Law Review*, 24:573–593; *Washington Law Review and State Bar Journal*, 14:1–29.

Hunting upon Federal Lands

Land owned by the United States as a proprietor and used for a purpose appropriate to the functions of the federal government. Examples: National forests, national monuments, national cemeteries.

Land owned by the United States and over which it exercises exclusive jurisdiction save for powers that the states have reserved. Examples: Some national parks, some military reservations.

Land owned by the United States and over which it exercises exclusive jurisdiction. Examples: Some national parks, some military reservations.

Control of lands of the United States, and its territories also, is vested in Congress,[1] but the *jurisdiction* of the states is not impaired by the fact of federal ownership, as the power delegated to Congress only empowers it to make necessary rules governing the property.[2] State game laws apply to federal lands, and a treaty with the Indians cannot authorize them to hunt there in violation of state laws.[3] But a type of "extraterritorial rights" within the states was granted to Indians by the Supreme Court when it held that Indians, unlike white people, may not be charged license fees because an 1859 Indian treaty granted their ancestors the right to fish in "their accustomed places of fishing" in common with citizens of the then territory.[4] "In common with citizens of the territory," it will surprise most people to learn, does not mean *in common with citizens of the territory* but means "continuing rights, beyond those which other citizens may enjoy."[5] But despite the grant by the Court of this racial autonomy to the Indians concerned, Indian fishing may be regulated by the state when such regulations are necessary for conservation purposes, although the state may not require a revenue license of Indians as of whites.[6]

It is apparent that, except for contradictory actions arising from solicitous concern for Indians, federal control may extend only to the use and protection of the federal property, unless the state has ceded the jurisdiction necessary for going further. Hunting rights as a part of exclusive use being an attribute of the land, it follows that Congress can regulate or prohibit these activities on federal land; an ordinary landowner has the same authority on his lands, but the Constitution confirms this in Congress and thereby adds the power of providing enforcement of the will of Congress under the federal criminal code. Without this constitutional provision, Congress would

---

[1] Constitution, Article 4, Section 3.
[2] *Utah Power and Light Co.* v. *United States*, 243 U. S. 389.
[3] *Ward* v. *Race Horse*, 163 U. S. 504.
[4] *Tulee* v. *State of Washington*, 315 U. S. 681.
[5] *U. S.* v. *Winans*, 198 U. S. 371.
[6] *Tulee* v. *State of Washington*, 315 U. S. 681.

probably have to depend upon the states for enforcement of regulations governing hunting on federal lands.

In a decision covering the much-publicized Kaibab deer case, the Supreme Court held that, under the Constitution, the power of Congress to protect federal property permitted the killing of deer that were damaging federal property, in this case forest reproduction.[1] The Court reasoned that state courts and laws, as well as custom and common laws, have long sanctioned the emergency destruction of game by private owners whenever the game is found to be injuring property, even though such destruction may be contrary to game laws. Hence the same power undoubtedly could be exercised by the federal government in protecting its property. Although the Supreme Court did not mention the means to be employed, the lower district court held that animals could be killed only by regular federal officers, obviously responsible to Congress. This does not authorize hunting seasons, and the game so killed still remains the property of the state.

Some challenge of the authority of the state to set seasons on federal lands has appeared from time to time, even in regulations issued for national forests by the Secretary of Agriculture,[2] but these challenges have been quickly revoked. Unless a rather nebulous position can be revolutionarily reinterpreted, the matter seems settled.

Indian Reservations and Miscellaneous Federal Lands. The application of state laws to federal lands, such as military reservations, parks, and other areas, depends upon whether the state in which the lands lie has ceded jurisdiction or the lands were exempted upon admission of the state to the Union. The purpose for which the jurisdiction of the federal government is sought, however, must be one for which the government may take jurisdiction and the state may cede it. No jurisdiction may be taken from a state without its consent. In most cases where federal jurisdiction is proper, the states have ceded it or the area was exempted upon admission, so that state laws, including game laws, do not apply or only partially apply.[3]

Indian reservations differ from federal lands in that they are Indian property under control of the federal government as the constitutional agency charged with control of commerce with Indian tribes. In general, if the Indian lands were situated within the boundaries of newly admitted states as organized reservations, the acts of admission have exempted them from jurisdiction of the new states and only

[1] *Hunt v. United States*, 278 U. S. 96.
[2] G-20-A.
[3] *Fort Leavenworth Railroad Co. v. Lowe*, 114 U. S. 525.

Congress has control. This control arises from the powers of Congress to regulate "commerce" with the Indian "tribes," [1] and state laws do not apply except where Congress may have provided.[2] The state laws apply if not exempted at the time of admission or if jurisdiction has not been ceded subsequently. If exempted land has been patented, even by an Indian, or restored to the public domain, the state laws immediately apply.[3]

Fishing and hunting upon navigable waters within the boundaries of the Indian reservations involve different considerations. The original colonies received rights from the Crown prior to and upon becoming independent and establishing a federal union. The federal government acquired no jurisdiction or powers over navigable waters except such as the states may have surrendered in matters of navigation as it affects commerce. As has been pointed out previously, the states admitted to the Union at later dates are upon an equal footing with the thirteen original states. It follows that, unless exemptions were made upon admission to the Union, the later states automatically received title to the soil under navigable waters and full jurisdiction over such navigable waters, which includes those within the Indian reservations. There appear to be no cases where the states have surrendered jurisdiction over navigable waters, and the Supreme Court of the United States has upheld the title of the states to lands under navigable waters.[4]

Many treaties with Indians granted them the right to hunt and fish upon ceded lands and elsewhere. Acts of admission, being laws of Congress, repeal treaties, and earlier Supreme Court decisions have universally held that the state laws apply to Indians off reservations, and treaties preceding the acts of admission do not deprive the states of full jurisdiction over all places within their borders,[5] even though treaties may impose a maintainable servitude on land itself.[6] But one must not overlook the fact that recent Supreme Court decisions have

[1] Constitution, Article 1, Section 8.
[2] *United States* v. *Kagama*, 18 U. S. 375; *in re Blackbird*, 109 Federal 139.
[3] *Clairmont* v. *United States*, 225 U. S. 551; *State* v. *Big Sheep*, 75 Montana 219; *State ex rel. Best* v. *Superior Court*, 107 Washington 238; *State* v. *Johnson*, 212 Wisconsin 301; *Kennedy* v. *Becker*, 241 U. S. 556; *Kitto* v. *State*, Nebraska 152 N. W. 380; *State* v. *Tilden*, 27 Idaho 262.
[4] *United States* v. *Holt State Bank*, 270 U. S. 49.
[5] *Kennedy* v. *Becker*, 241 U. S. 556; *United States* v. *Winans*, 198 U. S. 371; *Ward* v. *Race Horse*, 163 U. S. 504; *Lone Wolf* v. *Hitchcock*, 187 U. S. 553.
[6] *United States* v. *Winans*, 198 U. S. 371.

overturned earlier decisions and have even granted special racial autonomy to Indians.[1]

Despite the many apparent and real favors conferred upon Indians, in actual practice, however, reservation Indians are held in virtual peonage by the federal laws under the section of the Constitution that deals with commerce with Indian tribes.[2] As may be seen by the various court cases cited, as well as by many others, the federal government as protector of the Indian tribes zealously prosecutes their claims for special treatment over the whites, though the Indians have few of the recognized civil rights enjoyed by other citizens (including free or emancipated Indians). For example, by use of public funds, special regulations, and otherwise, attempts are made in parts of Alaska to eliminate competition from white herdsmen and trappers in favor of native reindeer herders and trappers. That the natives might suffer from free competition with the whites can neither be proved nor disproved, but they would most surely be stimulated to improved effort. Until free intercourse with other people comes and until Indians have the pride that goes with equality, wildlife conservation and management in Indian areas will be at a distinct and perhaps hopeless disadvantage.

It is the opinion of authorities that the title that the state has to all animals *ferae naturae* within its borders applies to animals on Indian reservations, national parks, and other reservations over which the state has no jurisdiction just as over lands within its jurisdiction.

Federal Agencies. The expansion of federal activities has brought on a multiplicity of agencies that touch upon wildlife in some of their many activities. Although it is next to impossible for the average man even to try to follow most of these, it seems appropriate to mention several of the more important or more orthodox bureaus and agencies.

The *Fish and Wildlife Service* was formed in 1940 by merging the Bureaus of Biological Survey and Fisheries and adding to it the wildlife division of the National Park Service. The Bureau of Fisheries originated in 1871 when Congress provided for the appointment of a Commissioner of Fisheries to be chosen from the employees of the government. The Commissioner was instructed to collect fish statistics, along with his regular duties, at no increase in salary.[3] An appropria-

[1] *Tulee* v. *State of Washington*, 315 U. S. 681.
[2] Constitution, Article 1, Section 8.
[3] 16 Stat. 594.

tion of $15,000 in 1873 provided for propagation and distribution of fishes in the "waters to which they are adapted." Appropriations for fish propagation increased to $30,000 in 1876 and $161,000 by 1887. It was these funds that paid the costs of introducing carp, considered since to have been one of the outstanding "conservation" blunders, on a par with the introduction of English sparrows and starlings. In sharp contrast to propagation money, appropriations for scientific work reached but $20,000 by 1887.

Fisheries existed as an independent commission until 1903, when Congress changed it to the *Bureau of Fisheries* in the Department of Commerce and Labor. Later the Bureau went to the Department of Commerce and in 1939 to the Department of the Interior. The Bureau handled matters of federal interest in regard to fish (its successor agency continues this work), and it also watched over the seal herds off the Alaska coast. Chiefs of the Bureau were:

Spencer F. Baird	1871–1887	George M. Bowers	1897–1913
G. Brown Goode	1887–1888	Hugh M. Smith	1913–1921
Marshall McDonald	1888–1895	Frank O'Malley	1921–1933
John J. Brice	1895–1897	Frank T. Bell	1933–1938

The *Bureau of Biological Survey* owes its origin to the influence of the American Ornithologists' Union. In 1885 Congress appropriated $5000 for the support of work on birds and mammals.[1] The work was carried on during the first year in the Division of Entomology and thereafter as a Division of Ornithology and Mammalogy in the Department of Agriculture. In 1896 it became the Division of Biological Survey and in 1906 the Bureau of Biological Survey. It remained in the Department of Agriculture until shifted to the Department of the Interior in 1939.

The work of the agency was scientific during the early years, when distinguished work centered around the distribution and economic aspects of birds and mammals. Law enforcement in connection with the Lacey Act was added in 1900, and a second major departure from scientific work took place in 1905 when the Division undertook suppression of wolves upon certain grazing areas. This work has grown into predator and poison campaigns that have outstripped scientific projects in funds and participants. Enforcement of the Migratory Bird Treaty Act was added to the duties of the Bureau in 1918. The expansion of federal interest in game activities resulted in a reorganization of the Bureau in 1934, largely to meet new responsibilities in

[1] 23 Stat. 353.

federal activities and waterfowl refuges, and later for work in connection with the Pittman-Robertson Act.

There have been six chiefs of the Bureau and two of the Fish and Wildlife Service:

C. Hart Merriam	1885–1910	Paul G. Redington	1927–1934
Henry W. Henshaw	1910–1916	J. N. Darling	1934–1935
E. W. Nelson	1916–1927	I. N. Gabrielson	1934–1940

Directors of the Fish and Wildlife Service:

I. N. Gabrielson 1940–46
A. N. Day 1946– —

The *National Park Service* was established in 1916 to administer the national parks. Formerly it maintained its own Wildlife Division as an integral part of its administrative organization, but the Division became a part of the Fish and Wildlife Service when this Service was formed.

The *Forest Service* has a dual origin in the Forest Reserves of the Department of the Interior [1] and the Division, later the Bureau, of Forestry, in the Department of Agriculture, which were joined in 1905. The Forest Service employs few personnel trained in wildlife management but assigns some wildlife work to regular forest officers. It maintains, however, a small but distinguished Division of Wildlife Management that oversees wildlife work carried on by the forest officers through regular administrative channels.

The *Soil Conservation Service* employs several wildlife managers and has done some of the most outstanding wildlife management of any federal agency, especially in its direct work with soil-erosion control on farms.

Other bureaus and agencies touch upon wildlife problems from time to time, such as the Grazing Service, Coast Guard, Customs Service, Army Engineers, Tennessee Valley Authority, Public Health Service, and a host of others.

SUGGESTED READING

Cameron, Jenks, 1929, *The Bureau of Biological Survey; Its History, Activities and Organization*, Brookings Inst., Serv. Mon. 54.

Connery, Robert H., 1935, *Governmental Problems in Wild Life Conservation*, Columbia Univ. Stud. in Hist., Econ., and Pub. Law 411.

[1] Act of March 3, 1891.

Suggested Reading

Fields, H. R., 1936, "Jurisdiction over Nationally Owned Areas within the States," *Calif. Law Rev.*, 24:573–593.

Gabrielson, Ira N., 1942, "Relations of the U. S. Fish and Wildlife Service to Sportsmen," *Trans. Seventh N. A. Wildlife Conf.:* 53–61.

Hayden, Sherman S., 1942, *The International Protection of Wild Life*, Columbia Univ. Stud. in Hist., Econ., and Pub. Law 491, New York.

Rupp, John N., 1939, "Jurisdiction over Lands Owned by the United States within the State of Washington," *Wash. Law Rev. and State Bar Jour.*, 14:1–29.

23

Provincial and Federal Wildlife Spheres in Canada

The systems of government within Canada and the United States differ surprisingly little in practice. In actual fact more variation often may be found between practices in the respective 48 states and 10 provinces than between the over-all general pattern of the two sovereign nations. The similarity of outlook arises from the simple geographical fact that the line dividing the newly independent colonies after 1783 and those retained as colonies separated a people of the same stock and with the same outlook. The second century of travel along independent pathways has seen them diverge little in practices and little in methods of handling their respective problems.

Canada and the United States base their judicial systems upon the same *English Common Law* (with an exception in the provincial judiciary of Quebec, just as the state of Louisiana largely uses the *Code Napoléon,* also because of its early French orientation). Even the names and titles of the common officials are the same—constable, warden, sheriff, justice of the peace, forest ranger, park ranger, and peace officer, all testifying to the unity of origin. Since much of the discussion of state and federal powers and spheres in Chapters 21 and 22 will therefore often be found singularly appropriate to many Canadian problems, it need not be repeated here. It is especially true of the more fundamental points of administrative organization, legislation, and judicial decision, for all have grown since the same colonial days from the same colonial and precolonial stems.

Generally speaking, provincial officials concerned with game and fish matters have somewhat more administrative power and latitude than their counterparts in the States, largely because policies in the States are set by duly elected law-making bodies that constitutionally may not delegate their powers, so that executive officers themselves seldom may promulgate regulations having the force of law. This in part stems from the days of 1776, when the revolting colonies had had enough of officials exercising legislative power; consequently such power became carefully defined by the early constitutions, state and federal. The issuing of restricted kinds of administrative regulations may be provided by law for carrying out duly enacted provisions, but the laws are always specific in definitions and rigidly circumscribe the practice. Courts hold that such provisions must be explicitly stated, not broad and general. The Canadian citizen has the greater respect for government, his fellow in the States the greater respect for the individual right. But a merging of ideas and outlook can be discerned by the traveler.

Division of Power. The fundamental law of Canada is the amended *British North America Act* of 1867, supplemented by the 1931 *Statute of Westminster*. In a sense this is the Canadian constitution, but it differs somewhat from a customary constitution in that it may be amended only by the British Parliament (a provision inserted by Canadian request) rather than by the people themselves. The Privy Council in London is the final court of appeal, though perhaps the Canadian Parliament could abolish such appeals.

The power of the federal government covers commerce, defense, navigation, banking, currency, marriage, and divorce. Those of the provinces include education, municipal government, property rights, civil rights, and licensing.

It might be well here to point out a very important basic difference in concept between the British North America Act and the Constitution of the United States, so that many of the general governmental problems and practices outlined in Chapters 21 and 22 will be better understood in their Canadian application. The British North America Act is specific in defining the powers of the provinces and federal governments. The provinces have only such powers as are stated therein; all others are reserved to the federal government. In the Constitution, however, the federal government gets only such powers as are delegated to it, all others being reserved to the states or to the people or prohibited entirely.

Ownership of Animals Ferae Naturae. Animals *ferae naturae* belong to the respective provinces, even though the provincial acts may not so state. Most of the provinces by law declare the ownership to be vested in the *Crown,* the sovereign power of the people ("His Majesty in the Right of the Province"),[1] and identical in effect with state ownership within the United States. The Canadian peace officer acts in the name of the Crown ("in the King's Name") and his States counterpart in the name of the people ("in the Name of the Law"), which, however phrased, means the same—the sovereign power of the people.

Provincial Organizations. Separate provincial game and fish commissions or branches of government departments have been established in all provinces. There is no unified conservation department, although one or two departments almost approach it. The organizational structure varies from province to province, but there is no independent commission in charge. The executive officer or officers are subordinate to a departmental minister. The executive appoints various members of the division. Policies laid down by law governing tenure, qualifications, and duties are generally not established.

The activities of the game divisions parallel those already outlined or to be outlined in Chapter 24, with the usual expected differences from province to province. Within democratic government, only certain activities may be allowed, and there are only so many ways of doing them.

A distinctive feature of the provincial administration is the establishment of *registered trap lines,* a procedure found, for example, in the more remote parts of British Columbia and Alberta. Such a trap line is a vested right granted to a trapper for exclusive trapping in a designated area. So long as the trapper complies with regulations on notices, reports, and trapping, the trapping right is his. Subject to regulations, he may sell his lease-right, along with trapping cabins, like any property-right, though the holder of a registered trapping line gains no claim upon the land itself. Actually trapping rights are analogous to mining claims so commonly staked out on public land in Mexico, the United States, and Canada.

North of the settled areas in some provinces and the territories white trappers have been discriminated against more or less in favor of Indians and Eskimos. Some areas have been closed entirely to white trappers and some largely so by prohibitive restrictions, such as 5 years of residence in the northern section demanded of a white man before he may qualify for a license. Registered trap lines may also be given to Indians only.

[1] For example, Chapter 36, Revised Statutes, 1927, New Brunswick; Chapter 4, Revised Statutes, 1946, Alberta; Chapter 252, Revised Statutes, 1940, Saskatchewan.

The general intent of these restrictions is to evict the white trapper or to prohibit his competition with the natives, but that the white man will permanently submit over so large an area seems unlikely, even though a native population of a few thousands lives off the fur bearers and a few fur companies depend upon the native trade.

The current provincial administrative organizations may be listed as:

British Columbia—Game Commission, Office of Attorney General.
Alberta—Fish and Game Branch, Department of Lands and Forests.
Saskatchewan—Game and Fur Branch, Department of Natural Resources and Industrial Development.
Manitoba—Game and Fisheries Branch, Department of Mines and Natural Resources.
Ontario—Fish and Wildlife Division, Department of Lands and Forests.
Quebec—Department of Fish and Game.
New Brunswick—Game Warden, Department of Lands and Mines.
Nova Scotia—Department of Lands and Forests.
Prince Edward Island—Department of Industry and Natural Resources.
Newfoundland—Department of Natural Resources.

Federal Sphere. The activities of the federal government in the wildlife field primarily concern migratory birds, wildlife in the national parks, and wildlife of the Northwest Territories. The federal government operates also in the field of commercial marine fisheries. Wildlife of the national parks and of the Northwest Territories is under complete jurisdiction of the federal government, as are fish in the Yukon Territory; control over migratory birds within the provinces is shared with the provincial governments. The Yukon Territory has been granted considerable local autonomy over all its wildlife except fish.

The enforcement of the Migratory Bird Convention Act, adopted in 1917 by Parliament to implement the Migratory Bird Treaty with the United States, is a federal activity carried on primarily through the Royal Canadian Mounted Police in cooperation with the provinces. The Wildlife Division, Development Services Branch, Department of Resources and Development, acts as adviser to the police in matters of birds and mammals and also has some enforcement responsibilities of its own in a few sanctuaries and some special areas. It carries on its activities with a small staff. Officers of the provinces of Alberta, British Columbia, Manitoba, New Brunswick, Ontario, Quebec, and Saskatchewan are *ex officio* enforcement officers for the Migratory Bird Convention Act, but officials of other provinces may not act except on provincial matters. The Royal Canadian Mounted Police enforce the Yukon territorial ordinances; by contract with several provinces the police enforce provincial acts, which include the provincial game and fish laws.

National Parks. In addition to special sanctuaries, there are now some 12,000 square miles of national parks of three types: scenic and recreational parks; wild animal parks (sanctuaries or refuges); and national historical parks. The provinces also maintain provincial parks, refuges, and sanctuaries, often of large size. The park system in Canada is of long standing; the first park was established in 1885 (now a part of Banff National Park).

SUGGESTED READING

Dawson, Robert MacGregor, 1947, *The Government of Canada,* University of Toronto Press, Toronto.
Hewitt, C. Gordon, 1921, *The Conservation of the Wildlife of Canada,* Charles Scribner's Sons, New York.
Innis, Harold A., 1930, *The Fur Trade in Canada; An Introduction to Canadian Economic History,* Yale University Press, New Haven.
Kennedy, W. P. M., 1938, *The Constitution and Canada 1534–1937,* London.
Lloyd, Hoyes, 1936, "The Administration of the Wildlife of Canada," *Proc. North American Wildlife Conf.:* 11–15.
Royal Commission, 1940, *Report on Dominion Provincial Relations,* 3 vols., Ottawa.

24

Administration and Regulation

Although we recognize that the operations of governmental agencies universally leave much to be desired, some progress towards betterment occurs in game departments. Examination shows, however, that not more than a handful of the departments are yet doing really good work.[1] Sources of waste and inefficiency exist in all human activities, though they seem to concentrate in some places more than in others. State game departments show this tendency toward inefficiency. Yet when we look at departments today in comparison with those of earlier years, we note definite improvements that will no doubt continue. We cannot afford to ignore the political aspects, however, for they will be with us as long as governments govern; be it noted, moreover, that the relations of people to each other are always matters politic, and we ought to distinguish sharply between the good politics that are essential and the bad that are not.

Establishment of State Game Departments. Political interference of the undesirable kind acted as a barrier to the union of game work with other forms of resources administration. The rise of forest conservation found its sponsors unwilling to trust their hopes to the mercies of politically run game-warden agencies. Instead of combining forest conservation with the game work, the proponents of forestry often succeeded in setting up separate forestry agencies. Other agencies frequently took over other conservation work as it developed: park boards, water commissions, pollution boards, mining bureaus, or oil commissions.

The administrations today fall into five or six general types, though modifications may cause individual agencies to assume some characteristics of another type:

[1] Gabrielson, Ira N., 1948, "What Is Wrong with Wildlife Administration?" *Sports Afield* (July).

Type	Governed by
Office of Game Warden	State Game Warden
Separate game or fish departments	Independent Commissions
Game and Fish Department	Independent Commission
Branch of Conservation Department	Commissioner of Department
Branch of Conservation Department	Independent Commission
Branch of a regular state department (as Agriculture)	Commissioner of Department

The department under a commission generally consists of a non-salaried commission composed of members "familiar with the field." Some states limit the number from any one political party, and some require sectional representation. Special or local qualifications and restrictions may be found also. Often the commissioners hold office at the governor's pleasure, but the incumbency may be a fixed term of years, with removal only for causes defined by law. Although the terms of commissioners may expire simultaneously, the general practice is for an overlapping in order to prevent all the terms from expiring during the same year. This is commonly called the "staggered system" and is in general favor because it provides stability in the service of the commission. The commission usually meets at intervals to pass upon matters of policy, whereas the actual administration is in the hands of a salaried director responsible to the commission.

It seems likely that in time most states and provinces will adopt the practice of unified conservation departments that administer state provisions for all natural resources. These departments are also governed by commissions whose members hold office by staggered terms. Maintaining a series of independent commissions or agencies for game, fish, waters, oil, parks, and the like does not provide the best administration; it also involves duplication of effort.

Departmental Powers and Responsibilities. Although the powers of state game departments vary from place to place, the general trend is towards a wider latitude in authority placed in the commissions by the legislatures. The legislatures themselves formerly undertook regulation, not only in legislative matters but also in those purely administrative. Some laws thus dictated purely administrative practice, even minute details of administrative procedure. Each term of the legislature brought a veritable flood of new bills to regulate seasons, bag limits, and a host of other game matters. This still occurs to some extent in several states.

The multiplicity of minor game laws clogs the legislative machinery and wastes valuable legislative time. A legislature rarely has knowledge of the subjects or any opportunity to investigate minor game bills, many introduced at the behest of groups or individuals. The inefficiency of trying to legislate for minor or administrative matters has given rise to the *discretionary power* of the game commission to regulate seasons, bag limits, and other matters not of primary legislative magnitude.

Discretionary power, when properly applied, gives flexibility to regulations, especially in those states where legislatures meet at long intervals; matters of immediate need can be expedited rather than forced to await the slow and cumbersome action of the legislature itself. Regulations can be adjusted also to meet situations as they arise; above all, they can be based upon findings of a technical staff under the direction of the regulatory body.

The powers of all game departments are provided by law, and no others are within their grasp. These powers usually cover enforcement, rearing and stocking, investigation, and the administration of refuges, but others may be included in the various states or provinces.

The general tendency of states to bar non-residents from positions in state departments handicaps the application of conservation technology. Such a provincial attitude may have popular appeal, but it hampers good administration by forcing the employment of less qualified men who are residents instead of better qualified men who are non-residents. The minimum effect of this policy appears in states where adequate technical training may be had in schools of higher learning; even so, departments may be forced to hire inexperienced help rather than seek more experienced employees in other states. The shifting of personnel from state to state is in itself a most important factor in preventing stagnation or "inbreeding."

Financial Support of Game Departments. Originally all costs of game-law enforcement came from appropriations from the general tax levies of the states, usually property taxes, or from fees collected from offenders, or from the general funds. The imposition of the license system, however, opened new sources of revenue. During the early period, the funds were spent for various purposes, chiefly for the support of schools or for county purposes. Most of these expenditures were eliminated, though, by the provision that those states that divert license money to public purposes other than support of the state game department may not qualify for federal aid under the Pittman-Robertson Act.[1] In itself such a provision must be looked upon as a federal

[1] Public Law 415, 75th Congress, September 2, 1937.

dictation to the states by a questionable method, since the use of public funds for all purposes within a state, worthy or unworthy, is the responsibility of the respective legislatures duly elected by the people of the state.

The general belief has grown up that, because hunters must pay to receive a license, the money so obtained should go for the benefit of their sport. This is not a proper premise, however attractive it may seem, because the license money actually is a regulatory fee paid for the privilege of converting a portion of a public property to private use. The payment of the license fee, contrary to widely held belief, does not give the licensee a vested interest in the game or the game department. There is no more a "sportsman's dollar" than a "theater patron's dollar" or a "cigarette smoker's dollar." All money so received by the public treasurer is public money like any other. So far as public policy or legality is concerned, there is no legitimate reason why a state should not turn into its general funds all money received from hunting licenses, as it does with corporation licenses or any other, and to appropriate the funds for such state purposes as the legislature in the exercise of its wisdom may determine to be in the best public interest. Spending hunting-license money, or money from any other charge on hunting, for the construction of highways or the erection of school buildings or any other state purpose is within the province of the legislature, however popular or unpopular such action might be. Game departments exist not as representatives of the license holders but as public administration bodies whose sole function is to carry out instructions and policies determined by the people through their constitutional channels.

Earmarked funds regularly available to the game departments bring many advantages, along with many disadvantages also. The fact that obtaining funds to carry on the work of game departments involves a minimum of political activity is a gain. Knowing that the game department has a steady income, politicians are sometimes tempted to use influence for job seekers. It is easier to transfer some costs, such as coyote control on sheep ranges, to the game fund from the sheep rancher's pocket when a public hearing is not held by a legislative committee. Having plenty of money may bring on wasteful practices when the licenses are plentiful, but when the licenses bring in too little, the game department is pinched and administration suffers. The dependence of a department upon licenses for its support sometimes creates a "vicious circle"; cutting the season would reduce the department budget, and few departments would be happy over restricting or recommending to the legislatures the restriction of hunting and thereby reducing the budget, even though technical study may indicate the advisability of lessening the hunting pressure.

It is probable that in some states earmarking license money for departmental purposes helps to build a stronger, though more strongly biased, game administration. Whether all the legislatures of the various states would have provided adequate funds is a question that cannot be answered. It seems entirely probable that the majority would have done so. Confidence in our governing system dictates that we believe in the wisdom of our duly elected representatives in the several legislatures.

Departmental Organization. The administrative establishment differs from state to state and from province to province, and no two have exactly the same departmental organization. Where fish and game work has been placed in a combined department, and sometimes otherwise, the *department* generally has a number of *divisions* each headed by a *chief* responsible to the *director*.

The main divisions usually are six:

Office. The office division, whatever it may be named, is the clerical division, headed by a chief clerk, that handles personnel, financial, and other records and files as well as routine mailings.

Protection. The protection division consists of wardens and district wardens in the field and a chief warden at the capitol. The protection force handles all law enforcement, as well as local administrative matters, and sometimes also the planting of hatchery fish and game birds. It may serve also as a forest-fire force in the fire season.

Biology. The biology division is generally a technical division that conducts studies of streams and lakes in addition to study of game problems in various areas. It may investigate administrative matters and recommend solutions to administrative problems. It frequently conducts research on the life history, ecology, and management of birds, mammals, and fishes. This division or its equivalent may direct actual management in states that provide it.

Fish Hatchery. Fish hatcheries are usually headed by superintendents, and the division is headed by a chief fish culturist.

Game Farm. Occasionally game farms are combined with fish hatcheries to form a division, though they are usually separate in those states still practicing artificial propagation.

Education. The education division serves as a bureau of information and public contact. It usually handles inquiries for information, and it may provide speakers and visual-aid material to schools and sportsmen's meetings. It may also publish a game magazine.

The organizational make-up of a unified conservation department is more elaborate and complete than that of a fish and game department. The conservation department generally has separate divisions handling forests, parks, minerals, along with fish and game. The game and fish divisions are separate, sometimes two or three of each, and handle matters in their respective fields. The warden force may be a major division or part of a field force including fire wardens, park rangers, and game wardens. The education work for all divisions centers in a single education division.

Educational Programs. A sound education program is one directed at the people needing it or desiring it most, rather than at those already informed or not likely to profit from it. Education programs especially need to be directed to the non-hunting and non-fishing public who make up the majority of citizens in states and provinces. Often the program, as measured by an informed public, accomplishes most with the more open-minded non-hunters and non-fishermen.

The main effort of an education program is supplying information and its explanation, especially of the department's work, rather than giving justification of the departmental operations.

A program can very profitably assist in the preparation of guides, state bird books, flower books, and material on life histories of animals. It should obviously strive to enlighten the public, not to glorify hunting and fishing as is done by sporting magazines.

A most important task of educational programs is to develop and foster an appreciation of the animal and plant as living organisms rather than as living targets. The idea that an organism must have some immediate good (i.e., hunting or economic use) before giving it consideration is not in the best public interest.

Purpose of Regulations. At the risk of repetition it should be emphasized anew that regulations concerned with fish, game, or any other form of wildlife have three functions in a democratic world, the first and most important of which is the protection of the public interest. We should bear in mind always that animals of the wild belong to the people as a whole, not to those who actually pursue them. The interests of future generations put obligations upon the present generation to assure continuance of the wildlife of a nation. Even though we recognize no important "use" or interesting attribute, future generations may.

A second function of regulations is to provide the measure of control over the human factor necessary for maximum care of life in the wild.

The third function of government in handling wildlife problems is to assure that each citizen, without infringing upon the rights of others, has equal political opportunity to exercise any privileges of citizenship if he so desires. Just as in football playing, auto driving, or card playing, it is the province of the individual to provide the economic and social opportunity for exercising these privileges.

Preparing Regulations. The procedures for *gathering* the information and *determining* the regulations is basically one of field work, and in principle the same in all states and provinces, even though authority for regulations and methods of implementing them vary.

The first essential of any regulation is assembling the facts upon which to develop the base for action; a regulation made and issued without this factual base may not be a sound one. The second essential is that the knowledge of these facts be available to the public as well as to regulatory officials. The third essential, associated with the second, is public explanation of the regulations and their purpose. The final one is enforcement.

Let us take a hypothetical example. The hunting season for species X runs for 10 days beginning September 25, with a bag limit of 4 a day. Several questions arise, among them: Is this the proper time for an open season? Is an open season justified, and is it the right length? Is this the proper bag limit? Obviously, it takes a lot of field work to answer these three questions.

In time, the allowable take can be determined in advance with a certainty comparable to gathering of honey from bee hives or cutting-out cattle on the range. The principle is fundamentally the same, but the operating conditions differ. Even so, the allowable take for most species in the wild seems to run under 20 per cent of the fall population.

The matter of the timing of seasons can be answered best on the basis of maturity of young, lateness of the season, the time of other seasons, and sometimes local customs. If the breeding season were late, the young might not be full grown by the opening date of September 25. Yet losses from natural causes begin the moment an animal is hatched or born, or even earlier, and continue throughout life. An early season allows the taking of an additional number that might otherwise perish in nature's survival mill. A season so early and warm as to cause spoilage of meat, as of big game, might not be suitable.

Whether a ten-day season is too long or too short depends upon the surplus of animals beyond that needed for breeding stock plus a margin of safety. This may be a local problem or a statewide one. Similarly, the amount of cord wood that may be cut must be determined in each woodlot and forest, tree by tree, rather than by blanket statewide or nationwide regulations. Statewide or provincewide fish and game regulations usually are established for administrative convenience, not for biological reasons.

The Gathering of Facts for Regulation. A sound procedure followed by some departments for gathering facts for administrative purposes, along with sound biological investigation, is the year-round employment of *district biologists* in the field, which makes it possible for trained men to follow wildlife throughout the year, to check sex ratios, nesting success, hatching success, brood success, spawning success, and similar governing factors. District biologists also check the land and water environment regularly to determine the available food and cover and its condition. The condition of the animals in the stand itself greatly concerns proper administration, and the biology force can keep account of this. Thus the sequence of fat utilization in the animal body tells the experienced biologist the condition of the animal, just as the sequence of palatability and consumption tells him of the food resources. The body consumes the fat reserves when food becomes scarce. Generally it uses these reserves in the order of dorsal, subcutaneous, visceral, cardiac, and marrow fat. In extreme starvation there is a similar sequence of muscle breakdown for energy, the heart muscle holding out to the last.

An increase or decrease in the stand can be noted readily by the biology force, the personnel of which is thoroughly familiar with the respective areas assigned. The probable demand can also be worked out satisfactorily for administrative purposes, just as can the anticipated sales of factory goods. The demand is the hunting pressure, and various sample methods already mentioned in earlier chapters will work sufficiently well for administrative use.

If closely supervised, *wardens* can assist very greatly in gathering information on hunting pressure and the hunting- or fishing-season kill. But their usefulness in gathering information on the abundance of animals is limited. The gathering of such information is a highly technical undertaking, and the warden is not equipped for it. Zeal and sincerity will not substitute for technical skill.

The testimony of *hunters* has little value in determining regulations because of their restricted time afield and the restricted nature of their "field work," along with their lack of training and experience. The bias of the hunter is proverbial. Public hearings on proposed legislation or regulations are part of the democratic system of providing a forum for expressing opinion and for assuring open conduct of public affairs.

They rarely uncover facts that a technical force misses, but they are essential to a democratic way of life.

Special Seasons. Animals living in environments disturbed by man often can cause trouble. Concentration of deer and elk in orchard land during heavy snow periods is an example; the competition of cattle and sheep for forage on the big-game range is yet another. Special seasons have developed as a method of reducing local concentrations or local abundance to control game damage and to serve other purposes. Such special seasons may be arranged for counties, lakes, or other areas; they may be in the form of antlerless-deer seasons after the main season. Usually no provisions are made for controlling the number of hunters except for big-game seasons or occasionally others. When the number is limited, a predetermined number of licenses is issued by lot drawing of applications if the number of applications is large.

Unbalanced Sex Ratios. The field man faces difficulties in determining sex ratios in animals that do not exhibit clearly visible sexual dimorphism. The general principle of sex ratios in the wild differs little from that of domestic stock on the range. The difficulties lie in the complications attendant upon determining proper sex ratios and checking sex ratios in the field. Once the biology of sex ratios has been established, checking the sex ratio becomes a problem in counting, but not an easy one. The sexes of large animals are determined by observation in the field, unless the observer is dealing with an extremely wary animal. Counts of other animals may have to be made by trapping and handling the animals themselves. A common method of some value in sex-ratio checking is to obtain data from hunters' bags, fishermen's creels, and the trappers' catch.

Contrary to popular opinion, unbalanced sex ratios can be corrected readily by closed seasons; a long-time closed season is not needed to correct the average shortage of males in big-game species. Although it may be more difficult to correct the unbalanced sex ratio in monogamous species, non-mobile species, and waterfowl, a one-year closure usually will correct the unbalanced sex ratio in big game. A two-year one most surely will, as can be seen in the following deer example, which assumes that a ratio of 1 to 5 is desired and that it gives 100 per cent of possible breeding success, whereas a ratio of 1 to 8 gives 75 per cent. (In the wild the maximum possible breeding success seems to be less than 70 per cent, though this figure is not considered in the example.) Death losses are not included, but they would not be likely to operate differently enough to distort the general picture.

First Year

	Bucks	Does	Sex Ratio	Fawns	Fawn Sex Ratio
Adults	10	80	1:8	60 (75% breeding)	30:30
One-year closed season Maturing from fawns	30	30			
Total adults	40	110	1:2.75	110 (100% of breeding)	55:55

Second Year

Adults	40	110			
Two-year closed season Maturing from fawns	55	55			
Total adults	95	165	1:1.7	165 (100% of breeding)	82:82

Third Year

Adults	95	165			
Three-year closed season Maturing from fawns	82	82			
Total adults	177	247	1:1.4	247 (100% of breeding)	123:123

Age Class Regulation. Normally the deer-season kill, for example, consists of about half, or a little less, of the animals maturing during the previous months, but the kill generally exceeds 50 per cent and may reach 75 per cent of the first-year birds in upland game birds and waterfowl.

Regulation of the age-class composition of the game stand has not yet received the attention that it deserves. Because the new crop of young usually outnumbers the adults in the fall, hunting and fishing pressure tends to operate more on the young than on the older individuals. If an excessively high proportion of young are killed during the hunting season, the breeding population may contain a high portion of older and presumably less capable breeders. Just how to determine rapidly most age classes in the field and how age-class composition should be regulated remains unknown.

Law Enforcement. The enforcement of game and fish laws differs not at all from other forms of law enforcement, though the procedures vary and the practices change from state to state. Enforcement generally is carried out by the game and fish departments through a regular staff of department wardens (they may be called protectors or officers or be given still other titles in some states) who serve on a full-time basis. Special commissions may be given to cooperating sportsmen, forest officers, and others. State wardens may also be commissioned as special federal wardens.[1] Some states do not issue commissions to federal officers or to cooperators.

Wardens may arrest without warrant anyone committing a crime in the presence of the officer, but courts are lenient in interpreting just what comes within the meaning of officers' view. Generally, positive evidence connecting the culprit with a crime or an immediate complaint is sufficient to justify arrest without warrant or issuance of a summons. Nevertheless courts will not tolerate indiscriminate arrest of people on mere suspicion, and officers must obtain warrants before making arrests for crimes not occurring in their "presence."

Enforcement officers, with few exceptions, may search, without warrant, cars, camps, warehouses, and the person of a suspect when the officers have reasonable grounds for believing that a crime has been committed and that the suspect or suspected place hides illegal articles. It is the duty of wardens to seize such articles for court action. Courts are very quick, in the Anglo-Saxon tradition of personal liberty, to frown upon promiscuous or arbitrary use of this power of search. Reasonable grounds for search must be just that. Search warrants are required to search homes, as well as buildings attached to and forming part of the home, but it is accepted in many states that game wardens may search outbuildings without warrants but with reasonable grounds for suspicion. In some states wardens are permitted to search cold-storage lockers without search warrants, but the trend is to extend to cold-storage lockers the protection of the home, just as this protection is extended to safe-deposit boxes in banks and similar special places for keeping personal property. The philosophy behind such protection is that the locker box, like the safe-deposit box, is an extension of the home facilities, which, though not economically feasible in the house itself, are a part of the home, nevertheless.

A question of nice legal judgment arises when dealing with cabins and shacks in the woods; some legal authorities hold that cabins and shacks are not homes in the constitutional sense and therefore are subject to search for probable cause without warrant. But others hold that permanent and semipermanent camps are legally homes and not

[1] Regular federal wardens have the misleading title of "game management agents."

subject to search without a search warrant. The same problem arises regarding the legality of searching house trailers and mobile homes, which in some states and provinces are accorded the full protection of homes, a trend that is likely to become general with the increase of trailer living. Precedents and court decisions need to be scrutinized carefully in each state to determine the method of handling all situations arising in matters of search. It should be remembered always that, in the English-speaking world, the rights and dignity of man are paramount; wardens should always give the benefit of the doubt to the individual, even though the practice may lose a case now and then.

Wardens may seize without warrant all game and contraband possessed or obtained in violation of the law and most implements used in such violation. In most states automobiles and boats used in illegal hunting may also be seized, but such drastic action is invoked only in extreme, repeated, or flagrant cases. Confiscated personal property must be held as evidence until the case has been settled. Confiscated equipment is forfeited to the state as provided by law, usually a court order only, upon conviction of the accused. Forfeited articles are disposed of as provided by law, but confiscated articles must be returned to the accused if he is acquitted.

Violations of game and fish laws universally are deemed misdemeanors, and the handling of charges filed for prosecution as provided by law differs little from that for other misdemeanors. Unfortunately the warden must usually carry the case to a finish himself, often with little help from county attorneys. Wardens may even have to furnish justices of the peace with the necessary information on law and precedents for carrying on the case.

Hunting Attitudes and Policies. The administrative policies and outlook of the various regulatory bodies—federal, state, or provincial—influence very greatly the success or failure of any conservation and management program. The general trend so far has been an increase in regulations and their complexity in the face of ever greater hunting and fishing pressure. But the increase in numbers of hunters and fishermen has in turn increased the drain upon the wildlife resources of the land, even though the number of game or fish taken per man has declined.

Improved farm efficiency and occupation of the land has reduced the available habitat or lessened its usefulness. In many areas hunting alone is the limiting factor to game abundance. A 40-acre field through which 100 hunters pass on the opening day cannot raise the game that its potentialities might indicate. In other areas the plow, the mower, and the harrow determine the game on the land, irrespective of hunters, regulations, or management practices. But in still other regions, only the regulations stand between the animals and extirpation. Management practices alone may seldom result in permanent increase in game without suitable regulations.

The general attitude of game departments is reflected by their policies, recommendations, and actions. This in turn usually reflects the public attitude, for game departments generally follow the public lead rather than anticipating future trends. The fact seems inescapable that the departmental attitude must be favorable to conservation and management at all levels of administration. It is necessary also that the legislative and judicial attitudes be favorable.

The attitudes, especially the unstated ones, toward the non-game species and the non-hunting and non-fishing public are particularly important and revealing. A department that concerns itself solely with the wants of the hunting and fishing segment does not shoulder its full obligation as a public administration agency. One that ignores or derides the non-hunting and non-fishing public actually impedes conservation progress. But the one that does so concern itself actively not only carries out its obligations to the public but also promotes good conservation policy.

The hunter or fisherman himself who looks upon game and fish as the inspiration for an outing and a source of outdoor recreation rather than the "target for today" has the right approach to the psychology of hunting and fishing. If he gets little or no game, he has nevertheless had a good day of recreation and the wildlife resources have served a useful purpose. If the hunter goes on from there and seeks to learn more of the habits of the wildlife and the outdoors, he is doing even better. The richer achievements in this world are likely to be emotional and intellectual rather than purely physical ones. The best future use of such wildlife resources as may be left to us is the satisfying pleasures in the outdoors that they bring. The administrative problems are always easier when this is the case.

SUGGESTED READING

Connery, Robert H., 1935, *Governmental Problems in Wild Life Conservation*, Columbia Univ. Stud. in Hist., Econ., and Pub. Law 411.
Gabrielson, Ira N., 1941, *Wildlife Conservation*, The Macmillan Co., New York.
Gerstell, Richard, 1937, "The Pennsylvania Bounty System," *Penn. Game Comm. Res. Bull.* 1.

Gordon, Seth, 1937, "Game Administration Policies and Methods," *Trans. Second N. A. Wildlife Conf.:* 26–32.

Grange, Wallace B., 1949, *The Way to Game Abundance with an Explanation of Game Cycles,* Charles Scribner's Sons, New York.

Hill, R. G., 1938, "Wildlife Extension Activities in Michigan," *Jour. Wildlife Management,* 2:235–238.

Leopold, Aldo, 1933, *Game Management,* Charles Scribner's Sons, New York.

Leopold, Aldo, and others, 1930, "An American Game Policy," *Trans. Seventeenth American Game Conf.:* 279–309.

Stevens, Ross O., 1944, *Talk about Wildlife for Hunters, Fishermen, and Nature Lovers,* Bynum Printing Co., Raleigh, N. C.

Turner, David B., 1948, *Professional Opportunities in the Wildlife Field,* Wildlife Management Inst., Washington, D. C.

Westerman, Fred A., 1934, "An American Fish Policy," *Trans. Twentieth American Game Conf.:* 161–166.

Wing, Leonard, 1943, "Employment in the Wildlife Field," *Jour. Wildlife Management,* 7:261–270.

Wire, Frank B., and A. B. Hatch, 1943, "Administration of Beaver in the Western United States," *Jour. Wildlife Management,* 7:81–92.

Index

Abies, see Fir
Abundance, absolute and relative, 55; and foods eaten, 24–25; designation of, 55
Accidents, 21, 34, 150, 232
Acer, see Maple
Acorn, 165, 166, 180
Acquisition, of private ownership of game, 329; of refuges, 337
Activity, and mitotic rhythm, 25; useful, of animals, 8
Activity recorders, 75
Adams, C. C., 138
Adaptation, of animals to forest conditions, 124; of musk ox, 229
"A"-deflector, 291, 292
Administrative costs, 4; limitations on, 4
Administrative reports, 88
Adult-young ratio in game kill, 360
Advance of spring, 221
Adverse weather, effect on woodcocks, 158
Aeration of water, 279
Aerial photographs, 68
Aestivation, 47–48
Africa, 41, 195
Age at maturity, 40
Age class, 151; of white sheep, 230; regulation, 360
Age indicators, 64, 359; of fish, 26, 40, 280; of sheep, 41, 230
Airplane, following birds by, 62; planting beaver by, 245
Airplane counts and censuses, 61–62, 182, 190, 198
Airplane dopes, use in marking birds, 76
Airplane photographs, 198
Airplane salting, 178, 205

Alabama, 15, 213, 214, 333
Alaska, 15, 143, 145, 146, 168, 173, 190, 201, 228–232, 250; caribou, 229; grassland, 223; land ownership, 222; need for local control, 223; timber, 223
Alberta, 145, 178, 199, 348, 349
Alces americana, see Moose
Alder, 150, 170, 191, 202
Aldous, Clarence M., 159
Aldous, Shaler E., 139
Aleutians, 223, 226
Algae, 191; control, 273
Aliens prohibited from hunting, 324
Alkali poisoning, 257–258
All-age classes, 132; forests, 34
Allan, Phillip F., 216, 283, 310
Allee, W. C., 36, 53
Allegheny Mountains, 252
Allen, Durward L., 105, 172
Allen, Glover M., 36, 317
Allen, Robert Porter, 317
Allen rule, 27
Alligator, 6, 215–216, 297; age, 215; biological data, 209; economic value, 216; food habits, 215; management, 216; maturity, 215; nests, 216; night lighting, 215; origin of name, 215; protection, 216; range, 215; size, 215; tourist distribution, 215; voice, 215
Alligator sinensis, 215
Allopatric species, 47
Alopex lagopus, see Fox, Arctic
Altamaha River, 333
Alternations of phase, 37
Altitudinal migration, 47, 140, 143, 155
Altitudinal temperature change, 33
Altitude, and life, 34; of migration, 46
Altitude range, valley quail, 114

Index

Amelanchier, see Serviceberry
American Ornithologist's Union, 343
American vessels and oceanic wildlife, 334
American Wildlife Conference, 298
Ammunition tax, 14
Amount of food needed, black-tailed deer, 183; moose, 191; prairie chicken, 200; sharp-tailed grouse, 202; white-tailed deer, 186
Amphibians, 6, 125
Anglo-Saxon hunting, 320
Anhimidae, 249
Animal normal, and phase alternations, 40
Animal population biology, 37, 219
Animal-proof fence, 56–57
Animal succession, 34
Animals, beyond 3-mile limit, 335; *ferae naturae* not owned by federal government, 333 (*see also Ferae naturae*); growth patterns, 40; status of, 7; trails of, 72; weeds eaten by, 136; work of, 7
Annuli in fish scales, 40
Anonymous author, 206, 216, 269, 283, 295, 331
Anseriformes, 249
Anteater, 214
Antelope, pronghorn, 65, 85, 203–205; breeding season, 196; census, 61; control of water holes, 205; crossings, 204; density, 203; environment, 196; fences, 205; food habits, 196, 204; gestation, 196; habitat requirements, 203; handling, 204; management, 204; mating, 196; migration, 203; minimum herd, 39; number of young, 196; original range, 203; overhunting, 204, 205; parturition, 196; poaching, 204; predation, 205; range, 194, 196, 203; refuges, 205; salt, 205; sex ratio, 196; trapping, 204, 205; water, 203–204, 205; weight, 196; winter range, 203
Antilocapra americana, see Antelope
Antlers, 73; caribou, 228; eating, 228
Apnoea, 260
Appalachian Mountains, 24, 49, 168
Apple, 15, 150

Apple rust and juniper, 300
Appropriations, for fisheries, 343; for game departments, 353
Aquatic plants, causes of failure, 273; methods of protecting from destruction, 273; requirements, 264; storage of, 264
Aquatic vegetation, 163; propagation of, 264
Arborvitae, 146, 147, 170, 185; rotation of, 187
Arborvitae-hemlock zone, 35
Arbutus, 16, 150
Arctic, 15, 27, 218, 242 (*see also* Northland); disease reduction, 210; food sources, 220; summer and winter in, 221
Arctic Circle, 218
Arctic conditions at high altitude, 34
Arctic prairie, 229
Arctic species at high altitude, 34
Areas, natural, 137; primitive, 137; roadless, 137; vanishing-species, 137; wild, 137; wilderness, 137
Argentina, 213, 215
Arizona, 11, 15, 152, 182, 207, 214; forage, 182
Arkansas, 15, 199, 203, 214
Armadillo, 214–215; biological data, 209; breeding habits, 215; burrows, 215; economic value, 215; food, 215; parturition, 215; range, 214; range extension, 215; relationships, 214
Army Engineers, 344
Arrest without warrant, 361
Artemisia, see Sagebrush
Arthur, Stanley Clisby, 247
Artificial propagation, 270; philosophy of, 271
Artificial stocking, 1
Ascension Island, 49
Ash, 153; green, 16; mountain, 133, 144, 176, 191, 301
Aspect measurements, 64
Aspen, 133, 141, 147, 161, 166, 170, 176, 185, 191, 202, 243
Atlantic salmon cycle, 51
Attwater prairie chicken, *see* Prairie chicken

Index 367

Auk, great, extinction of, 314
Australia, 49, 211; rabbits, 38
Authority to grant permission to hunt, 328
Autopsies, 74

Bachelor bobwhite, 112
Bachrach, Max, 247
Bacteria, botulism, 257
Badger, den, 237; economic relations, 240; habitat, 236; habits, 240; range, 240; sign, 74
Baffin Island, 250
Bag, adult-young ratios, 360
Bag censuses, 63; bag limit, determining proper size, 357–358; waterfowl, 265
Baird, Spencer F., 343
Baker, John H., 310
Baldpate, 250
Balsam, 146, 147, 191
Banding, 78, 79, 158
Banding together of prey, 20–21
Bands, aluminum, 77, 79; colored, 77, 79, 201; plastic, 77, 79
Banff National Park, 350
Barnes, Will C., 206
Bartlett, I. H., 192
Bar to hiring non-residents, 353
Bass, 21; stocking of, 270
    large-mouth black, 282, 283; food, 286; range, 286; spawning, 286
    small-mouth black, food, 286; range, 286; spawning, 286
    spotted black, food, 286; range, 286; spawning, 286
    striped, food, 286; range, 286; spawning, 286
    white, food, 286; range, 286; spawning, 286
Bassariscus astutus, see Ringtail
Basswood, 166
Bats, 15, 297
Baumgras, Philip S., 106
Bear, 40; cache, 75; hibernation, 48; sign, 74
    black, 173–175; breeding habits, 174; breeding season, 162; census method, 173; damage, 175; density, 173; environment, 162; food habits, 162, 174; gestation, 162; habitat requirements, 173–174; hibernation, 174; mating, 162; number of young, 162; open season, 174; parturition, 162; protection, 174–175; range, 162, 173; renegades, 175; sex ratio, 162; use of forest, 161; wallows, 174; weight, 162
    brown, 223, 226; age, 226; biological data, 224; breeding habits, 226; breeding season, 162; damage complaints, 226; environment, 162; fishing methods, 226; food habits, 223, 226; gestation, 162; habits, 223; hunting pressure, 226; King of Beasts, 223; mating, 162; number of young, 162; parturition, 162; range, 162, 223; relationships, 223; sex ratio, 162; spare needs, 226; weight, 162
    grizzly, 136, 162, 315; breeding season, 162; environment, 162; food, 162; gestation, 162; mating, 162; number of young, 162; parturition, 162; range, 162; sex ratio, 162; weight, 162
    polar, 226, 316; biological data, 224; decline in number, 226; distribution, 222; fat, 226; food habits, 226; habits, 226; pelage, 226; range, 226; vision, 219
Beard, Daniel, 317
Beard, Elizabeth B., 36, 247, 269
Beaver, 7, 124, 127, 242–246, 335; amount of aspen needed, 243; canals, 245; Carolina, 315; chief export, 234; control, 245, 246; cycles, 51; dam, 242, 243, 244, 245; dam construction, 243; dam repair, 243; decline in numbers, 234, 235; den, 237; determining food utilization, 244; emergency feeding, 245; empire builder, 235; enemies, 246; feeding, 75; food habits, 243; habitat, 236, 242; history, 234; lodges, 235, 236; management operations, 243–244; marking, 79, 246; meadows, 169; mountain streams, 242; original range, 242; poaching, 246; protection, 246; range, 242; sex

368 Index

determination, 246; sign, 75; state monopolies, 246; symbol for, 238; transplanting, 245; transplanting by airplane, 245; trapping, 245, 246; trout relationships, 245; value for water control, 243
Bed counts, 62, 190
Beech, 150, 153; blue, 133
Beechnuts, 165, 166
Beer, James, 144, 158
Beggarweed, 210
Behavior patterns, 27
Bell, Frank T., 343
Bells for tracing big game, 78
Benefits of settlement to wildlife, 91
Bennett, Hugh Hammond, 17, 106
Bennett, Logan J., 269
Bent, A. C., 122, 159, 206, 216, 232, 317
Bergmann principle, 23, 27
Bering Islands, 50
Berries, 142, 163, 184, 196; buffalo, 144
Bighorn, 41, 230; desert, 315, 316; Sierra, 315, 316
Binoculars and other optical instruments, 84–85; use in the field, 65
Biological aspects of hunting and fishing, 5–6
Biological balance, 40
Biological base of management, 19–53
Biological characteristics, 19
Biological eclipse, 311–312
Biological limitations, 4
Biological pressure, 20, 21
Biological principles, working with, 6, 19
Biological surplus, 5
Biological Survey, *see* Bureau of Biological Survey
Biology tables, farm game, 108; forest game birds, 142; forest game mammals, 162–163; Northland wildlife, 224–225; open-range game, 196; southern species, 208–209
Biomass and density, 43
Biomes, 35
Biotic potential, *see* Breeding potential
Biotic provinces, 35
Birch, 70, 133, 147, 150, 191, 202
Bird houses, specifications and use, 302

Bird islands, 50; of Peru, 15, 50
Bird Rock, 50
Bird rocks, 50, 268, 298
Birds, influx of, 84; protected by migratory bird treaties, 335–336; role of, 7
Bison, 22, 34; decline, 195, 197, 316; destruction to control Indians, 312; gregariousness, 41; promiscuity, 30; range, 194; slaughter of, 15
Bison bison, see Bison
Bitterroot, 16
Bittersweet, 141, 150, 161, 166
Blackberry, 121, 146, 150, 153, 166, 174, 301
Black duck, *see* Duck, black
Black-eyed Susan, 16
Black Hills, 143
Blair, W. Frank, 69, 89
Blake, James, 238, 247
Blinds, 78–80, 201; use for nest study, 75
Block cutting, 186
Block planting, 186
Blow-downs, 148
Blueberry, 144, 146, 150, 153, 166, 174, 185, 220
Bluebird, eastern, 16; mountain, 16
Bluebonnet, 16
Blue gill, 21, 282, 283; competition with bass, 271; food, 286; range, 286; spawning, 286
Boat rental, 9
Bobcat, *see* Wildcat
Bobwhite, 16, 19, 27, 110–114, 117, 140, 153, 307; ability to withstand high temperature, 44; advance and retreat, 49; breeding potential, 31; breeding season, 108; census methods, 113; controlled burning for, 134; cover type, 92–93; cover requirements, 111–112; covey range, 111; density, 111; dusting, 112; enemies, 113; environment, 108; food consumption, 105; food habits, 108, 112; grit, 113; habitat requirements, 110; hatching season, 108; improving food and cover, 112; in lake states, 49; incubation season, 108; introduction, 110; lespedeza, 210; losses, 97;

masked, 315; mating, 108; minimum covey, 114; mobility, 30, 110; nesting cover, 112; night roosting, 112; population build-up, 110; predator relations, 113; range, 108, 110; range extension, 110; roosting habits, 112; saturation point, 39; sex counts, 114; sex ratio, 108; territory, 111; transplants, 306; traps, 110; water needs, 112; weight, 108; whistling counts, 112; winter losses, 110
Body measurements of game, 64
Body size and weight, 26–27
Body temperature and air temperature, 52
Body weight fluctuations, 26–27
Body weight standards, 26
Bonasa umbellus, see Grouse, ruffed
Bond, Richard M., 206
Bonneville Dam, 289
Boom cover, 291
Booming grounds, counts, 201; location and use of, 28; prairie chicken, 30, 63, 199, 200
Bootleg of game and Lacey Act, 334
Borders, use of, 210
Borings, woodcock, 157
Botany, 2
Bottom sampler, 289
Botulism, cause, 257; conditions of occurrence, 257; diagnosis, 257; prevention, 257; treatment, 257; waterfowl, 256–257
Bounty system, 238, 239; failure of, 239; frauds, 239
Bovidae, 229
Bovine flocks, 42
Bowers, George M., 343
Bowfin, food, 286; range, 286; spawning, 286
Box elder, 161, 166; see also Elder
Branding, 78, 238
Brandt, F. W., 247
Brant, American, 249; American, decline in number, 226; black, 249
Break-up of rivers, 219, 221
Bream, 282
Breeding-bird census, 63
Breeding cycle, 39; and sex, 43

Breeding habits, black bear, 174; brown bear, 226; *see also* Mating habits
Breeding potential, 37–38; and life hazards, 40; and phase alternations, 40; and productivity, 30–31; in fish, 31
Breeding rate, muskrat, 246
Breeding season (*see also* Parturition); alligator, 209; antelope, 196; Arctic fox, 224; Arctic hare, 225; armadillo, 209; black bear, 162; black-tailed deer, 163; blue grouse, 142; bobwhite, 108; brown bear, 162, 224; caribou, 225; census of, 58; chachalaca, 209; cottontail rabbit, 108; cougar, 209; elk, 163; eyra, 208; fox squirrel, 163; Franklin grouse, 142; Gambel quail, 196; gray squirrel, 163; grizzly bear, 162; Hungarian partridge, 108; jack rabbit, 196; jaguar, 208; javelina, 209; marsh rabbit, 209; moose, 163; mountain quail, 142; musk ox, 225; muskrat, 247; ocelot, 208; opossum, 208; pheasant, 108; polar bear, 224; prairie chicken, 196; ringtail, 208; rock ptarmigan, 225; ruffed grouse, 142; sage hen, 196; sharp-tailed grouse, 196; spruce grouse, 142; success of, 58; swamp rabbit, 209; turkey, 142; valley quail, 108; white sheep, 225; white-tailed deer, 163; white-tailed ptarmigan, 225; willow ptarmigan, 225; woodcock, 142
Breeding stock, 5
Breeding success in the wild, 359
Brice, John J., 343
British Columbia, 15, 114, 145, 197, 211, 230, 348, 349
British Isles, 231
British North America Act (1867), 347
Brood counts, sage grouse, 198; waterfowl, 269
Brooding, 147
Broods, mixing of, 43; variation with latitude, 37
Brood success, 358
Bromus carinatus, 176
Browse, 163, 196; clipping, 67; determination, 65
Browse line, 180, 185

Browsing, black-tailed deer, 180
Brush and log shelters for streams, 290
Brush cutters, 116
Brush lanes, 95
Brush mats, 274
Brush piles, 95, 96–98, 102, 132, 133–134, 300; at feeders, 103; conifers, 133; construction, 96; escape cover, 96; hardwoods, 133; types of, 96; use for fish, 274
Brush shelters for fish, 275
Bryant, Harold Child, 159
Buck brush, 176
Buckeye, 16, 166
Buckwheat, 101, 102, 105, 200, 202
Buds, 23, 133, 142, 147, 149, 166, 196, 202, 225, 232
Buffalo, *see* Bison
Building cover, 96–99
Bulbs, 214
Bullhead, *see* Catfish
Bulrush, 259
Bunchgrass, 196, 204
Bunting, lark, 15
Bunting, Townsend, extinction of, 314
Bureau of Biological Survey, 63, 77, 342–343; activities, 343; chiefs, 344; origin, 343; shifted to Department of the Interior, 343
Bureau of Fisheries, 343; chiefs, 343
Bureau of Forestry, 344
Burning, and succession, 34; roadside, 309; stubble, 119
Burrows, 169; cottontail, 120; counting, 56; used for dens, 237; woodchuck, 120
Buss, Irven O., 122
Buttons, 15
Bypassing succession stages, 34

Cabbage palmetto, 16
Cache of food, 75
Cacomistle, *see* Ringtail
Cactus, 204
Cahalane, Victor H., 172, 192, 206, 216, 232, 247, 317
Cake, concentrated, 186
California, 15, 49, 114, 116, 146, 155, 168, 197, 201, 207, 211, 240

Calling males, bobwhite, 113
Caloric needs of animals, 23
Calories in foods, 22–23
Cameras, 9; choice of, 85; for obtaining sign, 75; Graflex, 85; motion-picture, 86; 35-mm, 85; types of, 85
Cameron, Jenks, 344
Camps, 136
Canachites cauadensis, see Grouse, spruce; *franklini, see* Franklin Grouse
Canada, federal government, power of, 347; provincial game departments, 348; provincial governments, 347
Canis latrans, see Coyote
Cannons for throwing nets, 269
Canvasback, 250; territorial demands, 28
Cape Hatteras, 50
Capital land values, 11–12
Capital outlay, 4
Caracara, Guadelupe, extinction of, 314
Carbon dioxide, 21, 272
Cardinal, 16, 301
Carex, see Sedge
Caribou, 41, 43; and reindeer industry, 228; antlers, 228; barren-ground, 228; biological data, 224; Dawson, extinction of, 314; decline in numbers, 228; dorsal fat, 221; enemies, 228; food habits, 228; gregariousness, 228; movements, 228; niche, 229; promiscuity, 30; relation to reindeer, 222; remnants, 229; season, 229; woodland, 228, 315
Carnation, 16
Carnivore, 316; amount of food needed, 24; foods, 22–23; response to meat, 27
Carolinas, 175, 207, 214
Carp, 278; food, 286; influence on waterfowl, 255; introduction, 343; range, 286; spawning, 286
Carrion, 174, 226, 242; insects, 74
Carrying capacity, 5, 21, 32; and winter range, 135; big-game range, 64; elk range, 177; forage acres, 66; forest, 132; range, 67
Castanea americana, 166
Castor canadensis, see Beaver

Index

Catch data, use of, 279
Cat family, 212–213
Catfish, and oxygen content of water, 33; food, 286; range, 286; spawning, 286
Catkins, 147
Caves used for dens, 237
Cedar, 191; browse, 185, 186; red, 147; swamps, 184, 185; white, see Arborvitae
Ceding of jurisdiction by a state, 318
Census methods (see also Censuses), airplane, 178, 190, 192; bed, 190; black bear, 175; black-tailed deer, 182–183; bobwhite, 113; booming-ground counts, 201; calling males, 113; covey counts, 113; crowing-ground counts, 119; dog counts, 119; drive, 113, 119, 122, 190; earthworms, 157; elk, 178; feces counts, 122; feeding-station, 119; flush counts, 113; form counts, 122; fox and gray squirrels, 168; frequency, 190; fur bearers, 238; horseback, 117; Hungarian partridge, 110; moose, 192; nest counts, 113, 119, 168; pellet-group, 190; prairie chicken, 201; quadrat, 168; random counts, 122; roadside counts, 122; roadside survey, 119; roost counts, 113; ruffed grouse, 151–152; sage grouse, 198; sample counts, 190; sharp-tailed grouse, 203; snowshoe rabbit, 171; spot counting, 168; track counts, 113, 119, 122, 190, 192, 201; transects, 122, 168; trap nights, 122; trapping, 113; turkey, 154; valley quail, 117; water-hole counts, 117; white-tailed deer, 190; woodcock, 158; yard counts, 190
Censuses (see also Census methods), airplane, 61–62; antelope, 61; bag reports, 63; bed counts, 62; booming grounds, 63; breeding-bird, 63; breeding season, 58; brood counts, 58; checking stations, 63; colonial birds, 63; concentration area, 62; coursing, 61; cover, 64; creel, 63; crowing grounds, 63; dancing grounds, 63; den counts, 58, 59; detection-distance technique, 60; drive, 61; elk, 61, 62; fall, 58; fish, 63; form counts, 62; ground crews, 62; hole-nesters, 63; King method, 59–60; late winter, 58; mule deer, 61; nesting, 58, 63; pheasant, 63, 119; post-hunting, 58; prairie chicken, 63; pre-hunting, 58; rabbit, 63; roadside, 60–61; rope counts, 63; seining, 63; sex, 58; sharp-tailed grouse, 63; singing bird, 63; tiger, 63; track counts, 62; trapping, 63; use of dog, 61; visual area, 60; waterfowl, 58, 61–62; winter, 58
Central America, 252
Centrocercus urophasianus, see Grouse, sage
Century of water levels, 254
Cervidae, 160, 173, 228, 229
Cervus canadensis, see Elk
Cestodes, 151
Cetacea, 316
Chachalaca, 216; biological data, 209; domestication, 216; habits, 216; territory, 216; water needs, 216
Chandler, Robert F., Jr., 138
Chaparral, 141, 161, 208, 209, 214, 216
Chapman, Herman H., 138
Chapman, Royal N., 53
Chase, Warren W., 36, 247, 269
Check areas, 83
Check dams, 153
Checking station, 63, 64, 164, 190
Check plots, crop damage, 84; range studies, 65
Chemical analysis of lakes, 272
Cherry, 133, 150, 166, 185, 191, 301
Chestnut, 166
Chickadee, 300, 304; black-capped, 16; Carolina, 16; species association, 43
Childs, Vandiver L., 216
Chilling, 151
China, 215
Chinquapin, 153
Chipmunk, pilfering of eggs by, 150
Chittenden, H. M., 247
Chufa, 153, 259
Cistotaemia, 214
Cittelus richardsoni, hibernation and aestivation, 48

Clams, 240; instinctive reactions of, 27
Classification of economic values, 8
Clear cutting, see Cutting
Clements, Frederic E., 36
Climate, influence of, 32; northward march, 49, 220, 221
Climatic changes, 51; maladjustment to, 45
Climax, 34, 35
Climographs, 45
Clipping, of feathers, for identification, 78; of toes, for marking, 78
Closed areas, for caribou, 229 for white sheep, 230
Closed seasons, of bird treaties, 336; on caribou, 229; on fish, purposes of, 281; on white sheep, 230; sex ratio control, 359–360
Clostridium botulinum, 257
Closure, of feeder streams, 285; of woods, 188
Cloudiness, 32
Clover, 16, 149
Club expenses, 13
Clubs, hunting and fishing, 10
Coast Guard, 344
Coccidiosis, in ruffed grouse, 151
Coconut, 16
Code Napoléon, 346
Cold-blooded animals, 32
Cold springs, 32
Cold-storage lockers, search of, 361
Colinus virginianus, see Bobwhite
Collecting, see Preserving and collecting
Collisions with automobiles, 182, 204, 307
Colony nesting, 50; birds, 63; gregariousness of, 42; nests, 298; requirements, 50
Colorado, 15, 110, 146, 152, 197, 199, 201
Color phases, Arctic fox, 226
Colorimetric sets, 272
Columbia black-tailed deer, 161
Columbia River, 50, 155, 183, 289
Columbine, Colorado, 15
Commerce with Indians, 340
Commercial clubs, 12
Commercial fishing, 9

Commercial species, number of, 6, 7
Commercial trapping, 9
Commissioner of Fisheries to collect statistics, 342–343
Committee for International Wildlife Protection, 298
Common fresh-water fishes, biology, 286
Competition, 8 (see also Conflicts); between elk and cattle, 176–177; between fishermen and others, 241; for nest holes, 304; interspecies, 43
Competitors, of stream fish, 285; of valley quail, 116
Concentrate, 186
Concentration areas, 47
Conditioned patterns, 27
Conditioning, by plant succession, 33; of water, 33
Condor, California, 312, 315; eggs, 312
Confinement and wildness, 32, 83
Confiscation of contraband and equipment, 362
Conflicts, 3 (see also Competition); between hunter and stockman, 135; between recreational and commercial uses, 9; deer and sheep, 180; in territory in animal life, 29; over use for game or food hunting, 319
Congress, control of Indians, 341; power of, to protect federal property, 340; prohibits importation of small sponges, 334; prohibits territories from passing local game laws, 334
Conifers, 141, 148, 161, 163, 180, 188; blocks of, 132; eaten by beaver, 243; furbearers, 236; needles, 142; plantations, 128, 132, 157
Conklin, W. Gard, 122
Connecticut, 16
Connery, Robert H., 331, 344, 363
Conservation, and management, 1; blunder of Commissioner of Fisheries, 343
Conservation departments, 129, 136; organization of, 3; unified types, and organization of, 352, 356
Conservation policy, 363
Constant-level dams, 277

Index

Constitution, 318, 321, 322, 327, 328, 337
Constitutional delegation of powers, 333
Construction, of dams, 262
  dust mounds, 131
  food hoppers, 103
Control, and jurisdiction over federal lands, 339; aquatic vegetation, 265; beaver damage, 245, 246; by special season, 177, 359; coyote, 195; damage, 182; disease, 7; eroding banks, 293; federal property, 333; fish derbies, 281; fish enemies, 278; fish populations, 278; insects, 7; local concentrations by special seasons, 359; measures, 1; oil pollution, 256; plants, 265; pond vegetation, 273–274; populations, 3; predators, *see* Predator control; rabbits, 122; roadside zoos, 14; silt on stream bottom, 290–291; snowshoe rabbit, 170–171; succession, 34; turtles, 255; unbalanced sex ratios, 359–360; waterholes, 215; water levels, 262–264, 276; water levels for plankton, 276; water temperature, 278; wave action, 277
Control areas, 83
Controlled burning, 116, 132, 134–135, 145, 153, 200, 203, 299
Controlled grazing, 145
'Coon hunting, 164; *see also* Raccoon
Cooperation studies, 83–84
Cooperatives, 10; land pools, 12
Coot, 249, 250; tearing loose vegetation, 260; time-depth ratio, 260
Coppice growth, 181
Corioli's force, 46
Cormorant, 15; Pallas, extinction, 314
Corn, 101, 102, 104, 105, 112, 166, 200, 202
Cornus, see Dogwood
Correction of unbalanced sex ratios, 359–360
Correlation of forestry and wildlife management, 128–129
Costs, 4; of fishing, 12; of game, 10
Cottam, Clarence, 259, 269
Cotton lands, 93

Cottontail, *see* Rabbit, cottontail
Cottonwood, 16, 141, 161, 202
Cougar, 136, 188, 209, 315, 316; biological data, 209; cache, 75; sign, 71; statements of "deer-a-week," 316
Counters, 61
Counting, 54; flocks, 58; migrating fish, 290; number of birds in rafts, 58
Courtship, communal, 29
Cover, 20 (*see also* Food and cover, Improving food and cover); availability of, 64; composition of, 64; farm, 95–96; fish, 291; measurements, 64; quality of, 64; quantity of, 64
Cover use tables, farm game, 92–93; forest game birds, 141; forest game mammals, 161
Covey counts, bobwhite, 113
Covey relations, valley quail, 114, 115
Covey territory, bobwhite, 111
Cow peas, 102, 153
Coyotes, 3, 23, 136, 171, 188, 195; and black-tailed deer, 182; control, 195; den, 237; den counts, 59; habitat, 236; marking, 238; valley quail, 117
Crab apple, 133
Cracidae, relationships, 216
Craig, Elberta, 17, 137, 317
Crane, sandhill, 314, 315; whooping, 314, 315
Crappie, food, 286; range, 286; spawning, 286
Crataegus, 98, 115, 121, 210, 299
Crayfish, 240
Creel census, 63, 279; cards, 83; data obtained, 279; methods, 279; use of, 279
Creeper, brown, species association, 43
Crepuscular animals, 33
Cretaceous, 141
Cripple loss, black-tailed deer, 181; waterfowl, 266
Crocodile, 6
Crop, damage, 84, 188; protection and damage control, 304–306; remnants, 99, 100
Croton, 210

Crow, 305; waterfowl predation, 255
Crowing ground, pheasant, 118, 156; census, 63, 119
Crown, as sovereign power of people, 248; capacities of, 320; powers of, 320
Crown land, 222
Cultivated crops, use for food and cover, 92–93
Curlew, Eskimo; extinction of, 314
Currant, 144
Curtis, Brian, 283, 296
Curtis, James D., 138
Customs Service, 344
Cutbacks, 61
Cutting, block, 186; clear, 166, 186; cycle, 186; group, 186; operations, 128; shelterwood, 186; single-tree, 186; strip, 186; timber, 132
Cycles, 127; Arctic fox, 227; Arctic hare, 227; blue grouse, 145; breeding, 39; breeding and sex, 43; causes of, 51, 52; drought, 253–254; El Nino, 52; estrus, 39; lemming, 22, 227; length, 52; lynx, 242; magnitude, 51; northern shrike, 54; ptarmigan, 231; rainfall, 254; range shift, 49; ruffed grouse, 50, 146, 151; snowshoe rabbit, 50–51, 169, 170, 227; snowy owl, 51; water levels, 253–254; white sheep, 230

Dabbling ducks, 250; water depth preferred, 261
Dakin, Edwin F., 53
Dalke, Paul D., 69, 123
Dall Mountain sheep, *see* Sheep, White mountain
Damage, 127 (*see also* particular species); black bear, 175; claims, 304; complaints, 84; complaints in Northland, 222; elk, 177, 178; federal property, 340; investigations, 84; rabbit, 122
Dambach, Charles A., 19, 48
Dams, constant-level, 277; construction, 262; kinds of, for stream fish, 291; loss of storage capacity, 291; preventing leakage, 263; protecting against wave action, 263; stone, 291; waterfowl, 262
Dancing grounds, 30, 63; sage grouse, 198; sharp-tailed grouse, 202
Darling, J. N., 344
Dasypus novemcinctus, see Armadillo
Data, collected by lake survey, 272; for regulation of fish seasons, 279; from hunters and fishermen, 83
Daubenmire, R. F., 36
Davenport, L. A., 138
Davis, Cecil N., 216, 283
Davis, H. S., 290
Davison, Robert MacGregor, 350
Davison, Verne E., 89, 106, 216
Day, Albert N., 269, 344
Day length, and migration, 26, 45; Arctic, 218
Deadhead shelter, 275
Dead limbs, 130
Dead trees, 130
Death by freezing, 25–26
Decimating factors, 34
Decisions, and reports, 88; problems, of, 19
Decline, 19; beaver, 234, 235; causes of, 311–313; fur bearers, 234–235; game species, 13; musk ox, 230
Declining quality, of game, 107
Decomposition sequence, 74
Deep diving, depth reached, 260; loon, 260; mechanism, 260; old squaw, 260; oxygen supply, 260
Deer, 39, 41, 55, 127, 128, 133, 160, 174, 204, 310; and laurel, 24; bells, 78; browsing, 67; census, 61; Columbia black-tail, *see* Deer, black-tailed; competition, 43; crossings, 182; damage, 182, 188; difference in keenness of senses, 41; effect on reproduction, 127; example of sex ratio control, 359–360; family, 160, 173; fence, 56; food, 133; increase, 136; live weight-dressed weight ratio, 164; migration, 47; mobility, 160; mule, *see* Deer, black-tailed; overgrazing 136; percentage of young in kill, 360; problem areas, 137; recog-

Index

nition of food differences, 24; sign, 73, 75; surveys, 182; track counts, 62

black-tailed, 41, 178–183; breeding season, 163; browsing, 180; census methods, 182–183; collision with cars, 182; coyotes, 182; cripple loss, 181; doe season, 181; environment, 163; food habits, 163, 180; forage condition, 181; forage requirement, 183; gestation, 163; grazing capacity, 181; gregariousness, 178; habitat requirements, 179; illegal kill, 182; improving food and cover, 180–181; irruptions, 181; key species, 181; mating, 163; migration, 179; number of young, 163; open season, 181; overpopulation, 181; parturition, 163; protection, 181; range, 163; refuge, 181; salt, 179, 180; sex ratio, 163, 183; sex ratio unbalance, 181; summer range, 179, 180, 181; trapping, 183; use of forest, 161; water needs, 179; weight, 163; winter range, 179, 180, 181

white-tailed, 2, 13, 24, 41, 136, 173, 178, 183–190; antlerless season, 188; bag limit, 188; breeding season, 163; census, 60, 190; concentration areas, 184; crop damage, 188; cutting timber, 186; daily food, 186; deferred maturity, 30; density reports, 31, 183–184; ecological succession, 183; environment, 163; evergreen blocks, 187; food habits, 23, 163, 185–187; gestation, 163; habitat requirement, 183; home range, 29, 183; illegal kill, 188; improving food and cover, 186–187; mating, 163; mobility, 30, 183; movement, 184; number of young, 163; nutrition, 185; overbrowsing, 184, 186, 187, 189; overpopulation, 183, 184, 187; parturition, 163; predation, 188; protection, 187–188; range, 163; range extension, 183; refuges, 187; salt, 184, 185; season, 188, 189, 190; sex ratio, 163, 188; starvation, 184, 186, 189; summer range, 184; swamps, 187; tolerance, 183; use of forest, 161; weight, 27, 163; winter feeding, 186; winter range, 184; wolf kill, 188; yarding, 184

Deer reeves, Massachusetts, 17, 64, 329
Deevey, Edward S., Jr., 53
Defense circle, of musk ox, 229
Deferred maturity, 29, 198; mowing, 96; plowing, 96
Deficits, 129
Deflection, by earth rotation, 46
Deflectors, in stream improvement, 291; kinds of, 291
Delaware, 16
Delayed implantation of ovum, armadillo, 215
Delegated powers of the federal government, 333
Dendragapus obscurus, see Blue grouse
Dens, 211, 235, 236; cavities, 165; location of fur-bearer, 237; ringtail, 212; sign, 74; symbol for, 238; trees, 130, 167; trees, number of, 165
Density, 66, 173; and cycles, 51; and saturation point, 31–32; antelope, 203; bobwhite, 111; brown bear, 226; cottontail, 120; cover, 64; elk, 176; fox, 165, 167; gray fox, 242; gray squirrels, 165, 167; Hungarian partridge, 109; measures of, 31; mixed, 43; moose, 191, 192; pheasant, 118; red fox, 242; ruffed grouse, 51, 127, 146, 147, 148; snowshoe rabbit, 51, 127, 170, 213; waterfowl, 262; white sheep, 231; white-tailed deer, 183–184
Departmental organization, 355–356; powers and responsibilities, 352–353
Department of Agriculture, 344
Department of Commerce and Labor, 343
Department of conservation, first, 330
Department of Resources and Development, 349
Department of the Interior, 344
Depth, of diving, 260; of snow, effect on Hungarian partridge, 107

Derbies, fishing and hunting, 14
Desert, 194, 207
Desert animals, adaptation to dry air, 33
  water needs, 24
Desiccation, 52
Designation of wildlife areas, 17
Desmodium, 153
Destruction, of Florida deer for disease control, 312; of property, 8; on oceanic islands, 304
Detection-distances, 60
Determinant growth, 40
Determination, of chief forage species, 65; of forage and range capacity, 67; of hunting pressure, 358; of plant density, 65–66; of proper-use factor, 64–65; of regulations, 357
Deterrents, 122, 182
Developmental costs, 4
Development Services Branch, 349
Dew, 110, 153
Dewberry, 153
Dewey, Edward R., 53
Dice, Lee R., 53, 69
Dickcissel, 49, 50
Didelphis virginiana, see Opossum
Diel rhythm, 218
Diet, 232; blue grouse, 143; cottontail, 121; mountain quail, 156; nestlings, 25; ruffed grouse, 150; sage grouse, 198; valley quail, 115
Differential sex wintering habits, 43
Digestive systems, in relation to food eaten, 22
Digger log, 292
Diminishing returns, law of, 4
Dingell-Johnson Act, 338
Direct income, 8–9
Director responsible to commission, 352
Disease, 21, 151; alkali poisoning, 258; and cycles, 52; botulism, 257; caribou, 229; control of, and wildlife destruction, 312; fish, 282; importance, 210; lead poisoning, 258; Northland, 220; South, 210; waterfowl, 256–258
Discretionary power, 353
Discrimination, against non-residents, 322–324; white man, 229, 348–349

Disintegrating shot, 258
Dissolved oxygen, 272
Distribution of Arctic animals, 221–222
District biologists, use of, 358
District of Columbia, 16
Diurnal animals, 33; migrants, 45
Diving ducks, 250; water depth preferred, 261
Division of Ornithology and Mammalogy, 343
Division of power, provincial and federal, 347
Divisions of a game department, 355
Dixon, Joseph S., 172, 192, 247
Dobie, J. R., 283
Doe seasons, 182
Dog counts, pheasants, 119
Dogwood, 16, 133, 150, 153, 166, 185, 191, 210, 301
Domesticated animals, 319
Domestication, of chachalaca, 216; relation to wild, 32
Domestic grazing, 135–136
Dominance, courtship grounds, 30; interspecies, 43; social, 44
Doves, and crop damage, 84
  mourning, 5, 107; flocks, 42; food habits, 30; mobility, 30; winter feeding, 103
  spotted, introduction of, 306
  white-winged, 315
Drainage, acreage, 252; failures, 252; mosquito control, 253; Swamp Land Act of 1850, 252
Drawings and sketches, 85
Drift fence, 181
Drive census, 61, 190; bobwhites, 113; pheasants, 119; rabbits, 122
Dropping counts, 171
Drought, 32, 112, 157, 158, 207, 208, 251, 261; and physiological stress, 52; areas, 253; cycles, 51, 253–254; cottontail affected by, 121; intensity index, 111; valley quail affected by, 115
Drumming logs, 56, 83, 147, 148, 149
Dry does, 182
Dry Tortugas, 50
Duck, black, 250; black duck winter range, 47; counts, 58; eider, 15; fac-

tory, 265; Labrador, 314; mottled, 28, 29, 250, 255; New Mexican, 250; ring-necked, 250; sickness, 256; traps, 269; tree ducks in relation to mottled ducks, 29; wood, 250; wood duck comeback, 313
Duck Stamp Act, 337
Duck stamps, issuance, 337; use of funds, 337
Dude ranches, 12, 136
Dufresne, Frank, 233
Dumping fish in earlier work, 270
Dust baths, 131; mounds, 112, 131; places, 112; sage grouse, 198; snowshoe rabbit, 169
Dwarfing, 148; of conifers, 99
Dyeing birds for identification, 77
Dyes, for marking, 76; to control water plants, 274
Dymond, J. R., 53
Dynamiting, 281

Eagle, 22, 188; bald, 41
Eakin, Henry M., 296
Earmarking license funds, 353–355
Early explorations and fur trading, 234
Early federal laws, 333–334
Ear tags, 78, 79, 238; tattooing, 78, 79
Earthworms, 142, 156, 157, 158; census method, 157
Easement refuges, 268
Ecological factors, 32–34; divisions, 35–36; evidence by photography, 85; unbalance, 33
Ecological succession, in Northland, 219; in South, 210; roadside maintenance, 93, 399; stages of, 34–35
Ecology, 2; fish predation, 278; nongame species, 298; Northland, 218; southern regions, 207
Economic limitations, 4; problems, 3
Economic values, Arctic hare, 227; classification of, 8; general, 7–8
Ecotone, 34
Edaphic conditions, 35
Eddy, Samuel, 283, 296
Edge effect, 34, 130, 132
Edminster, Frank C., 106, 159, 283
Educational programs, 356, 357
Edwards plateau, 57, 60, 289

Eel, 47
Eel grass, 259
Egg collectors, 312
Egg destruction, recognition of weasel and skunk feeding, 241
Eggs, number of, alligator, 209; blue grouse, 142; bobwhite, 108; chachalaca, 209; Franklin grouse, 142; Gambel quail, 196; Hungarian partridge, 108; mountain grouse, 141; pheasant, 108; prairie chicken, 196; rock ptarmigan, 225; ruffed grouse, 142; sage hen, 196; sharp-tailed grouse, 196; spruce grouse, 142; turkey, 142; valley quail, 108; variation with latitude, 37; white-tailed ptarmigan, 225; willow ptarmigan, 225; woodcock, 142
Egret plumes, 334
Eider, American, 250; king, 250; Pacific, 250; spectacled, 250; Steller, 250
Eiderdown, 15
Einersen, Arthur S., 206
Elder, 141, 144, 146, 150
Elderberry, 176, 301
Electric fence, 305
Elephant, 15
Elimination, of bats, 306; of birds from buildings, 307; of flying squirrels, 306; of unwelcome species, 306–307, 308
Elk (wapiti), 24, 163, 175–178, 359; breeding season, 163; carrying capacity, 177; census, 61, 62; census methods, 178; competition with deer, 43; controlled hunting, 177; damage, 177, 178; density, 176; environment, 163; extinction of Arizona elk, 314; food habits, 67, 163, 176–177; forage needs, 177; gestation, 163; habitat requirements, 175–176; key species, 176; management, 176–178; mating, 163; migration, 47, 175, 176; mobility, 160, 176; movements, 176; number of young, 163; open season, 177; palatability, 176; parturition, 163; range, 163; salt licks, 177; salting, 178; Selway Game Preserve, 176; sex ratio, 163, 177; stand, 177;

starvation, 177; summer range, 176; surveys, 67; tolerance, 175; tooth hunting, 313; wallows, 176; water needs, 177; weight, 163; winter feeding, 177; winter range, 176
El lagarto, 215
Ellis, M. M., 296
Ellis, Marion D., 296
Elm, 166
El Nino cycle, 52
Elton, Charles, 36, 53
Elymus glaucus, 176
Emerson, Alfred E., 36, 53
Emergency cover, 96
Emigration, 19, 51, 169; squirrel, 166
Emlen, John T., Jr., 123
Emotional appeals, 5
Empire builder, beaver as, 235
Enabling acts for purchase of federal land, 325
Endocrine, *see* Hormone
Endocrine glands, influence of, 24; light, 33
Enemies, 19, 34; of beaver, 246; of blue grouse, 144, 145; of bobwhite, 113; of caribou, 228; of fish, 278, 281; of mountain quail, 156; of ruffed grouse, 150–151; of songbirds, 303; of waterfowl, 254; of woodcock, 157–158
Energy cycle, 20; resources of Northland, 230; transfer, 20
Enforcement, of federal statutes, 321, 322; of game and fish laws, 360–362; of Migratory Bird Convention Act, 349; of regulations, 357; of will of Congress, 339
England, otter in streams, 241
English Common Law, as basis of American and Canadian Law, 346
Enumeration, 57
Environment, 34; alligator, 209; antelope, 196; Arctic fox, 224; Arctic hare, 225; armadillo, 209; black bear, 162; black-tailed deer, 163; blue grouse, 142; bobwhite, 108; brown bear, 162, 224; caribou, 225; chachalaca, 209; cottontail rabbit, 108; cougar, 209; eyra, 208; forest type, 140; fox squirrel, 163; Franklin grouse, 142; Gambel quail, 196; gray squirrel, 163; grizzly bear, 162; Hungarian partridge, 108; jack rabbit, 196; jaguar, 208; javelina, 209; marsh rabbit, 209; moose, 163; mountain grouse, 142; musk ox, 225; ocelot, 208; opossum, 208; pheasant, 108; polar bear, 224; prairie chicken, 196; ringtail, 208; rock ptarmigan, 225; ruffed grouse, 142; sage hen, 196; sharp-tailed grouse, 196; spruce grouse, 142; swamp rabbit, 209; turkey, 142; valley quail, 108; white sheep, 225; white-tailed deer, 163; white-tailed ptarmigan, 225; willow ptarmigan, 225; woodcock, 142
Environmental manipulation, 2
Environmental resistance, 21, 37–38; and breeding potential, 31; and phase alternations, 40
Epizoötics, 210
Equipment for note taking, 86, 87, 88
Erosion and silt control, 287–288
Errington, Paul L., 36, 53, 123
Escape cover, 96, 98–99, 132; at feeders, 103; tangles, 98, 132, 148; thickets, 132
Eschmeyer, R. W., 275, 283
Eskimos, 227, 228, 229; favored, 248; hunting, 226
Esthetic appreciation, 1, 297
Estimates, 57
Estrus cycles, 39
Euonymus, 150, 166
Europe, marten in parks, 241
Evans, C. A., 172
Evaporation, 33
Even-aged forests, 34, 186
Evidence of feeding, 74–75
Evolutionary adjustment of breeding pressure, 40
Evolutionary age, indications of, 312
Exclosures and inclosures, 56–57
Excluding birds from reservoirs and fish ponds, 306
Exclusive use of property, a right of ownership, 327
Exigencies, 19

Index

Exotics, 107; importation of fish, 270; in new environment, 38; successful introduction of, 183
Expenditures, 10; trout and pan fish, 285
Experimental areas, 83
Extended quadrat, 56
Extinction by biological eclipse, 311–312
Extinction threshold, 38, 312
Extinct species in America, 38, 311, 314; list of, 314
Extirpated species re-establishment, 309
Extraterritorial rights granted Indians, 339
Eye adaptation, 218
Eyesight of forest animals, 41
Eyra, biological data, 208; habitat, 213; habits, 213; range, 213

Facing down of shrubbery, 300
Factors, decimating, 34; influencing productivity, 31; welfare, 34; winter feeding, 105
Failure of exotics, 39
Falcon, aplomado, 315
  peregrine, 315; nesting on buildings, 315; pigeon control, 315; protection, 315
Falconiformes, reduction in number, 314
Fall census, 58
Fall food-patch plants, 101
Farallons, 50
Farm fish ponds, 210, 282–283; construction, 282; species, 282; stocking, 270, 282; yield of fish, 283
Farm game management, 91–123; biological table, 108; birds and mammals, 107–123
Farm practices and changed conditions, 91–95
Farmer-sportsmen cooperatives, 12
Farming operations, 91; South, 211
Fassett, Norman, 269, 283
Fat, Arctic animals, 219; deposition, 48; dorsal, of caribou, 211; polar bear, 226; sequence of utilization, 358; supply of Northern animals, 221

Feather identification, 80–81; marking, 76
Feces analysis, 81
Feces counts, rabbits, 122
Federal activities, agencies, 342–344; aid to states, 337–338; expansion of, 342; powers, Canada, origin of, 333; powers, United States, origin of, 333; prohibitions, 334–335; refuge law, 334; sphere, Canada, 349–350; sphere, United States, 333–345; types, 338–339; wildlife controls in the United States, 333–345
Federal government, created by former colonies, 318
Federal lands, denial of use for hunting, 322, 325
Federal wardens, 361
Feeding stations, 96, 99, 100, 102–105, 167, 202, 285, 300; counts, pheasants, 119; hoppers, 200; Hungarian partridge, 110; pheasants, 118; platform, 200
Fees, 3, 9
Felis, cacomitli, see Eyra; *concolor*, see Cougar; *onca*, see Jaguar; *pardalis*, see Ocelot; range, 27
Fence, cat-proof, 304; electric, 305
Fence laws, 194
Fence rows, 92, 93
Fencing, 95, 153, 182; exclosures, 56
Ferae naturae, 320, 321, 322, 323, 324, 326; definition, 319; ownership in Indian reservations and national parks, 342; state ownership, 319–320
Feral animals, definition, 319; ownership, 319
Fericology, 2
Fericulture, 2
Fern, 146, 170
Ferret, black-footed, 315
Fertility, 15; and fish production, 276; and sea water, 33
Fertilizing lakes, 273
Fescue-wheat grass zone, 35
Feterita, 101, 102
Field collecting, 86; see also Preserving and collecting
Field experimentation, 82–83
Field notes, 86–88

Field observation, 81–82
Fields, H. R., 332, 345
Financial support of game departments, 353–355
Finch, purple, 16
Fir, 141, 144, 146, 147, 161, 180
  Douglas, 16, 23, 144; zone, 35; seeding, 132
Fire, use of, *see* Controlled burning
Fire conditions in succession, 35
Fire hazard, 130; conifers, 133; hardwoods, 133
Fire lanes, 131, 186
Firing lines, 132
First-class forest sites, 128
Fish, 124, 125, 174; and the population curve, 38; awareness of disturbance, 273; catch limits, 281; census, 63; control, 270; counting houses, 289; culture and planting of, 270; enemies, 281; general management methods, 270; growth in relation to food, 276; hatcheries, expansion period, 270; hatchery requirements, 271; loss in irrigation ditches, 293; management, 1; marking, 280; migration, 46, 47; population, gathering data on, 279–280; preventing movements of, 293; production, and temperature, 276; production, of northern and southern waters, 276; scales, 64; screens, 294; senses, 273
Fish and Wildlife Service, 77; directors, 344; organization, 342–343
Fish shelters, 275; brush piles, 274; natural, 273; supplying, 272–274; tree tops, 274
Fished-out lakes, 282
Fisher, 21, 235; den, 237; extirpation, 241; habitat, 236; tolerance, 235
Fishing, by brown bear, 226; in streams, 327; methods prohibited, 281–282; year-round, 295
Fishing and hunting derbies, control of, 14, 281; policy toward, 281
Fishing regulations, paralleling hunting regulations, 282
Fishways, at dams, 293; conveyor, 293; elevators, 293, 294; ladder, 293, 294; transport in trucks, 293

Fixed-unit count, 55
Flash guns, 305
Flicker, yellow-shafted, 15; number of food items, 22
Flies, black, 220
Flight power, rock ptarmigan, 231
Flight years, 51; northern birds, 40
Floating covers, 291
Floating devices, for fish management, 274
Flock counts, 154; counting birds, 58; counting method, 269; habits, 43; minimum size, 39; size, 42; size and security, 39; size, reactions of small flocks, 39
Flocking, inception of, 42
Flocking habits, 41–42; by sex and age, 42–43; forest birds, 140
Flocks, American raven, 42; blue goose, 43; bovine, 42; brown creeper, 43; cat family, 42; chickadee, 43; downy woodpecker, 43; forest birds, 140; Fringillidae, 43; Hungarian partridge, 109; Icteridae, 43; icterids, 42; interspecies, 43; merganser, 42; migratory bird, 42; mourning dove, 42; nuthatch, 43; Parulidae, 43; passenger pigeon, 42; prairie chicken, 43, 199; ruffed grouse, 43; scaup duck, 42; sedentary birds, 42; sharp-tailed grouse, 43; snow goose, 43; turkey, 153; white-necked raven, 42; white sheep, 231; wren family, 42
Floods, and muskrats, 247; and stream fish, 287
Florida, 16, 152, 164, 173, 183, 216; destruction of deer in disease control, 312
Fluctuating water levels, 277
Fluke, 213
Flush counts, bobwhite, 13; Hungarian partridge, 110
Flushing, 158, 190
Flushing bar, 93, 109, 119
Flushing distance, 59–60, 151, 171
Flushing hole-nesting birds, 75
Fly fishing as "highest use," 285
Fly season, effect on caribou herds, 228
Flyways, 45, 252; Atlantic, 252; Central, 252; Mississippi, 252; Pacific, 252

Index

Food and cover conditions, 358 (*see also* Improving food and cover); and shelter, 19–20; Arctic supply, 220; for attracting birds, 301; hot-weather, 23; items, number of, 22; loss of plants to drainage, 254; needs of animals, 22–24; on farms, 95–96; quality, 24; quantity, 22–23; recognition of differences by wildlife, 24; requirements of body, 24; shortage, 150; types used by farm game, 92–93; use, 141

Food-bearing trees, 133

Food borders, 131

Food chains, 20; place of forage fish, 276

Food fishes, 7

Food habits, 82; alligator, 209, 215; American eider, 259; American golden-eye, 259; antelope, 196, 204; Arctic fox, 224; Arctic hare, 225, 227; armadillo, 209, 215; badger, 240; Barrow golden-eye, 259; beaver, 243; bison, 22; black bear, 162, 174; black-tailed deer, 163, 180; blue grouse, 143–144; bobwhite, 108, 112; brown bear, 162, 223, 224, 226; bufflehead, 259; canvasback, 259; caribou, 225, 228; chachalaca, 209; cottontail rabbit, 108, 121; cougar, 209; dabbling duck, 260; deer, 22; diving duck, 259, 260; elk, 67, 163, 176–177; eyra, 208; fox squirrel, 163; Franklin grouse, 142; Gambel quail, 196; goose, 259; gray fox, 242; gray squirrel, 163; greater scaup, 259; grizzly bear, 162; harlequin, 259; herbivores, 22; Hungarian partridge, 108, 109; jack rabbit, 196; jaguar, 208; javelina, 209, 214; king eider, 259; lesser scaup, 259; lynx, 242; marsh rabbit, 209; mergansers, 259; mink, 241; moose, 67, 163, 191; mountain quail, 142, 156; musk ox, 225, 229; muskrat, 246; northern eider, 259; ocelot, 208; old squaw, 259; opossum, 208, 211, 212; otter, 240; Pacific eider, 259; pheasant, 108; polar bear, 224, 226; prairie chicken, 196, 199; ptarmigan, 232; raccoon, 240; red fox, 242; redhead, 259; research, 64, 81; ring-necked duck, 259; ringtail, 208; rock ptarmigan, 225; ruddy, 259; ruffed grouse, 142, 147, 149, 150; sage hen, 196, 198; sharp-tailed grouse, 196, 202; snowshoe rabbit, 170; spruce grouse, 142; Steller eider, 259; surf scoter, 259; swamp rabbit, 209, 213; swan, 259; turkey, 142, 153; valley quail, 108; waterfowl, habits of, 258–260; weasel family, 240; white sheep, 225; white-tailed deer, 163, 185–187; white-tailed ptarmigan, 225; white-winged scoter, 259; wildcat, 242; willow ptarmigan, 225; woodcock, 142, 156, 157

Food patches, 96, 99, 100–102, 153, 167, 202, 301; exhaustion, 101; Hungarian partridge, 110; mixtures, 102; pheasants, 118; plants, 101; prairie chicken, 200; size, 100, 200; sowing, 101; success, 100; valley quail, 116

Food plants for birds, 300–301

Food supply to increase fish production, 276

Food web, 20

Fool hen, 146

Forage, 160; acre, 66; and range capacity determination, 64; black-tailed deer, 181; census, 182; condition, 181; determination, 64–65; division, between stock and big game, 136; preference, 160; requirement, 66, 182

Forage fish, 283; role of, 276

Forbs, 180, 184, 191

Forest, all-age classes, 166; animals, keenness of senses, 41; big-game, 173–193; canopy, 20; carrying capacity, 132; dependent species, 124, 125; even-age, 166, 186; fires, 1; game mammals, biology table, 162–163; game mammal management, 160–193; grazing, 135; openings, 130, 131; products, 129; recommended future status, 129; single species, 166; types, 141

Forest area, 129–130

Forest conservation rise and game-warden agencies, 351
Foresters and game needs, 136
Forest game birds, biological requirements, 140, 142; distribution, 140; instinctive needs, 140; range essentials, 140; reserves, 344; topography, 140
Forest Reserve Commission, 337
Forestry, 1, 2; and wildlife management, 124–139; Arctic, 223; general considerations, 130–132; modifications for wildlife, 128; practices and wildlife, 128
Forest Service, 11, 137, 138; Division of Wildlife Management, 344; origin, 344
Forest wildlife, definition, 124; needs, 124
Forget-me-not, 15
Forms, for field notes, 87; hunting, 83; multiple-copy, 87
rabbit, 120, 121; counts of, 62, 122; snowshoe rabbit, 169
Formula, drought intensity index, 111; for forage-acre factor, 66; forage-acre requirement, 67; grid census, 59; live-dressed weight, 164; populations, 31, 38; proper-use factor, 66; range carrying capacity, 67; range carrying numbers, 67; winter hardness test, 111
Fox, 22; den, 237; den counts, 59; fur value, 242; hunting as a higher form of use, 242; hunting versus trapping, 242; instinctive reactions of, 27
Arctic, 226–227; biological data, 224; color phases, 227; cycles, 227; distribution, 222; economic value, 227; fur, 227; habitat, 236; habits, 226; movements, 227; pelage, 226; range, 226
blue, 227
gray, 241–242; density, 242; food, 242; habitat, 236; predation of, 242; range, 241; tolerance of man, 242
kit, 315

Fox, red, 241–242; density, 242; food, 242; habitat, 236; predation of, 242; range, 241; tolerance to man, 242
Foxtail, 100, 112
Frauds, statute of, 329
"Free" hunting, 3; a political right, 325–326
Freezing to death, 25–26
Frequency of occurrence, 55, 190
Freshwater fishes, 6
Frightening birds from crops, 305
Fringillidae, species association, 43
Frost, Edward M., 206
Fungi, 166, 180
Fungus diseases in South, 210
Fur, see name of animal; Arctic fox, 227; badger, 240; nutria, 50; opossum, 212; ringtail, 212; wildcat, 242
Fur abundance, 237; change in emphasis, 234, 235; examination at fur houses, 236; low-value pelts, 235; primeness, 237; quotations, fictitious, 239; reports, 236; resources, Northland, 223; royalty, 240; size, 237; surveys, 237, 238
Fur bearers, 6; decline in numbers, 234–235; gathering data, 236–238; habitat requirements, 235–236; home sites, 235–236; management, 1, 234–248; predatory, 238–239; protection, 234, 239–240; relation to other animals, 238–239; seasons, 239; sign, 237, 238; tolerance, 235
Fur farming, 234
Fur seal, 316
Fur trade, 234

Gabrielson, Ira N., 17, 269, 283, 296, 344, 345, 351, 363
Gadwall, 250
Galliformes, feeding time, 115
Gallinaceous guzzlers, 116
Gallinule, 249; Florida, 250; purple, 250
Game, and food animals defined, 319; damage by, 359; food and cover for, 95–96; number of species of, 6, 7; open-range management, 194–206;

Index

quality, decline of, 107; refuges for, on federal lands, 325
Game area, 17; cooperative, 17; farms, 1; management, 1; management area, 17; pools, 12, 17; stands, 37; survey, 54
Game birds of the forest, 140–159
Game commission, 352
Game departments, as public administrative bodies, 354; attitudes toward non-game species, 363; attitudes toward non-hunting and non-fishing public, 363; divisions of, 355, 356; inefficiency of, 351; power of, 352 (*see also* State powers); use of funds, 354
Game management of the open range, 194–206
Game warden, *see* Warden
Game ways, 102
Gar, 278; food, 286; range, 286; spawning, 286
Gates, Frank C., 69
Gathering of information and technical skill, 358
Gaultheria shallon, *see* Salal
Gaylussacia, *see* Huckleberry
Geese, 62; migration, 46
Genetic variations, 37
Geographic variations, of broods, 37; litters, 37; number of eggs, 37
Georgia, 16; controlled burning, 134
Gerstell, Richard, 106, 247, 363
Gestation period, antelope, 196; Arctic fox, 254; Arctic hare, 225; armadillo, 209; black bear, 162; black-tailed deer, 163; brown bear, 162, 224; caribou, 225; cottontail rabbit, 108; cougar, 209; elk, 163; eyra, 208; fox squirrel, 163; grizzly bear, 162; jack rabbit, 196; jaguar, 208; javelina, 209; marsh rabbit, 209; moose, 163; musk ox, 225; ocelot, 208; opossum, 208; polar bear, 224; ringtail, 208; swamp rabbit, 209; white sheep, 225; white-tailed deer, 163
Gigging, 281
Giles, LeRoy W., 216
Girard, George L., 206

Girdling, 75, 167, 170; identification of, 75
Glading, Ben, 106, 123, 206, 216
Goat, mountain, 316
Goat's rue, 132
Goldeneye, American, 250; Barrow, 250
Goldenrod, 15
Goldfinch, 16, 22, 40
Goldman, Edward A., 317
"Good" and "bad" animals, 3
Goode, G. Brown, 343
Goodrum, Phil, 172
Goose, blue, 43, 249; species association, 43
  Canada, 249; migration, 45
  emperor, 249
  Ross, 249, 315
  snow, 43, 249; species association, 43
  white-fronted, 249
Gooseberry, 144
Gordon, Seth, 364
Gordon, Seth, Jr., 17, 69
Gorsuch, David N., 123
Goshawk, 151, 171; predation, 97
Government, functions of, 356–357
Grackle, and squirrel relations, 166
Graham, Edward H., 17, 106, 331
Grain, amount eaten, 105; kinds of, in winter feeding, 104; preventing waste of, at feeding stations, 102
Grand Banks fishing, 333
Grand Manan bird island, 50
Grange, Wallace B., 17, 36, 53, 92, 93, 106, 123, 138, 141, 159, 161, 172, 192, 206, 331, 364
Grant of hunting and fishing rights, 329
Grape, 98, 141, 147, 150, 152, 153, 161, 166, 301; tangles, 166
Grass, panic, 132; paspolium, 132; seed, 100
Grasshoppers, 22, 153
Grassland environment, 34
Grayling, Michigan, extinction, 314; extinction threshold, 312
Grazing, 128, 135; capacity, 67, 181; rights, 10
Grazing service, 344
Great Lakes, 50, 211, 240
Great Salt Lake, 50

384   Index

Great Slave Lake, 230
Grebe, 249; botulism, 256
Greeley, John R., 296
Green, R. G., 172
Greenbrier, 141, 150, 161
Green Island, 50
Greenland, 227, 229, 230, 231
Greenland hare, 227; incisors, 227
Gregariousness, see Flocking, Flocks; caribou, 228; deer, 160; javelina, 214
Grid census system, 59–60
Gridiron reconnaissance. 66
Grinnell, Joseph, 138, 159, 172, 247
Grit, 103, 131, 149, 202; amount, 115; bobwhite, 113; general rule, 115; pheasants, 118; sources of, 131; supply, 103; valley quail, 115
Grizzly, California, extinction, 314
Grosbeaks, 40; rose-breasted, 16
Ground crews and airplane counts, 62
Ground hemlock, 191
Groundhog, see Woodchuck
Group selection, 186
Grouse, black, 143; adaptation, 143
   blue, 143–145; broods, 43; cycles, 145; deferred maturity in, 30; enemies, 144, 145; environment, 142; food habits, 23, 25, 142, 143–144; habitat requirement, 143; improving food and cover, 144–145; incubation, 142; mating, 142; migration, 143; mortality, 145; nesting, 143; nesting season, 142; nest losses, 145; number of eggs, 142; protection, 144, 145; range, 142, 143; sex ratio, 142; snowshoes, 143; species association, 43; species groups, 44; use of forest, 141; water, 143, 145; weight, 142; wintering habits, 144
   dusky, see Grouse, blue
   Franklin, 145–146; environment, 142; food habits, 142, 146; habitat requirement, 145; incubation, 142; mating, 142; nesting habits, 145; nesting season, 142; number of eggs, 142; protection, 146; range, 142, 145; sex ratio, 142; use of forest, 141; weight, 142

Grouse, pinnated, see Prairie chicken
   red, 231; loss of white winter plumage, 231
   Richardson's, see Grouse, blue
   ruffed, 16, 83, 143, 146–152, 156; accidents, 150; birch seeds, 147; brood, 43; brood cover, 147; census methods, 59–60, 151–152; cold, 150; conifer plantations, 132; cycles, 50–51, 127, 146, 151; density, 127, 146, 148; disease, 151; enemies, 150–151; environment, 142; feeding stations, 149; food habits, 142, 147, 149–150; food plants, 150; grit, 149; habitat requirements, 146–147; habits, 133; improving food and cover, 148–150; incubation, 142; instructive behavior pattern, 28; juvenile mortality, 151; marking, 152; mating, 142; minimum area, 39; molting cover, 147; nest, 72; nest destruction, 150; nesting, 147; nesting season, 142; number of eggs, 142; parasites, 151; predation, 150; predator control, 150; protection, 150; range, 142, 146; refuges, 151; roosting, 147; sampling populations, 56; saturation point, 146; seasons, 151; sexing, 152; sex ratio, 142; snow, 147; species association, 43; starvation, 150; territory, 147; trapping, 152; use of forest, 141; water needs, 149; weight, 142; wind, 147; winter cover, 147
   sage, 195–198, 315; breeding season, 196; census methods, 198; dancing grounds, 198; deferred maturity, 198; diet, 198; dusting, 198; environment, 196; flocks, 198; food habits, 196, 198; habitat requirements, 198; hatching, 196; incubation, 196; instinctive behavior pattern, 28; mating, 196, 198; mating by only a few males, 198; number of eggs, 196; promiscuity, 30; range, 195, 196, 197; sex ratio, 196, 198; water needs, 198; weight, 196

Index

Grouse, sharp-tailed, 16, 194, 199, 201–203; breeding season, 196; broods, 43; census methods, 63, 203; dancing grounds, 202; environment, 196; food consumption, 105; food habits, 22, 23, 25, 196, 202; food need, 202; food patches, 202; grit, 202; habitat requirements, 201–202; habits, 133; hatching, 196; improving food and cover, 202; incubation, 196; marking, 202; mating, 196; migration, 201; night roosting, 202; number of eggs, 196; range, 196; sex ratio, 196; species association, 43; trapping, 203; water needs, 203; weight, 196; winter feeding, 103, 202

sooty, see Grouse, blue

spruce, 145–146; environment, 142; food habits, 142, 146; habitat requirement, 145; habits, 143; incubation, 142; mating, 142; nesting habits, 145; nesting season, 142; number of eggs, 142; protection, 146; range, 142, 145; sex ratio, 142; specialization, 140; use of forest, 141; weight, 142

Growth, 40; and body weight standards, 26; determinant, 40; indeterminant, 26, 40, 41

Growth rate, 40–41; determinations, 64; determination from scales, 280; use of studies, 279

Guano, 15; birds, 15, 50; cycle, 51; industry, 15

Guides to migration, 46

Guiding and guide hunting, 9, 231

Gulf Coast, 100, 252

Gulf of Mexico, 242

Gull, 16, 298, 310; botulism, 256; islands, 298

Gum, 153, 166, 167

Guns, loaded, in car, 107

Habit, 3; action of, 28; and foods eaten, 24–25; and tradition, 28; and water conservation, 24; definition of, 28; knowledge of, 2; solitary, 41

Habitable territory, 4

Habitat, 4; choice and instinctive patterns, 28; destruction of fur bearer, 234; forest game, 160; open, 41; preference, reduction of, 362; relations and cycles, 51; roadside, 93

Habitat requirements, antelope, 203; Arctic fox, 236; beaver, 236, 242; black bear, 173–174; black-tailed deer, 179; bobwhite, 110–112; chachalaca, 216; coyote, 236; elk, 175–176; eyra, 213; fisher, 236; fur bearers, 235–236; fur seal, 236; gray and fox squirrels, 164–165; jaguar, 213, 214; lynx, 236; marsh rabbit, 214; marten, 236; mink, 236, 241; moose, 190–191; mountain quail, 155; muskrat, 236, 246; ocelot, 213; opossum, 211, 236; otter, 236; pheasant, 117; prairie chicken, 199–200; raccoon, 236, 240; ringtail, 212; sage grouse, 198; sea otter, 236; sharp-tailed grouse, 201–202; skunk, 236; snowshoe rabbit, 168–169; turkey, 152; valley quail, 114; weasel, 236; white-tailed deer, 183; wildcat, 236; wolf, 236; wolverine, 236; woodcock, 156–157

Habits, Arctic fox, 226; Arctic hare, 227; badger, 236, 240; chachalaca, 216; gray fox, 236; javelina, 214; marsh rabbit, 214; mink, 241; ptarmigan, 231, 232; red fox, 236; valley quail, 114; white sheep, 230

Hadwen, Seymour, 233

Hair and feather identification, 80–81

Half-cutting limbs, 98

Hamerstrom, F. N., Sr., 69, 89, 123, 238, 247

Hamilton, W. J., Jr., 36, 138, 172, 192, 216, 233, 247

Handling trapped big game, 204

Hanson Refuge, 183

Hardness test for winter, 111

Hardwood, 141, 146, 147, 161, 162, 163, 236

Hare, Arctic, 227; biological data, 224; cycles, 227; economic value, 227; food, 227; habits, 227; pelage, 227; range, 227; reduction of ear size, 27

386   Index

Hare, snowshoe or varying, see Rabbit, snowshoe
Harlequin, 250
"Harmless" species, number of, 6, 7
Hatch, A. B., 364
Hatcheries, 1
Hatchery stock and disease spread, 282
Hatching success, 358
Hatching season, alligator, 209; bobwhite, 108; chachalaca, 209; Gambel quail, 196; Hungarian partridge, 108; pheasant, 108; prairie chicken, 196; rock ptarmigan, 225; sage hen, 196; sharp-tailed grouse, 196; valley quail, 108; white-tailed ptarmigan, 225; willow ptarmigan, 225
Havemeyer, Loomis, 17
Hawaii, 16
Hawk, broad-winged, 42; Cooper, 47; destruction of, 313; duck, see Peregrine falcon; Harris, 315; Mexican black, 315; migration, 42; mountain sanctuary, 315; Sennett, white-tailed, 315; sharp-shinned, 47; short-tailed, 315; Swainson, 42
Hawkins, Arthur S., 105, 123
Hawley, Ralph C., 138
Hawthorn, 16, 133, 300
Hayden, Sherman S., 345
Hayfield nests, 94
Hazel, 147, 150, 166, 191, 299
Heat balance, 26; production, 25–26; conservation and radiation, 23
Heat distress, symptoms of, 52
Heath hen, 199; extinction, 314; extinction threshold, 38, 312
Heavy fishing, to prevent overpopulation in farm ponds, 283
Hedges and hedge rows, 92, 93
Hegari, 101, 102
Hemlock, 16
Hemp, 102
Henderson, Junius, 17, 310, 317
Henshaw, Henry W., 344
Herbage, 162, 163, 180, 184, 196, 209, 225
Herbivores, 20, 21; amount of food needed, 24; cycles, 51; forage requirements, 64; promiscuity, 30

Herbivorous foods, calories of, 22–23
Herding, see Gregariousness
Heron, 298; botulism of, 256; great white, protection, 314, 315
Hesse, Richard W., 36
Hewitt, C. Gordon, 233, 350
Hibernation, and aestivation, 47–48; and fat deposition, 24; and light, 33; black bear, 174; food of mammals in, 221; polar bear, 226
Hibiscus, 16
Hickey, Joseph, 89
Hickie, Paul, 123
Hickory, 165, 166
High plains, 253
High water, 287
Highway, species killed most on, 307
Hill, R. G., 364
Hillcourt, William, 17, 69
Hochbaum, H. Albert, 269
Hole-nesting birds, interspecies strife, 29; censuses, 63
Hollow logs, used for dens, 237
Hollow square shelter, 225
Hollow trees, 211, 237
Holly, 16, 133, 150, 301
Holt, Ernest G., 106
Home range, 29; cottontail rabbit, 120; snowshoe rabbit, 169; white-tailed deer, 183
Homoiothermous, definition of, 32
Honess, Ralph F., 206
Honeysuckle, 191
Hook and line, inefficiency of, compared with gun, 282
Hopper, 102, 103, 104
Hormones, and fat deposition, 24, 48; gregariousness, 42; light, 24, 33; migration, 45
Hornaday, W. T., 197, 317
Horton Creek, Arizona, 11
Hosley, Neil, 138
Hours afield in hunting, 10
Hubbs, Carl L., 275, 283, 296
Huckleberry, 150, 153, 166, 185
Hudson Bay, 250
Humanitarian appeals, 5
Humid conditions and animal life, 33
Humidity, 32, 33, 207, 208

Index

Hunters, claims upon game resources, 326; testimony of, 358
Hunting, along streams, 327; and fishing, as outdoor recreation, 363; attitudes and policies of game departments, 362–363; for sport and trophies, 312; from aircraft, 336; in Mexico, 252; subject to police power, 321; upon federal lands, 338–340
Hunting camps, 11; grounds, 4
Hunting rights in the land, 325–327, 328
Hunting season, determining proper time and length, 357–358
Hydrosere succession, 35

Ibis, glossy, 315; eggs, 312
I.B.M. tabulation cards, 87
Ice encrustments on body, 25
Iceland, 15
Icterids, flocks, 42; species association, 43
Idaho, 16, 196, 197
Ideas and counting, 54
Ilex, 301
Illegal kill, deer, 182, 188
Illinois, 16, 213
Imler, Ralph H., 317
Immature classes and predation, 21
Impervious core, 157
Impoundable water, 4
Improvements, for hunters, 138; for lake fish, 270–284; for stream fish, 285–296
Improving food and cover, black-tailed deer, 180–181; blue grouse, 144–145; bobwhite, 112; cottontails, 121–122; fox and gray squirrel, 166–167; moose, 191–192; mountain quail, 156; pheasants, 118; prairie chicken, 200; ruffed grouse, 148–150; sharp-tailed grouse, 202; snowshoe rabbit, 170; turkey, 153; valley quail, 115–116; waterfowl, 264; white-tailed deer, 186–187; woodcock, 157
Inclosures, 56–57
Income, direct, 9–10; indirect, 9; from leasing, 10, 11; recreational, 9
Increasing food, by changing water levels, 276; by mast, 130; oxygen in lakes, 279

Increment borings, 86
Incubation period, bobwhite, 108; alligator, 209; blue grouse, 142; chachalaca, 209; Franklin grouse, 142; Gambel quail, 196; Hungarian partridge, 108; mountain quail, 142; pheasant, 108; prairie chicken, 196; ruffed grouse, 142; rock ptarmigan, 225; sage hen, 196; sharp-tailed grouse, 196; spruce grouse, 142; turkey, 142; valley quail, 108; white-tailed ptarmigan, 225; willow ptarmigan, 225; woodcock, 142
Indeterminant growth, 40–41
Index, of drought intensity, 111; of hard winters, 111
India, tiger census, 63
Indiana, 16
Indian lands, difficulty of conservation, 342; prohibition of hunting, 333
Indian reservations, and miscellaneous federal lands, 340–342; and state laws, 340; ownership of game, 342
Indians, 8, 128, 228, 229; extraterritorial rights, 339; favored, 348; held in virtual federal peonage, 342; lack of civil rights, 342; racial autonomy, 339; special fishing privileges, 339; special privileges, 341; treaties with, and acts of Congress, 341
Indian sites as game indicators, 127
Injurious species, number of, 6, 7
Inks for note taking, 87
Innate patterns, 27
Innis, Harold A., 248, 350
Inroads of settlement, 312
Insects, 74
Insectivores, amount of food needed, 24
Insectivorous birds, 22; of the forest, 126
Insolation, in relation to altitude and latitude, 34
Instinct, cover needs of bobwhite, 111; feeding, 27; food responses, 25; food selection, 24, 258; meat eating, 27; needs, 19, 27, 140; preying, 27; reactions to cold, 26; requirements for shelter, 27; size balance, 39

Instinctive behavior pattern, 19; bass, 27; fish, 273; musk ox, 229; ptarmigan, 232; security, 20; sharp-tailed grouse, 202
Internal adjustment factors, 37-38
International Ornithological Congress, 298
International protection of sea mammals, 316
International Zoological Congress, 298
Interpreting sign, 71
Interrelation of cycles, 51-52
Interspecies dominance, 43; flocks, 43; strife, 29
Interspersion, 34, 116, 132
Interstate commerce, 333
Interstate shipment of game, prohibition of, 323
Interviews, 10
Intestinal worms, 24
Intolerance and evolutionary age, 312
Introduced species, 306
Introduction, and species groups, 45, 306; antelope, 204; bobwhite, 110; Hungarian partridge, 107; valley quail, 114
Invasion, ptarmigan, 231
Inventory methods, 53
Inverse relationships, 40
Investigation of complaints, 88
Iowa, 16, 60, 250
Iris, 16
Ironwood, 133, 150, 153
Irreversible nature of succession, 34
Irrigation ditches, 182; screening, 293
Irruptions, deer, 181
Islands, as inclosures, 57
Isle Royale, 191
Isolated remnants and survival, 39
Ivory, 15

Jack lighting, 281
Jackson, C. F., 310
Jackson, Hartley H. T., 233
Jaguar, biological data, 208; damage claims, 213; food, 213; habitat, 213; habits, 213; range, 213
Javelina, 214; biological data, 209; economic use, 214; food habits, 214; gregariousness, 214; habitat, 214; habits, 214; predators, 213
Jessamine, 13
Jetties, 278
Junco, slate-colored, concentration area, 47
Junipers, 300
Juniperus ashei and apple rust, 300
Jurisdiction, of the state overall land, 318; over Indian reservations, national parks, and military reservations, 319
Juvenile mortality, 158

Kaffir, 102
Kaibab deer case, 340
Kalmbach, E. R., 89, 216, 269, 310
Kalmeia, see Laurel
Kansas, 16
Kelker, G. H., 192
Kennedy, W. P. M., 350
Kentucky, 16
Kestrel, 22
Keys, hair and feather, 80
Keysort cards, 87
Key species, 65; black-tailed deer, 181; elk, 176; shifting over range, 25
Kill evidence, 72
King census method for ruffed grouse, 59-60, 151
King of Beasts, 223
King of Canada, 297, 335
Kingfisher, destruction of, 313
Kite, eggs, 312; everglade, 315; Mississippi, 315; reduction in number, 314; swallow-tailed, 315; white-tailed, 315
Knapp, Frank T., 286
Korstian, Clarence F., 139
Kortright, Francis H., 269
Krefting, Laurits W., 192
Kyle, H. M., 36

Laboratory experimentation, 82
Labrador, 15, 145, 146, 168, 173, 226, 228, 250
Lacey Act (1900), 334; enforcement, 343
Lagler, Karl F., 283, 296
Lagopus leucurus, mutus, rupestris, see Ptarmigan

Index

Lake fish management and improvement, 270–284
Lake Michigan, 39; water levels at Milwaukee, 254
Lake states, 253
Lake surveys, 271–272; carbon dioxide, 272; chemical analysis, 272; dissolved oxygen, 272; map symbols, 272; maps, 272; pH of water, 272
La Monte, Francesca, 283, 296
Land, changes, 3; kept on tax rolls, 267; utilization, 2
Landowner permission laws, 240
Landowner rights, 3, 13
Land pools, 12; rental, 9, 10–11; rental value, 11
Larch, 144, 146; see also Tamarack
Larix, see Tamarack, Larch
Lauckhart, Burton, 180
Laurel, 150; mountain, 16, 185; toxic effects of, 24
Laws, 2; enforcement, 360–362; enforcement simplified by state monopoly of beaver trapping, 246; uniform application of, to all land, 322
Lay, Daniel W., 123
Leading bird foods, 301
Lead poisoning, 258; cause, 258; prevention, 250; treatment, 258
Lead shot, and X-ray or fluoroscope, 266
Leasing land for hunting and fishing, 10–11
Lechuguilla, 214
Legislatures, and game administration, 352; determination of state policy, 354–355; regulations, 352
Legumes, 112, 115
Lehman, Valgene W., 123, 206
Lemming cycle, 22, 227
Leopold, Aldo, 17, 36, 53, 54, 69, 89, 101, 106, 111, 123, 192, 364
Lepus, see Rabbit; *americanus*, see Rabbit, snowshoe; *arcticus*, see Hare, Arctic; *bairdii*, see Rabbit, snowshoe; *groenlandicus*, see Greenland hare; *washingtonii*, see Rabbit, snowshoe
Lespedeza, 132, 153, 210; use of, 210
Lethal openings, protection from, 97
Leucocytozoan bonasa, 151

Lewis mock orange, 16
License fee, 13
License money, 4; public policy aspects, 354
Licenses, 3, 4, 9, 14; cats, 303; denying to chronic offenders, 331; examinations for, 331; federal duck stamp, 331; first in Virginia Colony (1631), 330; local, 331; need of license tests, 353; New Jersey (1719), 331; non-residents, 323; North Carolina (1795), 331; number of, 10; public money, 354; qualifications to hold, 331; special, 359; to control overhunting, 265; to raise money, 330; trapping, 239
License system, 353; growth of, 330–331; state controls, 329–330; warden system, 329–330
Lichen, 180, 184
Life essentials and carrying capacity, 31
Life hazards and breeding potential, 40
Life zones, 35
Light-gathering power of binoculars, 84
Light penetration, 64
Ligon, J. Stokley, 159, 216
Lilac, 16
Lime, for control of acid water, 273
Limitations, of numbers by territory demands, 28; right to hunt, 326; saturation point, 31, 32; space for animals in the wild, 38; to management, 4
Limited license, 330
Limiting factors, 362–363
Limit of Trees, 164, 219, 226, 229, 242
Limits, body temperature, 32; population, 3; range, 4; renewability, 312; size of food, 21–22; structural, 22
Limpkin eggs, 313
Lincoln, Frederick C., 89, 216
Lincoln index, 59, 269
Linsdale, Jean M., 172, 247, 310
Litters, variation with latitude, 37
Live traps, 182
Living snow fences, 300
Lloyd, Hoyes, 350
Loaded guns in car, 107
Local cycles, 52
Lodges, hunting, 11

Logging, 132
Lophortyx californica, see Quail, valley; *gambeli, see* Quail, Gambel
Lopping limbs, 98, 148; conifers, 99
Lord Proprietor, 320
Loss, of title to game, 327; of vigor, 19; of young waterfowl, 254
Lotka, A. J., 53
Louisiana, 16, 50, 199, 214, 216, 323, 346
Lower California, 114
Low reproduction, 19
Lutz, Harold J., 138
Lynx, 188; and bobcat, 242; cycle, 242; den, 237; food habits, 242; fur value, 242; habitat, 236; protection, 242; range, 27, 242; tolerance, 235
Lyrurus, 143

Macaw, extinction of Cuban tricolored, 314; Gosse, 314; Guadeloupe, 314
Mackenzie Delta, 250
MacLulich, D. A., 53, 172
Macrocycles, 51
Magna Charta, 320
Magnolia, 16, 133
Mail-order research, 83, 236
Maine, 16, 145, 152, 305, 329
Maize, 153
Mallard, 47, 250; number of food items, 22; winter range, 47
Mammals, 6, 125; *see also* name of mammal
Management operations, *see* Improving food and cover; elk, 176–178; muskrat, 246; pine areas, 131; pocket gophers, 20
Manatee, 312, 315
Mangels, Frederick P., 89
Manipulations in field study, 83
Manitoba, 49, 156, 178, 203, 250, 349
Manzanita, 144
Maple, 16, 150, 166, 176, 185, 191
Mapping, 67–69; fur survey, 237; fur survey symbols, 238; plane table, 272
Maps, base, 68; contour, 68; cover, 68; for lake survey, 272; outline, 68; size, 69; soil, 68; symbols, 68; topographic, 69
Margin of safety, 5

Marine mammal breeding grounds, 50
Maritime provinces, 250
Market hunting, 9
Marking game to show ownership, 326
Marking methods, 76–79 (*see also* name of animal); beaver, 79; day-old birds, 78; fish, 77, 280; fur bearers, 238; incubating birds, 76; prairie chicken, 201; rabbits, 79, 122; ruffed grouse, 152; to determine territory, 29; use of airplane dopes, 76
Marsh control, 263; ecology, 253
Marshes, muskrat, 11; ungrazed, 93; waterfowl, 11
Marsupials, 211
Marten, 21, 235; den, 237; extirpation, 241; tolerance to man, 235, 241
Martin, 63, 304
Martin, A. C., 269
Maryland, 16
Massachusetts, 16
Mass data, 83
Mass in relation to surface, 27
Mast, 16, 112, 142, 153, 154, 174, 184, 210, 211, 214, 240
Mast trees, 133; number, 130; benefited by space, 130
Mathiak, Harold A., 89
Mating habits, 29; alligator, 209; antelope, 196; Arctic fox, 224; Arctic hare, 225; armadillo, 209; black bear, 162; black-tailed deer, 163; blue grouse, 142; bobwhite, 108; brown bear, 162, 224; caribou, 225; chachalaca, 209; cottontail rabbit, 108; cougar, 209; elk, 163; eyra, 208; fox squirrel, 103; Franklin grouse, 142; Gambel quail, 196; gray squirrel, 163; grizzly bear, 162; Hungarian partridge, 108, 109; jack rabbit, 196; jaguar, 208; javelina, 209; marsh rabbit, 209; moose, 163; mountain quail, 142; musk ox, 225; ocelot, 208; opossum, 208; pheasant, 108; polar bear, 224; prairie chicken, 196; ringtail, 208; rock ptarmigan, 225; ruffed grouse, 142; sage hen, 196, 198; sharp-tailed grouse, 196; spruce grouse, 142; swamp rabbit, 209; turkey, 142; valley quail, 108; white

Index

sheep, 225; white-tailed deer, 163; white-tailed ptarmigan, 225; willow ptarmigan, 225; woodcock, 142
Maturity, and hunting season, 357; deferred, 29–30; physical, 41; sexual, 41; white sheep, 230
Maximum possible breeding success, 359
May, John Richard, 317
Mayr, Ernst, 36
McAtee, W. L., 6, 36, 92, 93, 123, 139, 141, 161, 269, 283, 301, 310
McCabe, Robert A., 123
McDonald, Marshall, 343
Meadowlark, western, 16; winter range, 47
Measuring cover, 64
Meat-eater, 20, 21, 22, 162; and cycles, 51; decline of, 51
Meat hunger, 25
Mechanical devices for obtaining sign, 75
Meehean, O. L., 283
Meleagris gallapavo, see Turkey
Mendall, Howard L., 159
Merganser, 22; flocks, 42; American, 250; hooded, 250; red-breasted, 250
Merriam, C. Hart, 344
Mershon, William Butts, 317
Metabolic water, 24
Mexico, 110, 120, 152, 173, 178, 203, 207, 211, 212, 213, 240; treaty clause, 336; waterfowl hunting, 266; waterfowl migrating to, 252
Mice, 22, 40, 83; species groups in deer, 44
Michigan, 16, 49, 145, 185, 191, 201; Department of Conservation, 330; State Game, Fish, and Forest Fire Warden, 330; white-tailed deer, 183, 184
Microcycles, 51
Microfauna of soil, 33
Microflora of soil, 33
Migration, 45–47; altitudinal, 140; anadromous, 47; and fat deposition, 24; and increase of fat and body weight, 27; and light, 33; and pairing, 46, 47; antelope, 203; black-tailed deer, 179; blue grouse, 143; broad-winged hawk, 42; catadromous, 47; cover preferences, 300; elk, 175, 176; fish, 46, 47, 293; flyways, 45; geese, 46; guides, 46; hawks, 42; in animal classes, 45; latent tendencies, 51; pathway, 45; prairie chicken, 199; rock ptarmigan, 231; sequence, 45; sharp-tailed grouse, 201; Swainson hawk, 42; time of, 45; turkey, 152; white-tailed ptarmigan, 232; willow ptarmigan, 231; woodcock, 156
Migratory Bird Conservation Act, 337
Migratory Bird Conservation Commission, 337
Migratory birds, and day length, 26; food, 210; game, list of, 335, 336; insectivorous, list of, 335; non-game, list of, 336; ownership of, 333; winter homes, 210
Migratory bird treaties, as evolution of thought, 336
Migratory Bird Treaty, 6, 249, 297, 335–337; implemented, 349
Migratory Bird Treaty Act, 336–337; enforcement, 343
Migratory fish counting, 290
Mild winters, 110
Miller, J. Paul, 106, 248
Millet, 101, 102, 153, 200, 202
Milo, 101, 102
Mineral shortage, 228; soil, 132
Mine wastes, pollution of streams, 288
Minimum numbers, 38–39; for breeding success, 39; valley quail, 114
Mink, den, 237; food, 240; habitat, 236, 241; habits, 241; symbol for, 238
sea, extinction, 314
Minnesota, 16, 145, 150, 244; state game warden, 330
Mirror, 158; transparent, 76
Miscellaneous products, 14–15
Mississippi, 16
Mississippi River, 259
Mississippi Valley, 252
Missouri, 16, 146, 175, 185
Mistletoe, 16
Mitotic rhythm, 25
Mixed forests, 34, 141, 157, 161, 162, 163

Mixed stands, 43–44
Mixing of plant species, 34
Mobility, and study areas, 83; bobwhite, 110; elk, 176; forest game, 160; open range game, 160; predator and prey, 30; white-tailed deer, 183
Moccasin flower, 16
Mockingbird, 14, 15, 16, 20
Mohr, Carl O., 53
Molting, 147; sign, 74
Monogamy, 29; *see also* Mating habits
Montana, 16, 62, 145, 178, 204, 205
Moore, Elwood B., 101, 106, 139
Moose, 190–192; aquatics, 191; areas, 83; breeding season, 163; browse, 191; census methods, 192; density, 191, 192; environment, 163; food habits, 67, 163, 191; food need, 191; gestation, 163; gregariousness, 190; habitat requirement, 190–191; hearing, 219; improving food and cover, 191–192; Isle Royale, 191; marking, 192; mating habits, 163; number of young, 163; Nova Scotia, 191; overbrowsing, 191; parturition, 163; range, 163; salt, 192; sex ratio, 163; shelter, 190; use of forest, 161; vision, 219; wardens, 329; weight, 163; wildness, 191
Morgan, Ann Haven, 283, 296
Mortality, 145; bobwhite, 112; differential sex, 29; highway, 307, 308; juvenile, 145, 151; muskrat, 246; woodcock, 158
Morton, James N., 122
Mosquito, 220; control, 253; season, 228
Moss, 184, 225
Motion pictures, 85; sound, 86
Mountain goat, 316
Mountain lion, *see* Cougar
Mount McKinley National Park, 230
Mountain mahogany, 176
Mountain tundra, 34, 232
Mouse sign, 75
Movements, altitudinal, 140; Arctic fox, 227; associated with settlement, 49; caribou, 228; cottontail rabbit, 120; elk, 176; opossum, 211; seasonal, 140; turkey, 152
Mulberry, 166, 301, 306

Multiple-purpose land, 4
Multiple use, 128, 135
Multiscope, 68
Murie, Adolph, 14, 89, 191, 192, 233, 248, 317
Murie, Olaus J., 233
Museums, roadside, 14; trailside, 14
Muskellunge, food, 286; range, 286; spawning, 286
Musk ox, 229–230; adaptations, 229; biological data, 224; food habits, 229; killing by aborigines, 229; niche, 229; original number, 230; pelage, 219, 229; predators, 229; present number, 230; protection, 229, 230; range, 229; range shrinkage, 229; relationship to bison, 229; restoration, 229; weight, 229
Muskrat, 10, 234, 235, 246–247; breeding rate, 246; breeding season, 247; burrows, 246; den, 237; depth of water, 247; food habits, 246; habitat, 236, 246; houses, 235, 236, 246; management practices, 246; mortality, 246; open season, 247; overtrapping, 247; protection, 246; range, 246; relations with waterfowl, 255; resting places, 247; symbol for, 238; tearing loose vegetation, 260; trapping, 247
Mustelidae, *see* Weasel family
Mynah, crested, introduction, 306

National Audubon Society, 297, 334
National forests, 137
National parks and monuments, Canada, establishment in (1885), 350; failure to protect wolf, 316; ownership of animals, 342; United States, 129, 136
National Park Service, 342–343, 344
Natural areas, 137
Natural deaths, 74
Natural extinction, 311
Natural openings, 131
Natural resources utilization, 2
Nature hikers, 14; trails, 14
Navigable waters in Indian reservations, 341
Nebraska, 16, 178, 197, 250, 252
Need for combination of practices, 363

Index

Needham, Paul R., 296
Needs, of animal life, 19; of forest wildlife, 124
Neff, Johnson A., 159
Nelson, E. W., 344
Nematodes, 151
Neotropics, 216; animals, 207; region, 214
Nest boxes, 164; for observation, 75; fox and gray squirrel, 167; waterfowl, 262, 265; song and non-game birds, 303–304
Nest counts, 63; bobwhite, 113; Hungarian partridge, 110; pheasants, 119; sage grouse, 198; waterfowl, 269
Nest destruction, 150; blue grouse, 145; Hungarian partridge, 109; pheasant, 118; valley quail, 115; waterfowl, 255
Nesting, 47 (*see also* name of species); blue grouse, 143; colonies, 50; material for, 302–303; mountain quail, 155; prairie chicken, 199; sites for, 302–303; turkey, 153; woodcock, 156
Nesting cover, 202; bobwhite, 112; controlled burning, 134; Hungarian partridge, 109; pheasant, 118; supplying nesting conditions, 302
Nesting season, *see* Breeding season, name of species
Nest observation, 85
Nests, alligator, 216; snowshoe rabbit, 170; valley quail, 115
Nest success, 358
Nest traps, 158
Nets, 158
Nevada, 16, 114, 197
New Brunswick, 349
Newfoundland, 349
New Hampshire, 16, 329
New Jersey, 16
New Mexico, 16, 110, 143, 168, 175, 197, 199, 207, 214, 232, 252
New York, 16, 145, 194, 211
Nice, Margaret Morse, 36
Nichol, A. A., 193
Night, lighting, 158; roosting, 300
Noble, G. Kingsley, 283
Nocturnal animals, 33; migrants, 45, 46
Non-biological aspects, 6

Non-breeding, 21
Non-game species, general requirements of, 298
Non-resident licenses, history, 323
Norman, J. R., 283
Normans, and ownership of game, 320
North Carolina, 16, 146, 215; State Audubon Society as state game department, 330
North Dakota, 16, 197, 203
Northland, 15, 51, 141, 218, 219 (*see also* Arctic); aboriginal population ratio, 223; animal numbers, 219–220; definition, 218; ecology, 218; economy of, 223, 227; land ownership, 222; land productivity, 223; local rule, 223; march of climate, 220–221; natives, 223; phenology, 220–221; problems, 218
Northland wildlife, 218–233
Northward extension of southern species, 34
Northward march of climate, 49, 220–221
Northwest Territories, land ownership, 222; wildlife controls, 349
No-see-ums, 220
Notebooks, selection of, 87
Note pads, 88
Note taking, 87
Nova Scotia, 190, 191, 349
Number of young, antelope, 196; Arctic fox, 224; Arctic hare, 224; armadillo, 209; black bear, 162; black-tailed deer, 163; brown bear, 162, 224; caribou, 225; cottontail rabbit, 108; cougar, 209; elk, 163; eyra, 208; fox squirrel, 163; gray squirrel, 163; grizzly bear, 162; jack rabbit, 196; jaguar, 208; javelina, 209; marsh rabbit, 209; moose, 163; musk ox, 225; ocelot, 208; opossum, 208; polar bear, 224; ringtail, 208; swamp rabbit, 209; white sheep, 225; white-tailed deer, 163
Nut grass, 259
Nuthatch, 300; red-breasted, 40; species association, 43
Nutria, spread in America, 50
Nutritional deficiencies and soil, 33

Nutritional needs, study of, 24
Nuts, 163

Oak, 16, 150, 153, 167, 185
Oak-hickory, 164; zone, 35
Obeliscoides, 213
Observational skill and notes, 87
Observation blinds, 78, 80
Observation nest boxes, 75
Observations, recording of, 80
Obstructions to free passage of fish, 293–294
Oceanic bird islands, protection of, 334
Ocelot, biological data, 208; fur, 213; habitat, 213; habits, 213; range, 213
Odocoileus hemionus, see Deer, black-tailed; *virginianus, see* Deer, white-tailed
Ogden, Adele, 248
Ohio, 10, 16, 49, 60, 333
Ohio hunt, 173
Oil pollution and waterfowl, 256; control of, 256
Oklahoma, 16, 213, 214, 333
Old Mexico, *see* Mexico
Old squaw, 250
O'Malley, Frank, 343
Ondatra zibethica, see Muskrat
Ontario, 211, 349
Oosting, Henry J., 36, 69
Openings, 116, 128, 130, 131, 148, 186
Open season, 188, 189, 190; black bear, 174; black-tailed deer, 181; elk, 177; fur bearers, 236; muskrat, 247; opossum, 212
Operations of state officials on federal land, 325
Opossum, 211–212, 235; biological data, 208; den, 237; economic value, 212; food habits, 210, 211, 212; fur, 210; habitat, 211, 236; open season, 212; range, 211; spread in California, 49
Orange blossom, 16
Oreamnos americanus, 316
Oregon, 16, 114, 145, 155, 201, 212
Oregon grape, 16
Oreortyx picta, see Quail, mountain
Original forest area, 129
Oriole, Baltimore, 16

Ortalis vetula, see Chachalaca
Otter, 235; extirpation, 241; food, 240; habitat, 236; slides, 71; symbol for, 238; tolerance to man, 241 sea, 315, 316; habitat, 236; protection, 313; pursuit of, 313, 316
Outdoor recreation, 136
Outline of reports, 88
Overbrowsing, 186, 187, 189, 191; deer, 184
Overfishing, salmon, 226
Overgrazing, 135, 195; and deer increase, 136; jack rabbits, 136; rodents, 136; tundra, 228
Overhead costs, 4
Overlapping, of deer and elk requirements, 43; of pheasant and quail requirements, 44
Overmature trees, 167
Overpopulation, 137, 184, 187; and special seasons, 359; black-tailed deer, 181; fish, 295; pan fish, 278
Overshooting, 13
Overtrapping, 234; muskrat, 247
Ovibos moschatus, see Musk ox
Ovis canadensis, see Bighorn; *dalli, see* Sheep, white mountain
Owl, 130, 151; destruction, 313; Florida burrowing, 315; great horned, 171; screech, 307; snowy, cycle, 51
Ownership, of animals *ferae naturae,* 319–320, 347–348; of animals in territorial water, 322; of exotic animals, 327; of feral animals, 319; of land under water, 322; of migratory birds, 333; of property and exclusive use, 327; public, of game, 323; similarity of American and European systems, 321
Owners-in-fact of animals, 320
Oxidation in cells, 26
Ox, musk, *see* Musk ox
Oxygen, content of air, 33; content of water, 33; deficiency in lakes, 279; supply in deep diving, 260; supply in streams, 285
Oxyhemoglobin, 260
Oxymyoglobin, 260
Oyster, 297

Index

Pack rat, 117
Paedogenesis, 41
Painted cup, 16
Pairing, 49; and migration in waterfowl, 46, 47; duration of, 29
Palatability, 64–65, 66, 160; elk foods, 176; food patch species, 102; variations with season, 25; winter foods, 105
Palmer, E. Laurence, 17
Palmer, L. J., 233
Palmer, T. S., 332
Palouse region, Hungarian partridge, 109; pheasant, 109
Panama, 119, 212, 240
Pan-American Union, 298
Paraguay, 213
Paralysis, waterfowl, 257, 258
Paramount rights created by Supreme Court, 322
Paraquet, extinction of Carolina, 314: Louisiana, 314
Parasites, 64, 145, 151, 213
Parental fear, 19
Park, Orlando, 36, 53
Park, Thomas, 36. 53
Parks, 14; see also National parks
Partridge, Hungarian, 107–110, 118; altitude, 109; and population curve, 38; breeding season, 108; census methods, 110; cover, 109; cover type, 92–93; coveys, 109; density, 109; environment, 108; feeding stations, 110; food consumption, 105; food habits, 108, 109; food of young, 110; food patches, 110; habitat, 109; habits, 109; hatching season, 108; incubation, 108; introduction, 306; mating, 108, 109; nest destruction, 109; nesting, 109; number of eggs, 108; range, 108; restocking, 109; sex ratio, 108, 109; spread, 49; successful establishment, 109; trapping, 110; water needs, 110; weight, 108; winter feeding, 103, 109–110; winter food, 109
Partridge pea, 132
Parturition, antelope, 196; Arctic fox, 224; Arctic hare, 225; armadillo, 209; black bear, 162; black-tailed deer, 163; brown bear, 162, 224; caribou, 225; cottontail, season of, 108; cougar, 209; elk, 163; eyra, 208; fox squirrel, 163; gray squirrel, 163; grizzly bear, 162; jack rabbit, 196; jaguar, 208; javelina, 209; marsh rabbit, 209; moose, 163; musk ox, 225; ocelot, 208; opossum, 208; polar bear, 224; ringtail, 208; swamp rabbit, 209; white sheep, 225; white-tailed deer, 163
Parulidae, species association, 43
Pasque flower, 16
Passalunis, 214
Passenger pigeon, *see* Pigeon, passenger
Patagium, 78, 79
Patterns of behavior, 27
Peach blossom, 16
Pearce, John, 139
Pearls, 15
Pearse, A. S., 36, 53
Pearson, Allen N., 216
Pearson, T. Gilbert, 310
Peat marshes, 252
Pecan, 16, 165
Pecari ungulatus, *see* Javelina
Peccary, *see* Javelina
Peck dominance, 44; order, 44; right, 44
Pedioecetes phasianellus, *see* Grouse, sharp-tailed
Pelage, *see also* Fur; Arctic fox, 226; Arctic hare, 227; musk ox, 229; Northland animals, 219; polar bear, 226; wetting of, 25
Pelican, brown, 16
Pellet-group count, 190
Pellets, 71, 82; analysis, 81
Pencil notes, 87; smudging, 87
Penguin migration, 47
Pennsylvania, 16, 168, 190; bounty payments, 238
Perdix perdix, *see* Partridge, Hungarian
Permafrost, effect on wildlife, 219; map of, 219
Permanent escape cover, 99
Permits, 14
Peromyscus, *see* Mice, deer
Persecuted species, 311
Persimmons, 212

396   Index

Personal interview method of gathering data, 236
Personal rights and dignity of man, 362
Peru, 15, 50, 51
Peruvian Guano Commission, 15
Petrel, 304; black-capped, extinction, 314
Pettingill, Olin Sewall, Jr., 159
Phase alternations, 37, 39–40
Phasianus, see Pheasant
Pheasant, ring-necked, 56, 102, 107, 109, 110, 117–119, 307; Asia, 117; biological surplus, 119; breeding season, 108; censuses, 63, 119; climate, 117; cock hunting, 119; cover type, 92–93; crowing ground, 118; density, 118; environment, 108; flushing bar, 119; food consumption, 105; food habits, 108, 118; grit, 118; habitat choice, 118; habitat requirements, 117–118; hatching, 108; hen season, 119; hunting season, 119; improving food and cover, 118; increase of population, 38; incubation, 108; introduction, 117, 306; marking, 76; mating, 108; mobility, 117; movement, 118; nest cover, 118; nesting, 119; nest losses, 118, 119; number of eggs, 108; polygamy, 118; predation losses, 118; protection, 118–119; range, 108; roadside census, 60–61; sex ratio, 108, 118, 119; snow, 117; trapping, 119; weight, 108; winter feeding, 103, 118; winter habits, 117, 118
Phenological indicators, 220
Phillips, John C., 269, 310
Philohela minor, see Woodcock
Phoebe, 304; instinctive reactions of, 27
Phosphorous poisoning, 117
Photo-electric cells, 75
Photographic stations, 85
Photographs, aerial, 68; use in counting flocks and rafts, 58
Photography, 85–86; color, 85; from blinds, 78, 80
Photosynthesis, 20, 21
Physical maturity, 41

Physiological activity and hibernation, 48
Physiological disturbance and cycles, 52
Physiological requirements and food eaten, 24–25
Physiological stress, prolonged, 52–53
Physiological variations of populations, 14
Phytoplankton, 21
Piedmont, 175
Pigeon, 305, 306; control by falcons, 315 passenger, 127; and squirrel relations, 166; extinction, 314; extinction threshold, 312; flocks, 42 white-crowned, 315
Pike, food, 286; range, 286; spawning, 286
Pike-perch, food, 286; range, 286; spawning, 286
Pinch period, 5, 31, 130
Pine, 15, 16, 21, 141, 145, 146, 161, 170, 180; cane and tassel, 16; jack, 145, 170; lodgepole, 21, 145, 170; ponderosa, 35; white-barked, 144; zone, ponderosa, 35
Pine straw, 134
Pinnepedia, 316
Pintail, 250
Pirnie, Miles David, 269
Pitelka, Frank A., 36
Pittman-Robertson Act, 337–338, 353; division of funds, 338; projects, 338; public shooting grounds, 338
Plane table mapping, 68, 276
Planetary wind system, 46
Plankton and fish, 276
Plant density, 65
Plant-eater, 20, 21; cycles, 51
Planting, 149, 150; aquatic vegetation, 264, 273; and succession, 34–35; food plants, 132
Plants, recommended, 132
Plastic markers, 77; tags, 77
Platform brush pile, 96
Platform feeder, 104, 105, 200
Plowing, and succession, 34; of stubble, 119
Plum, 166

Index

Plumage, importation prohibited, 334; Northland birds, 219; red grouse, 231; trade in, 15, 313, 334; wetting of, 25
Poaching, 188; antelope, 204; beaver, 246; fur bearer, 239; ptarmigan, 232; rare bighorns, 316
Pocket gophers, 20
Poikilothermous, definition of, 32
Point observation method, 66
Poison, use of, by animals, 22
Poison campaigns, 117, 171, 313; and fur bearers, 239
Pole trap destruction, 313
Police power and state controls, 319, 320–322
Political appeals, 5
Political interference in game work, 351
Pollution, and oxygen content, 33; chemical, 255; effect of chemicals, 255; excess organic, 256; fertilizing effect, 255; oil, 256; sewage, 255; sewage sludge, 255; stream, 288
Polygamy, 29
Polygonum, 259
Pond weeds, 259
Poplar, 150
Poppy, 15
Population, ability to establish, 38; cycles, 50–51; estimates of wildfowl, 265; fluctuations in, 38; in relation to breeding potential, 31; pressure of, and growth rates, 40; reservoirs, 48; studies of, use of, 279
Population counts of fish, 280
Population curve, 38
Populus, see Aspen
Porcupine sign, 74, 75
Porpoise, 316
Post-mature classes and predation, 21
Post-mortems, 74
Post oak, 207; zone of, 35
Potamogeton, 259
Potential surplus, 5
Pough, Richard H., 317
Powell, Burwell B., 106, 248
Prairie, 194, 195

Prairie chicken, 199–201; Attwater, 199, 315; booming ground, 199, 200; booming ground counts, 201; breeding season, 196; broods, 43; brush piles, 201; census, 63; census methods, 201; confusion of name, 199; diet, 200; environment, 196; feeding stations, 200; flock counts, 201; flocking habits, 199; food consumption, 105; food habits, 199; food need, 200; food patches, 200; habitat requirement, 199–200; habits, 133; hatching, 196; improving food and cover, 200; incubation, 196; instinctive behavior pattern, 28; lesser, *see* Prairie chicken; marking, 201; mating, 196; nesting, 199; number of eggs, 196; original range, 199; promiscuity, 30; range, 196, 199; return to booming grounds, 28; sex migration, 199; sex ratio, 196; species association, 43; tolerance, 199; tradition, 199, 200; trapping, 201; water needs, 199; weight, 196; winter feeding, 103, 200
Prairie dog, 41
Prairie grouse group, 30; adaptations, 143; courtship habits of, 30
Precipitation, 32
Predation, 8, 20–21; alligator, 213; antelope, 205; Arctic fox, 222; bobwhite, 113; caribou, 228; deer, 188; fox and gray squirrels, 168; foxes, 242; fur bearers, 238, 239; in burned-over marshes, 255; musk ox, 229; pheasants, 118; ptarmigan, 232; ruffed grouse, 150; snowshoe rabbit, 169, 171; stream fish, 285; turkey, 154; valley quail, 116, 117; white sheep, 230; woodcock, 157
Predation loss, 21; molting ducks, 255; pheasant, 118; waterfowl, 254–255
Predator, 20, 21, 150, 175; and domestic stock, 136; and poison campaigns of Biological Survey, 343; and prey relations to cycles, 52; and territory demands, 28

Predation campaigns, 311; and rodent poisoning, 239; disturbance from, 255; failure to increase waterfowl, 254; fur decline, 234; game species, 136
Predator-prey relationships, 311
Predator protection measurements, 64
Predator sign, 74
Preservation, of ptarmigan remnants, 232; of rare bighorns, 316; of woodland caribou remnants, 229
Preserve, 17
Preserving and collecting, 86; amphibians, 86; birds, 86; fish, 86; feathers, 86; mammals, 86; material, 74; plants, 86; reptiles, 86; seeds, 86; soil samples, 86; stomach contents, 81; tree ring samples, 86; water samples, 86
Pressure for cheaper hunting and fishing, 3
Prevention, of fish movement, 293; of botulism outbreaks, 257; of wastage of grain, 102, 104
Prey, 20, 21
Price lists, fictitious, 239
Primary refuges, 268
Prime years, 21; white sheep, 230
Primitive areas, 137; conditions, 14
Primitive man, 8
Prince Edward Island, 349
Priorities, 3; of mining, 288
Private ownership, maintained in game, 326–327
Private waters, fishing on, 327
Privilege of hunting, 13
Privilege tax, 14
Privy Council in London, 347
Prizes, 14; fish derbies, 281; offered for best prepared fur, 239, 240
Problems, beaver, 245; of southern ecology, 207–208; of the wildlife manager, 3–4
Procyon lotor, see Raccoon
Production, 1
Productivity, 30–31
Products, useful, of animals, 8
Programs, success dependent upon administrative attitude, 362
Progressive changes, 32

Prohibition, of alien hunting, 324; of alien ownership of guns, 324; of hunting practices, 266; of importation of eggs, 334
Prolificness, of fish compared to land animals, 271
Promiscuity, 30
Pronghorn, *see* Antelope
Property interest in game, acquiring, 326
Property rights, 11; and hunting rights, 327–329
Proper-use factor, 64–65; tables, 65
Proprietary capacity of government, 320
Prosecution of violations, 362
Protection, 270; alligator, 216; antelope, 204–205; beaver, 246; black bear, 174–175; black-tailed deer, 181; blue grouse, 144, 145; bobwhite, 113; buildings, from birds, 307, 308; costs of, 4; crops, from birds, 304; den trees, 167, 168; eroding banks, 274, 278; fish, 281–282; fox and gray squirrels, 167–168; Franklin grouse, 146; frogs, 297; fur-bearer, 234, 239–240; high seas wildlife, 335; lynx, 242; mountain goat, 316; mountain quail, 156; muskrat, 246; non-game mammals, 297; oceanic birds, 304; of the public interest, 354, 356; on paper only, 314; pheasants, 118, 119; rare fur bearers, 241; ruffed grouse, 150; sea otter, 313; shore, from wave action, 273; song and insectivorous birds, 297, 303; sponges, 334; spruce grouse, 146; turkey, 154; valley quail, 116; waterfowl, 265–266; white sheep, 230; white-tailed deer, 187–188; woodcock, 157
Protein lack, 25
Providing shelter for stream fish, 290
Provincial and federal wildlife spheres in Canada, 346–350; origin of, 347
Provincial game and fish departments, 348–349
Provincial organizations, 248
Pruning, 145
Prunus, see Cherry
Pseudotsuga, see Fir, Douglas

Index

Psittacosis, 315
Psychological needs of animals, 27–28; and minimum numbers, 39
Ptarmigan (rock, white-tailed, and willow), 23, 231–232; accidents, 232; adaptation, 143; biology table, 225; cycles, 231; distribution, 221; economic value, 232; food habits, 232; habitat, 141; habits, 231, 232; hunting, 232; migration, 231, 232; predators, 232; range, 231, 232; remnants of white-tailed, 232; seasonal plumage, 231, 232; winter food, 232
Public administration, 2, 3
Publication of data, 89
Public attitude, reflected in game department, 363
Public domain, 195
Public explanation of regulations, 357
Public funds, 3
Public Health Service, 344
Public hearings on regulations, 358
Public policy, 5; limitations on, 4
Public shooting grounds, 12–13, 267
Puget Sound, 50
Punching holes in webbing, as a marking technique, 79
Purchase of land, by federal government, 325
Pursuit, for plumage, fur, and other products, 313; of rarities, 312

Quadrats, 56, 66
Quail, 110; hunting of, 11
 bobwhite, see Bobwhite
 Gambel, breeding season, 176; food habits, 196; environment, 196; game ways, 96; hatching, 196; incubation, 196; mating, 196; number of eggs, 196; range, 196; sex ratio, 196; weight, 196
 mountain, 155–156; altitudinal migration, 155; enemies, 156; environment, 142; food habits, 142, 156; habitat requirements, 155; improving food and cover, 156; incubation, 142; mating, 142; nesting, 155; nesting season, 142; number of eggs, 142; protection, 156; range, 142; range extension, 155; roosting, 155; sex ratio, 142; transplantation, 155; water needs, 155, 156; weight, 142; winter range, 155
 valley, 15, 114–117, 155; altitude range, 114; breeding season, 108; brush cutters, 116; census methods, 117; competitors, 116; controlled burning, 116; drought, 115; environment, 108; feeding time, 115; food habits, 108, 115; food items, 115; food patches, 116; grit, 115; habitat requirements, 114; habits, 114; hatching season, 108; hawks and owls, 116; improving food and cover, 115–116; incubation, 108; interspersion, 116; introduction, 114; mating, 108; minimum covey, 114; nest destruction, 115; nests, 115; number of eggs, 108; openings, 116; original range, 114; overgrazing, 116; predator control, 116; protection, 116; range, 108; roosting habits, 115; sex ratio, 108; shade, 116; size of food, 115; snow limits, 114; territory, 114; transplants, 306; water needs, 114, 115, 116; weight, 108
Qualitative lacks, 19
Quantitative lacks, 19
Quebec, 190, 201, 346, 349
Quercus, see Oak
Questionnaires, 83, 236

Rabbit, 21, 102, 242, 307; Australia, 38; damage, 122; density limit, 38; escape cover, 98–99; exotics, 38; fence, 56–57; forage food, 51; forms, 63; home range, 29; ice and cold, 99; instinctive reactions, 27; length of ears and Allen's rule, 27; marking, 79; sign, 74, 75; spread in Australia, 49; thinning, 121
 cottontail, 107, 119–122; breeding season, 108; burrows, 120, 222; census methods, 122; conifers, 122; cover, 120; cover grading system, 64; cover type, 92–93; density, 120; diet, 120; drought, 121; eastern, 119; environment,

108; food consumption, 105; food habits, 108, 121; forms, 120, 121; gestation, 108; girdling, 121; habitat requirements, 120; home range, 120; improving food and cover, 121–122; marking, 122; mating, 108; movements, 120; nests, 120; number of young, 108; overlap of habitat with swamp rabbit, 213; parturition season, 108; range, 108, 119–120; range extension, 120, 127; Rocky Mountain, 119; sex ratio, 108; snares, 122; tattooing, 122; trails, 120; transplanting, 120; trapping, 122; water needs, 121; weight, 108; western, 120; winter, 120

jack, 307; breeding season, 196; environment, 196; food, 196; gestation, 196; mating, 196; number of young, 196; overgrazing, 136; parturition, 196; range, 194, 196; sex ratio, 196; weight, 196

marsh, 214; biological data, 209; habits, 214

snowshoe, 168–172; census methods, 171–172; control, 170–171; cycles, 127, 169, 170, 227; density, 127, 170; dust baths, 169; effect on reproduction, 127; emigrations, 169; food habits, 170; forage animal, 169; forage, value to fur animals, 242; forms, 169; girdling, 170; habitat requirement, 168–169; home range, 169; improving food and cover, 170; injury to forest, 170–171; marking, 171; populations, 170; predators, 169; range, 168–169; transect-count, 171; use of forest, 161; value of forestry, 170; winter feeding, 170; young, 170

swamp, 213–214; biological data, 209; density, 213; enemies, 213; food habits, 213; habits, 213; management, 214; parasites, 213

Raccoon, 130, 164, 240; den, 237; food habits, 240; extirpation, 240; habitat, 236, 240; management, 240; range, 240; symbol for, 238

Rack feeders, 103, 104
Raft cover, 291
Rafts, counting birds in, 58
Ragweed, 100, 102, 112, 210
Rainfall, cycles, 254; deficiency on breeding grounds, 253; effectiveness, 194
Raiz, Erwin, 69
Rallidae, 249
Rand, A. L., 233
Random chance, 39
Random counts, 122; data, 39; sample, 158; selection of sample plots, 56
Range, area, 194; capacity determination, 64–65; carrying capacity, 67; conversion to forms, 194; country, 194; definition, 4; depletion of, of white sheep, 231; management of, 64, 67; open, definition of, 194; original, 194; ownership, 194; preference, 160; shifts in, 49, 50; shrinkage of, of musk ox, 229

data, alligator, 209, 215; antelope, 196, 203; Arctic fox, 224, 227; Arctic hare, 225, 227; armadillo, 209, 214; badger, 240; beaver, 242; black bear, 162, 173; blue grouse, 142; bobwhite, 110; brown bear, 223, 224; caribou, 225; chachalaca, 209; cougar, 209; eyra, 208; flying squirrel, 164; Franklin grouse, 142; Gambel quail, 196; gray fox, 241; jack rabbit, 196; jaguar, 208; javelina, 209; lynx, 242; musk ox, 225, 229; muskrat, 246; marsh rabbit, 209; mountain quail, 142; ocelot, 208; opossum, 208, 211; polar bear, 224; prairie chicken, 196; raccoon, 240; red fox, 241; ringtail, 208; rock ptarmigan, 225; ruffed grouse, 142; sage hen, 196; sharp-tailed grouse, 196, 201; snowshoe rabbit, 168–169; spruce grouse, 142; swamp rabbit, 209; turkey, 142, 152; white sheep, 225, 230; white-tailed ptarmigan, 225; wildcat, 242; willow ptarmigan, 225; woodcock, 142

Range extension, 91; armadillo, 215; bobwhite, 110; cottontail rabbit, 120, 127; mountain quail, 155; opossum, 211; robin, 127; sharp-tailed grouse, 201; song sparrow, 127; white-tailed deer, 183
Rangifer, see Caribou
Rare species, 311; American birds, 313–315; list of, 315; mammals, 315–316; sea mammals, 316
Raspberry, 121, 146, 166, 174, 185
Rat, black, spread on Ascension Island, 49
Ratio, of live to dressed weight, 164
Raven, flocks, 42; sign, 73
Reading sign, 71
Recolonization, 209, 310
Reconnaissance survey for range studies, 66
Recording, of data, 86, 87; of observations, 86; of tracks, 72
Recreation, 8, 14; areas, 136; expenditures, 8–12; goods, 9; income, 9; measures of pleasure, 10; pleasure derived, 9; services, 9; use of forest, 136–137; use of wildlife, 3, 7, 9, 128; value of, 12; value of streams, 285
Redbird, 16
Redhead, 250
Redington, Paul G., 344
Redwood, 15
Reese, Albert M., 217
Re-establishing extirpated species, 309–310; antelope, 204; white sheep, 230
Refuges, 4, 13, 17; and hunting control, 267; black-tailed deer, 181; deer, 187, 188; kinds, 268; negative values, 267; measures of usefulness, 268; permissible activities, 268; programs, and wildfowl increase, 265; ruffed grouse, 151; size, 187; special, 268; value, 267; waterfowl, 266–267
Registered trap lines, 348
Regulation, by state of federal lands, 322; of environment and plant composition, 298; of fish seasons and need for data, 279; of hunting by foreign governments, 321; of roadside zoos, 14

Regulations, 2; for hunting migratory birds, 337; gathering facts for, 357–359; increase of, 362; preparing, 359; purpose of, 356–357
Reindeer, distribution, 222; industry, 228; predators, 222
Release cuttings, 133–135, 150, 153, 166
Remnant populations, 309
Remnant species, 309
Renegade bears, 175
Renewability powers, of a species, 312
Rents, hunting, 11
Repellents, 122, 182; for protecting seeds, 305; in buildings, 306, 307
Reports, 88–89; condensing, 89; preparing, 89; trapper, 236
Reproductive rate change with numbers, 37
Reptiles, 6, 125
Research, "mail-order," 83, 236
Reservations, 195
Reserve, 17
Reservoir fluctuations, 277
Resorts, and wildlife values, 11; owners of, 13
Resources administration, separation of, 351
Resources, public, used for private purposes, 14
Resting places, muskrat, 247
Restocking, Hungarian partridge, 109; stream fish, 285; turkey, 154
Restrictive combinations, of game laws, 325
Rhode Island, 16
Rhododendron, 16
Rhus copalina, see Sumac
Rhythm, mitotic, 25
Ribes, 115, 300; see also Gooseberry
Rice, 259; amount of waste, 100
Ricker, William E., 69
Ridgepole brush pile, 96, 97
Ringtail (cacomistle), 212; biological data, 208; den, 212; food, 212; fur, 212; habitat, 212; range, 212; relation to raccoon, 212
Rio Grande, 213, 215, 216, 249, 315
River break-up, 220
Road counts, 60–61

402   Index

Road hunting, 107
Roadless areas, 137
Road-runner, 16
Roadsides, 93; acreage, 307; burning, 309; census, 60–61; census, of pheasants, 119; counts, of rabbits, 122; cutting, 309; maintenance, 93–94; museums, 14; note taking, 88; tables, 136; zoos, 14
Robin, 16, 20, 305, 307; range extension, 127
Robinette, W. Leslie, 70, 90, 193
Rock cover, 292
Rocky Mountains, 168, 183
Rodents, 7, 127, 174, 211, 212, 242; and badgers, 240; and valley quail, 117; as forage food, 51, 239; burrowing, 41; colonies, 127; control of, and fur decline, 234; counting burrows, 56; damage, 136; fences, 56–57; forage food for fur bearers, 239; home range, 29; overgrazing, 136; poisoning, 117; promiscuity, 30; sign, 74
Rookeries, visits to, 298
Roost counts, bobwhite, 113
Roosting habits, bobwhite, 112; chachalaca, 216; mountain quail, 155; sharp-tailed grouse, 202; valley quail, 115
Rose, 16, 150, 301; American beauty, 16; Cherokee, 16; multiflora, 210; prairie, 16; wild, 16
Rotary fish screens, 294
Rotation, in cedar swamps, 187; in valley quail range, 116
Rough fish control, 278
Rouse, Charles H., 233
Royal Canadian Mounted Police, enforcement of game laws, 349
Royal Commission report, 350
Royalties, 9; and taxes, 14–15
Rubus, see Blackberry, Raspberry
Ruddy, 250
Runoff, 287
Runs of three, 39
Runways, 71, 169
Rupp, John N., 332, 345
Ruppia, 259
Rural zoning, 188
Rut, 189, 190
Rye, 153

Safety strips, 131
Sagebrush, 16, 196, 198, 204; and sage grouse, 28, 198
Sagebrush-grass zone, 35
Sage hen, *see* Grouse, sage
Saggitaria, 259
Saguaro, 15
St. Lawrence River, 20, 250
Salal, 144, 155
Sale of wildlife, 9
Salinity of sea water, 33
Salix, see Willow
Salmon, 40, 128; canneries, 226; cycle, 51; migration, 47; overfishing, 223; relation to brown bear, 223, 226; run, 226
  Atlantic, range, 286; spawning, 286
  Pacific, range, 286; spawning, 286
Salt, 184; antelope, 205; black-tailed deer, 179, 183; elk, 177
Salt lick, 185, 192
Sample area, 55–56; census, 55–56; counts, 190; in determining abundance, 55–56; plots, 55–56, 157, 171; selection of, 55–56; quadrats, 171
Sampling stations, in stream surveys, 289
Sanctuary, 17
Sarber, Hosea A., 317
Saskatchewan, 16, 197, 203, 250, 252, 349
Sassafras, 133
Saturation point, 31
Savanna, 41
Scale-reading machines, 280
Scales, age and growth of fish determined from, 26
Scale samples, 280; gathering, 280; methods of reading, 280; use of, 280
Scandinavia, 15, 232; spread of animals, 49
Scarcity of food, 99
Scarecrow, 305
Scats, 71
Scattered grain, 99, 102
Scatter stations, 102
Scaup duck, flocks, 42; greater, 250; lesser, 250
Schmidt, Karl P., 36, 53
Schultz, Leonard P., 283
Scirpus, 259

Sciurus carolinensis, see Squirrel, gray; *niger,* see Squirrel, fox
Scoter, American, 250; surf, 250; white-winged, 250
Screening fish from irrigation ditches, 293
Sea cow, 316; extinction of Steller, 314
Seal, elephant, 315; hunting, 313, 316; migration, 47; trapping, 239; West Indian, 315
Seal lions, 50; pursuit of, 313, 316
Search, and seizure, power of, 361–362; buildings, 361–362; by wardens, 361–362; camps, 361; cold-storage lockers, 361; mobile homes, 361
Seasonal plumage, ptarmigan, 231, 232
Seasons, on does, 182; on federal lands, 340; on ruffed grouse, 146, 151; on waterfowl, 265; special, 359
Sea water, fertility, 33; salinity, 33
Secchi disc, use of, 271
Secondary refuges, 268
Secretary, of Agriculture, 337, 338, 340; of Commerce, 337; of the Interior, 337, 338
Sectioning hair, 80; method of, 81
Sedge, 191, 225, 232
Sedge-grass zone, 35
Seed-eaters, 22
Seeding, 132
Seeds, 196; collecting, 86
Seed trees, 131, 186
Sego lily, 16
Selective logging, 166
Selway Game Range, 176
Serological tests, 81
Service berry, 133, 144, 170, 185, 301
Seton, Ernest Thompson, 90, 123, 172, 193, 206, 217, 230, 248, 253, 317
Settlement, and animal movements, 49; effect on range extension, 91; inroads of, 312
Severance tax on furs, legality of, 324
Sex, and age flocks, 42–43; and breeding cycle, 43; maturity, 41
Sex counts, 58; bobwhite, 114
Sex migration, prairie chicken, 199
Sex packs, 42
Sex ratio, biology, 359; check methods, 359; communal courtship, 29; deferred maturity, 29; determination, 359; differential mortality, 29; gathering data on, 237; polygamy, 29
Sex ratios, 29–30, 48, 358; alligator, 209; antelope, 196; Arctic fox, 224; Arctic hare, 225; armadillo, 209; black bear, 162; black-tailed deer, 163, 181; blue grouse, 142; bobwhite, 108; brown bear, 162, 224; caribou, 225; chachalaca, 209; cottontail rabbit, 108; cougar, 209; deer, 188; elk, 163, 177; eyra, 208; fox squirrel, 163; Franklin grouse, 142; Gambel quail, 196; gray squirrel, 163; grizzly bear, 162; Hungarian partridge, 108, 109; jack rabbit, 196; jaguar, 208; javelina, 209; marsh rabbit, 209; moose, 163; mountain quail, 142; musk ox, 225; ocelot, 208; opossum, 208; pheasant, 108; polar bear, 224; prairie chicken, 196; ringtail, 208; rock ptarmigan, 225; ruffed grouse, 142; sage hen, 196, 198; sharp-tailed grouse, 196; spruce grouse, 142; swamp rabbit, 209; turkey, 142; valley quail, 108; waterfowl, 266; white sheep, 225; white-tailed deer, 163; white-tailed ptarmigan, 225; willow ptarmigan, 225; woodcock, 142, 158
Shade, 136; along streams, 124, 131, 290; in dry regions, 116
Shade tolerance of trees, 33, 150
Shallows and plankton, 276
Shantz, H. L., 206
Sharp-tail, see Grouse, sharp-tailed
Sheep, bighorn, 41; desert bighorn, 315, 316
 Dall, see Sheep, white mountain
 white mountain, 230–231; age classes, 230; age determination, 230; bands, 231; breeding season, 225; density, 231; environment, 225; food habits, 225; gestation, 225; habits, 230; mating, 225; number of eggs, 225; parturition, 225; population cycles, 230; predation, 230; prime years, 230; protection, 230; range, 225, 230; sex ratio, 225; taxonomy, 230; weight, 225
Shelford, Victor E., 36, 69, 90

Index

Shell-fish, 297; management, 1
Shelter, 19, 34 (*see also* Fish shelters); construction, for stream fish, 290; for feeders, 103; instinctive requirements of, 27; natural, for fish, 273; tree-top, for fish, 274
Shelterwood cutting, 166, 186
Shivering with cold, 26
Shocking grains, 101
Shooting preserve, 17
Shore, 162
Shorebirds, 252; botulism, 256
Shoveller, 250; reaches South America, 252
Shrike, caches food, 75
Shrimp, 297; shipment in interstate commerce, 324
Shrubs for escape tangles, 98
Shultz, Leonard P., 296
Sierra Nevada, 168
Sigmoid curve, 38
Sign, 71; obtaining evidence, 75–76; obtaining evidence by mechanical device, 75
Silt, in fish water, 278; streams, 288
Silver, James, 310
Silvics, 2
Silviculture, 2, 128, 132, 134, 166, 170
Singing bird censuses, 63, 158
Singing ground, 156, 157
Single-species forest, 34, 128, 132
Single-tree cutting, 186
Sirenia, 316
Sites, 128, 129
Size, limits of fish, 279; of alligator, 215; of animals and growth rates, 40; of blind to build, 80; of control areas, 83; of experimental areas, 83; of food, 21–22; of food items, 115; of food patches, 100; of forest openings, 131
Sketches, 85
Skunk, 235, 307; den, 237; eating eggs, 241; food, 240, 241; fur, 212; habitat, 236
Skyline from overbrowsing, 180
Slash disposal, 133–134
Slick and clean farming, 91
Sloth, 214

Small game of forest, 164–172
Smartweed, 112, 259
Smilax, 153
Smith, Arthur D., 18, 69, 206
Smith, Clarence F., 139
Smith, Gilbert M., 283
Smith, Hugh M., 343
Snags, 130
Snake River, 287
Snares, 171
Snipe, Wilson, cover type, 92–93
Snow fences, living, 309
Snow limit, bobwhite, 114; pheasant, 114, 117; valley quail, 114
"Snowshoes," on grouse feet, 143
Snow trailing, 65
Social appeals, 5
Social hierarchy, 44
Socialized hunting, *see* Public shooting grounds
Soils, 127; and succession, 34; conditions in succession, 35; contamination of, 103, 153; deficiencies of, and nutritional deficiencies, 33; in relation to flora and fauna, 33; nutrients, 21; of food patches, 101; of the South, 210
Soil Conservation Service, 282, 344
Soil sickness, 33
Solar radiation and cycles, 52
Solitary habits, 41
Songbirds, and food patches, 100, 101; and non-game conservation and management, 297; supplying cover for, 300
Soper, J. Slewey, 233
Sorghum, 101, 102, 153, 200
Sorting cards, 87
South, water needs, 207
South America, 214, 215; waterfowl wintering in, 252
South Carolina, 16
South Dakota, 16, 110, 197, 203
Southern wildlife species, 207–217; water needs, 210
Southward extension of Northern species, 34
Souvenirs, 9
Sovereign capacity of government, 320

Index

Sowing methods, for food patches, 101, 102
Sowls, Lyle K., 101, 106, 192
Soybean, 100, 101, 102, 153, 200
Space needs of animals, 38
Sparrow, Cape Sable seaside, 315
   English, *see* Sparrow, house
   European tree, 306
   house, 26, 49, 304, 306, 307; introduction, 306; spread in America, 38, 49
   song, range extension, 127
   tree, concentration area, 47
Spawning, interfered with by vegetation, 273; of forage fish, 276; success of, 258
Spawning beds, 274–275; covered by silt, 278; floating devices, 274; kinds, 274; size, 274
Spawning structures, providing, 276
Species association, 43
Species groups, 44–45
Speeding up successions, 34
Spencer, David L., 192
Spencer, Donald A., 90
Sperry, Charles C., 248
Sperry, Omer E., 57
Spheres of influence, state and federal, 324–327
Spicebush, 150
Sponges, protection, 334, 335
Spoonbill, roseate, protection, 314, 315
Sport, 14
Sporting arms and ammunition tax, 338
Sporting-goods tax, 14
"Sportsman's dollar" attitude, 354
Spot burning, 135
Spot counting, 168
Spotting scopes, 85; use in the field, 65
Spray devices for marking, 77
Spread, into new or unoccupied range, 49–50; of neotropical animals, 207
Sprout growth, 133
Spruce, 141, 147, 161, 170, 180, 191; blue, 15, 16
Spruce-fir zone, 35
Spurr, Stephen H., 69
Square food density method, 66, 67
Squirrel, 10, 55, 130, 210; food cache, 75; food consumption, 105; preventing waste of grain, 104; wasting grain, 103
   flying, 164, 297, 306; nesting, 164; range, 164
   gray and fox, 164–168; bag limit, 168; breeding season, 163; census methods, 168; clear cutting, 166; dens, 165; density, 165–167; den trees, 165; emigration, 166; environment, 163; food habits, 163, 165–166; food storage, 165; gestation, 163; grazing, 167; habitat requirements, 164–165; hibernation, 48; improving food and cover, 166–167; making dens, 167; marking, 168; mating, 163; nest boxes, 167; nest counts, 168; nest material, 167; nests, 165; number of young, 163; open season, 167–168; parturition, 163; predation, 168; protecting dens, 167; protection, 167–168; quadrat, 168; range, 163; selective logging, 166; sex ratio, 163; shelter-wood cutting, 166; spot counts, 168; transect, 168; trapping, 168; use of forest, 161; wastage of grain, 167; water needs, 166; weight, 163; winter, 165; winter feeding, 167; young, 165
   ground, 23, 41, 117; hibernation and aestivation, 48; hunting, 107
   pine, *see* Squirrel, red
   red, 21, 157; feeding, 75; pilfering grouse eggs, 150; sign, 75
   tufted-ear, 164
   western gray, 164
Staggered system of appointing commissioners, 352
Stagnation and oxygen content, 33
Starling, 304, 305; introduction, 306; spread in America, 38, 49
Starvation, 19, 34, 150; and body requirements, 25–26; and cold, 25–26; and sequence of fat utilization, 358; and weight change, 26; deer, 186, 189; elk, 177; white-tailed deer, 184, 186, 189
State, as source of people's power, 333; as unit of government, 318

State birds, trees, and flowers, list of, 15–16
State forests, 137
State game departments, types of, 352
State game wardens, titles of, 361
State jurisdiction, exempting and ceding, 340
State laws, and federal lands, 340; and Indian lands, 340–341; applying to Indians, 341
State monopolies of beaver trapping, 246
State ownership, dóctrine of, 320
State powers, and controls, 318–332; federal challenge to, 340; origin of, 131
Statute of Westminster (1931), 347
Stebler, A. M., 90
Steelhead, *see* Trout, rainbow
Steese Highway, 229
Stefansson, Vilhjalmur, 233
Steppe, 194
Stern, Edith M., 283, 296
Steven, Ross O., 18, 217, 332, 364
Stock industry and overgrazing, 135
Stock-proof fence, 57
Stoddard, Herbert S., 106, 123, 139, 217
Stoddart, Laurence A., 69
Stomach analysis, 81; and hard foods, 259; in range studies, 65
Stomach worm, 213
Stone dams, 291
Stone walls, 93
Storer, Tracy Irwin, 159
Stream and lake management relations, 285
Stream fish, competitors, 285; food improvement, 290; predators, 285; providing shelter, 290; recreational value, 285; restocking, 285
Stream regimen, 287
Streams, bottom sampling, 289; fluctuations of, 287; improvement and management, 285–296; intermittent, 287; runoff and vegetative cover, 287
Stream sides, 130; surveys, 237, 238; timber, 131
Stream survey, 288–289; data collected, 289

Strigiformes, reduction in number, 314
Strip selection, 186
Strips, for quail, size of, 210; use of, 210
Strawberry, 144, 149
Stubble cutting, 95
Studies, recommended for lakes, 279
Stuewer, Frederick W., 248
Stumps, used for dens, 237
Stunted fish populations, 278, 281
Sturgeon, 39; food, 286; range, 286; spawning, 286
Sturkie, D. G., 216
Subarctic, 218
Subclimax, 35
Submarginal land, 11
Succession, 132; forest regions, 35; grass regions, 35; Pacific Northwest, 35; Tennessee Highlands, 35
Succession stages, 34, 35; annuals, 35; bare ground, 35; climax, 35; crustose lichens, 35; Douglas fir, 35; floating, 35; foliose lichens, 35; forbs, 35; forest, 35; grass, 35; hemlock, 35; lichens, 35; moss, 35; perennials, 35; reed swamp, 25; sedge meadow, 35; shrubs, 35; submerged, 35
Succulent vegetation, 110, 149, 153
Suckers, food, 286; range, 286; sparrows, 286
Sudan grass, 101, 102
Sumac, 121, 210, 301
Summer camps, 9
Summer fallow, 93
Summer homes, 136
Summer range, 4, 160; black-tailed deer, 179, 180, 181; elk, 176; white-tailed deer, 184
Sunfish, food, 286; range, 286; spawning, 286
Sunflower, 16, 101, 102, 301
Sunlight, 21
Sun River Range, 62
Super refuges, 268
Supreme Court grants, extraterritorial rights to Indians, 339; racial autonomy to Indians, 339
Surber, Thaddeus, 283, 296
Surface cover devices, 291
Surplus, biological, 5

Surveys, ground, 178
Survival, and cold, 25–26; of native and exotic birds, 26; and winters, 221
Sustained deficits, 129
Sustained yield, 129
Swamp Land Act of 1850, 252
Swan, mute, 249, 319; trumpeter, 249, 314, 315; whistling, 249
Swift, chimney, 63
Sylvilagus aquaticus, see Rabbit, swamp; *auduboni*, see Rabbit, cottontail; *floridanus*, see Rabbit, cottontail; *nuttalii*, see Rabbit, cottontail; *palustris*, see Rabbit, marsh
Symbols, in field notes, 87; in fur survey, 238
Sympatric species, 47
System of government, Canada and United States, 346

Tabulation cards, and handling data, 87; for ease of handling, 89
Tagging, 78, 79; fish, 281; traps, 239
Tamarack, 141, 161; see also Larch
Tangles, 300
Tanks, 153
Tanner, James T., 317
Tapeworm, 214
Tariff act, of 1895, 334; of 1913, 334
Tarzwell, Clarence, 292, 296
Taste and eating habits, 25
Tattooing, 78, 79, 238; of rabbits for marking, 122
Tax-delinquent land, 10
Taxes, 10, 14
Tax rolls, 13; loss of public land, 267
Taylor, Walter P., 69, 206
Teal, 62
 blue-winged, 250; migration, 45; South America, 252
 cinnamon, 250; South America, 252
 green-winged, 250
Technical reports, 88
Techniques, of field investigation, and practice, 54–90; miscellaneous, for fish, 277
Telephoto lens, 86
Telescopes, 85
Temperature, 32; control of animal body, 32; influence on plants and animals, 32; maintenance of body, 25; measurements, 64; of body and hibernation, 48; relation to fish production, 276; water control, 278
Temporary cover, 99
Tendon of Achilles, tagging, 238
Tennessee, 16, 146
Tennessee Valley Authority, 344
Tepee brush pile, 96
Terns, 298; Aleutian, 315; roseate, 315
Territorial demands and food chain, 20
Territorial needs, 28
Territorial waters, ownership of animals, 323
Territory, 4, 49, 143; block, 28; bobwhite, 111; breeding, 28; chachalaca, 216; colonial birds, 28; consciousness of, 28; cottontail rabbit, 120; determining, 29; kinds of, 28; predators, 28; role of, 28–29; roosting, 28; valley quail, 114; winter, 28
Tetraonidae, 216; flocking habits, 198; foot habits, 218; origin, 141
Texas, 10, 11, 16, 39, 57, 136, 147, 152, 164, 183, 199, 203, 207, 211, 213, 214, 240, 252, 253
Thalarctos maritimus, see Bear, polar
Thallium, used in poison campaigns, 117
Thelon Game Sanctuary, 230
Theroux, Frank R., 269
Thimbleberry, 150
Thinning, 133, 166
Thrasher, brown, 16
Threatened species, 311; list of, 315
Three Arch Rocks, 50
Threshold, extinction, 38
Thrush, hermit, 16; wood, 16
Thuja occidentalis, see Arborvitae
Thunderbird, 15
Ticks, 151
Tick trefoil, 100, 132, 150
Tiffany, Lewis Hanford, 283
Tiger census, 63
Timber, cutting, 128; improvement of stands, 133; land, 129; production, 128; stands, 37; type choice, 160; value in valley quail range, 116
Time afield, for game bagged, 10

408   Index

Time-depth ratio, 260
Title to game, acquiring, 323, 324
Titmouse, 300
Toe, clipping of, in marking animals, 78, 238; punching, 238
Tolerance, 151; marten, 241; otter, 241; red fox, 242; to man, gray fox, 242
Tonto Creek, Arizona, 11
Topographical influences, 33
Topping trees to control growth, 144
Toumey, James W., 139
Tourist lodges, 12
Tourists, 13, 14; attractions for, 13, 91; deer, 187; effect on distribution of alligator, 215
Track album and registers, 72
Track counts, 62, 190, 201; bobwhite, 113; Hungarian partridge, 110; rabbits, 122
Tracking snow, 71
Tracks and trails, 71, 72, 74
Tradition, action of, 28; black-tailed deer, 179; prairie chicken, 199, 200; relation to winter and breeding grounds, 28
Trailside museums, 14
Transect, 56, 171; counts by, of Hungarian partridge, 110; of rabbit, 122; of snowshoe rabbit, 171
Transfer of title to animals *ferae naturae*, 322
Transparent mirrors, 76
Transplanting, and species groups, 45; cottontail rabbit, 120; mountain quail, 155
Transportation, 9
Transverse sketching reconnaissance, 66
Trap, bobwire, 119, 152; cock and hen, 152; extended jaw, 152, 158; funnel, 119, 152; nest, 158; padded jaw, 152
Trap-nights, 55, 63, 122, 171
Trappers, reports by, 236; restriction on white, 348
Trapping, 183; along banks of streams, 327; beaver, 245, 246; bobwhite, 113; Hungarian partridge, 110; marking and censusing waterfowl, 268–269; muskrat, 247; pheasant, 119; prairie chicken, 201; ruffed grouse, 152; small mammals, 63;   snowshoe rabbits, 171; woodcock, 158
Travel lanes, 95; of caribou, 228
Treaties protecting aliens, 324
Treatment of rare, threatened, and persecuted species, 311–317
Treaty, between Canada and United States, 335–337; between United States and United Mexican States, 335–337; of Paris, 333
Treaty-making power, 333, 337
Tree duck, black-bellied, 249; fulvous, 249
Trees, dens, 165; nests, 165; rings, 86
Tree-top shelter for fish, 274
Trespass, 4, 8, 12; a civil offence, 328; a criminal offence, 328; for hunting, 328
Triangulation reconnaissance, 66
Trichostrougyhus, 213
Trippensee, Reuben Edwin, 106, 123, 139, 159, 172, 193, 317
Trophy hunting, 226
Trouble-shooting reports, 88
Trout, and oxygen content of water, 33, 285; relation to beaver, 245
  brook, food, 286; range, 286; spawning, 286
  lake, food, 286; range, 286; spawning, 286
  rainbow, food, 286; range, 286; spawning, 286
  steelhead, *see* Trout, rainbow
Trout streams, value of, 11–12
Truck logging, 132
Tularemia, 151
Tulip tree, 16
Tundra, 34, 141, 224, 225, 229, 231; Alaska, 223; amount, 223; map of, 219; overgrazing, 228
Tundra grouse, adaptations, 143
Turbidity of water, 278
Turkey, 152–154; breeding age, 153; census methods, 154; controlled burning, 134, 153; deferred maturity in, 29; environment, 142; flock counts, 154; flocking, 153; food habits, 142, 153; food patches, 153, 154; gobbling counts, 154; green food, 153; habitat requirements, 152; illegal kill,

Index

154; improving food and cover, 153; incubation, 142; mating, 142; migration, 140, 152; nesting, 153; nesting season, 142; number of eggs, 142; predation, 154; protection, 154; range, 142, 152; restocking, 154; roosting, 154; sex ratio, 142, 154; soil contamination, 153; use of forest, 141; water needs, 153; weight, 142; wildness, 154; winter feeding, 153
Turner, David B., 364
Turtle, 6, 297; control, 255
Tympanuchus, see Prairie chicken

Uhler, F. M., 269
Ultra-violet rays and cycles, 52
Unbalanced sex ratios, 359–360; correction, 359–360
Underplanting, 95, 148
Undersized fish, 281
Ungulates, 127
Uphill planters, 126
Urocyon cinereoargenteus, see Fox, gray
Ursus americana, see Bear, black; *gyas, see* Bear, brown; *horribilis, see* Bear, grizzly
Utah, 16, 114, 146, 197, 201, 252
Utilization, higher forms of, 9

Vaccinium, see Blueberry
Vallisineria, 259
Vandal fishermen and rookeries, 298
Van Dersal, William R., 18, 106, 310
Vanishing species, *see* Threatened species; areas of, 137
Varying hare, *see* Rabbit, snowshoe
"V"-deflector, 291
Veery, 16
Vegetation zones, 35
Velvet, 73
Venison, identification of, 81
Vermont, 16
Vertebrate species, status of, 6
Viburnum, 150, 301
Vigor, 19
Vines, 48, 61; for escape tangles, 98; for food and cover, 92, 141
Violations, and prosecution, 362

Violet, 16
Vireo, red-eyed, protecting forest trees, 126
Virgin forests, and animal abundance, 127
Virginia, 16, 199
Virginia creeper, 141, 150, 161
Virgin timber, 141, 161
Visibility, 64
Vision, of Northland animals, 219
Visual distance census, 60
Vitality, 151
Vitis, see Grape
Volume palatability method, 66
Vorhies, Charles T., 206, 217
Vulpes fulva, see Fox, red

Wade, Douglas E., 90
Wadkins, L. A., 90
Walkinshaw, Lawrence, 317
Wallows, bear, 174; elk, 176
Walnut, 166
Walrus, 15, 316
Wandering habits, 19, 30
Wanton destruction, 313; of sea birds, 313; of sea otter, 313
Wapato, 259
Wapiti, *see* Elk
Warbler, black-polled, migration of, 45; Kirtland, 312, 315; Sutton, 315
Warbles, caribou, 228
Ward, Henry Baldwin, 284, 296
Warden, first appointed, 330; first state game, 329; local (1739), 331; paid wardens, 330; use in gathering data, 358; variously named, 361
Warden system, origin and growth, 329–330
Warm-blooded animals, 32
Warning signs, for road crossings, 204
Warrant, arrest without, 361; need for search, 361
Warren, E. R., 248
Washburn, G. N., 283
Washington, 16, 155, 232
Waste, grain, 96, 100; rice, 100
Waste land, 95
Water, 21, 34; conservation of, by desert animals, 24; depth for ducks, 261; depth for muskrat, 247; fluctu-

ations, 287; metabolic, 24; mineral and organic content, 33

Water areas, fur bearers, 236

Waterfowl, 85; algae control, 265; alkali poisoning, 257–258; areas and flyways, 250–252; botulism, 256–257; breeding grounds, 250–251; brood counts, 269; catching on nesting grounds, 269; census, 61–62; censusing, 269; control of vegetation, 265; counting, 269; cripple loss, 266; crow, 255; dams, 262; decline in numbers, 265; definition, 249; density, 262; dikes, 263; disease, 256–258; drainage, 252, 253; drain on population, 252; drought, 251; drought area, 252; effect of oil pollution, 256; failure of predator control, 254; flight ways at ponds, 261; flock counts, 269; flocking habits, 42; food habits, 258–260; food plant propagation, 264; food plants, 264; food relations to muskrat and coot, 260; grazing, 255; hawks, 255; hole-nesters, 267; hunting pressure, 249; increase in numbers, 265; influence of carp, 255; instinctive food selection, 258; kill in Mexico, 266; kill in United States, 265; lead poisoning, 258; lead shot in body, 266; loss of food and cover plants, 254; loss of young, 254; management, 249–269; marking, 269; marsh control, 263; Mexican hunting, 252; migration, 252; muskrat relations, 255; need for deep water in drought, 261; nest boxes, 265; nest counts, 269; nest losses, 255; nesting far from water, 262; nesting habits, 261; netting, 269; number shot, 252; overhunting, 251, 252, 265; owls, 255; percentage of young in kill, 359; per cent nesting in Canada, 251; per cent shot in United States, 252; planting aquatic vegetation, 264; pollution, 255, 256; predation, 254–255; providing flight ways, 261; providing resting places, 261; raft counting, 269; range improvement, 260–262; refuge program, 267; refuges, 266–267; sex ratio, 266; shrinkage of breeding grounds, 250, 251; status, changes in, 252–254; stomach analysis, 259; suitable vegetation, 261; time of feeding, 260; traps, 269; wintering grounds, 251, 252

Water holes, 130

Watering devices, 116

Water levels, control of, 262–264; cycles, 253–254; diversions, 264; pumping, 264; stabilizing, 262–264

Water needs, antelope, 203–204, 205; black-tailed deer, 179; blue grouse, 143; bobwhite, 112; chachalaca, 216; cottontail rabbit, 121; elk, 177; Hungarian partridge, 110; moose, 192; mountain quail, 155, 156; prairie chicken, 199; ruffed grouse, 149; sage grouse, 198; sharp-tailed grouse, 203; South, 207; southern region, 210; squirrel, 166; turkey, 153; valley quail, 114, 115, 116; woodcock, 157

Water requirements, variations in, 24

Wave action control, 277

Weakness, of animal, 19; environmental, 21

Weasel, 21, 151; den, 237; food, 240; eating eggs, 241; habitat, 236

Weasel family, 240–241

Weather cycles, 51, 52

Weather hazards, 21; conditions and physiological stress, 52; influence on northern animals, 220

Weaver, J. E., 36

Webb, William L., 70

Webster, R. L., 289, 293, 294, 295

Weeds, animal, 136; control of, for waterfowl, 265; poisons for water plants, 273–274; seed, 96, 100, 301

Weed trees, 133

Weight, 164; alligator, 209; antelope, 196; Arctic fox, 224; Arctic hare, 225; armadillo, 209; black bear, 162; black-tailed deer, 163; blue grouse, 142; bobwhite, 108; brown bear, 162, 224; caribou, 225; chachalaca, 209; change, as indication of conditions, 26; cottontail rabbit, 108; cougar, 209; elk, 163; eyra, 208; fox squirrel, 163; Franklin grouse, 142;

Index

Gambel quail, 196; gray squirrel, 163; grizzly bear, 162; Hungarian partridge, 108; jack rabbit, 196; jaguar, 208; javelina, 209; moose, 163; mountain quail, 142; marsh rabbit, 209; musk ox, 225, 229; ocelot, 208; opossum, 208; pheasant, 108; polar bear, 224; prairie chicken, 196; ringtail, 208; rock ptarmigan, 225; ruffed grouse, 142; sage hen, 196; sharp-tailed grouse, 196; spruce grouse, 142; swamp rabbit, 209; turkey, 142; valley quail, 108; white sheep, 225; white-tailed deer, 163; white-tailed ptarmigan, 225; willow ptarmigan, 225; woodcock, 142
Weight estimate method, 66
Welch, Paul S., 70, 90, 283, 296
Welfare factors, 34
Westerman, Fred A., 364
Western duck sickness, 256
Western range, 206
Westfall, B. A., 296
Westveld, R. H., 139
West Virginia, 16, 168
Wetmore, Alexander, 53, 90
Whaling, 9, 313, 316; regulations, 316; treaties, 316
Wheat, 105, 153
Wheat grass-blue grass zone, 36
Wheat rust and barberry, 300
Whipple, George Chandler, 284, 296
Whistling counts of quail, 112
Whitefish, food, 286; range, 286; spawning, 286
White hunters, discriminations against, 229
White pine blister rust, 300
Widgeon, European, 250
Widgeon grass, 259
Wight, Howard M., 70, 90, 310
Wild areas, 137
Wildcat, 130, 171, 188; den, 237; food habits, 242; habitat, 236; range, 242; rodent control value, 242; valley quail, 117
Wild celery, 259
Wild indigo, 132
Wilderness, 1, 14; areas of, 1; management, 1; wildlife, 1, 137

Wildfowl, decline in numbers, 265; definition, 249; management, 249–269
Wildlife, and the highway, 307–309; as a tourist attraction, 13–14; investigations of damage, 84; relation to forest, 124–127
value of, attraction, 15; capital land, 11; crop saving, 7; cultural, 15; dollars-and-cents, 7; economic, 7; esthetic, 7, 8, 9; insect suppression, 7; land rental, 11; meat, 11, 12; recreational, 7, 8, 12; subsistence, 8; to forest, 125–127; trout waters, 12
Wildlife areas, 17
Wildlife Division, 249
Wildlife economy, 7; people supported by, 8–9
Wildlife management, and allied fields, 2–3; branches, 1; definition, 1
Wildness, 154; and confinement, 83; moose, 191; turkey, 154
Wild plant management, 1
Wild-raised game and fish, 4
Wild turkey, see Turkey
Williamston Plan, 12
Willow, 147, 166, 170, 176, 185, 191, 243
Wind, 32; and caribou movement, 228; and migration, 46; damage by, 131; exposure to, 25; protection from, 64
Windbreaks, 92, 300; and wave action, 277
Wing clips, 78, 79
Wing, Leonard William, 269, 310, 364
Winter census, 58; deer surveys, 182
Winter feeding, 96, 99 (see also Feeding stations, Food patches); beaver, 245; elk, 177; non-game birds, 301; non-game species, 301; objectives of, 99; pheasants, 118; ruffed grouse, 149; sharp-tailed grouse, 202; snowshoe rabbit, 170; turkey, 153; white-tailed deer, 186
Winter foods, 232; patch plants, 101; use of, 105
Wintergreen, 150
Wintering habits, blue grouse, 144; ruffed grouse, 147

Winter losses, bobwhite, 110
Winter range, 4, 130, 160; big game, 135; black-tailed deer, 179–181; elk, 135, 176; mountain quail, 155; white-tailed deer, 184
Winters, measure of mild and hard, 221; severe, 32
Wire, Frank B., 364
Wisconsin, 16, 49, 100, 145, 185, 259; state game warden, 330
Witchhazel, 150
Wolf, 2, 22, 136, 188, 195, 315; cache, 75; den, 237; habitat, 236; peck order, 44; unprotected in national parks, 316
Wolf predation, caribou, 228; musk ox, 229; white sheep, 230
Wolf trees, 20, 167
Wolverine, den, 237; extirpation, 241; habitat, 236; tolerance of man, 235
Wood Buffalo Park, 195, 197
Woodchuck, benefit to burrow users, 241; den counts, 59; hunting, 107
Woodcock, 156–157; banding, 158; census methods, 158; cutting timber, 157; drought, 157, 158; enemies, 157–158; environment, 142; flushing, 158; food habits, 142, 156, 157; habitat requirements, 156–157; improving food and cover, 157; incubation, 142; mating, 142; migration, 140, 156; mortality, 158; nesting, 156; nesting season, 142; number of eggs, 142; predators, 157; protection, 157; range, 142; sex determination, 158; sex ratio, 142, 158; singing birds, 158; singing ground, 156, 157; trapping, 158; use of forest, 141; water needs, 157; weather, 158; weight, 142

Woodlands, kept in brush, 299
Woodlots, 161; grazed, 93, 94, 95; ungrazed, 93, 94, 95; use, 141
Woodpecker, 130, 307; downy, 125; downy, and species association, 43; holes, 165; ivory-billed, 125, 126, 315, 321; pileated, 42; white-headed, 126
Woods rule of drawing first blood, 326
Wood substitutes, 129
Wren, 304; cactus, 15; Carolina, 16; flocks, 42; house, 16
Writing notes, 87
Wyoming, 16, 114, 143, 190, 197

Xerosere succession, 35

Yard counts, 190
Yeatter, Ralph E., 123, 248
"Y"-deflector, 291, 292
Yield tables, for beaver food determination, 244
Yocom, Charles F., 123
Young, Stanley P., 317
Young, Vernon A., 70, 90, 193, 206
Yucca, 16
Yukon, 143, 230; aboriginal ratio, 223; land ownership, 222; wildlife control, 349
Yukon River, 220; opening and closing, 222

Zinnia, 16
Zizania, 259
Zoology, 2
Zooplankton, 21
Zoos, roadside, 14
Zostera, 259